Course	PRINCIPLES OF CHEMISTRY
Course Number	**CHE 151-CHE152**

Montgomery County
Community College

Chemistry

http://create.mcgraw-hill.com

ISBN-10: 039070914X   ISBN-13: 9780390709141

Contents

Credits

Experiment 1

1

Introduction to Laboratory Techniques

PURPOSE AND LEARNING OBJECTIVES

To become familiar with common laboratory equipment and techniques. To understand the uncertainties of measurements, significant figures, and the propagation of errors.

PRINCIPLES

Chemistry is an experimental science that relies upon accurate measurements and observations from scientists. All observations and measurements have uncertainties associated with them. It is therefore important to know and understand the precision of each piece of equipment used and record data with the appropriate number of significant figures. In order to draw conclusions from the data, any limitations in the reliability of the data must be taken into account. In this experiment, you will learn how to use basic laboratory equipment that you will be using throughout the year. You will also become familiar with the uncertainties associated with the equipment and how errors in measurements propagate in calculations.

Originally, our system of weights and measures was based on the properties of water, as summarized in Table 1.

Table 1. Metric Units of Measurements

Measurement	Definition	Units
Mass	quantity of matter in an object	Gram (g) = weight of 1 cm^3 of water at 4°C and 760 mm Hg
Length	extent of something along its greatest dimension	Meter (m) = 100 cm = 1000 mm
Volume	quantity of space occupied by an object	Liter (L) = volume of 1 kilogram (kg) of water at 4°C
Temperature	measure of heat intensity on a defined scale	Degree Celsius (°C) is based upon the melting and freezing points of water
Heat	transfer of energy between two objects of differing temperatures	1 calorie (cal) = amount of heat required to raise 1 g of water 1°C from 14.5 to 15.5°C
Density	mass of an object per unit volume	g/mL for liquids; g/L for gases

In each of these measurements, the uncertainty will depend on the laboratory equipment used to make the measurement. The precision associated with various pieces of equipment is summarized in Table 2.

Table 2. Uncertainties in Laboratory Equipment

Equipment	Uncertainty
100-mL graduated cylinder	± 0.2 mL
10-mL graduated cylinder	± 0.1 mL
50-mL burette	± 0.02 mL
25-mL pipette	± 0.02 mL
5-mL pipette	± 0.01 mL
Thermometer (10°C to 110°C, graduated to 1°C)	± 0.2°C
Top-Loading Balance	± 0.001 g

Keeping track of errors as they propagate through calculations can be tedious. However, in the experiments done this quarter, you will simply record the appropriate significant figures for each of the measurements taken. The significant figures in the calculated results are determined by following some simple rules, which are outlined in the following table and examples.

Table 3. Significant Figures

Quantity	Number of Significant Figures
155	3
160	2 or 3
160.	3
150.00	5
0.0013	2
0.001300	4
0.0170	3
6.022×10^{23}	4

Carefully note the significance of the zeros in each of the quantities. In general, zeros used to hold a decimal place are not significant. Thus, 0.0013 only has two significant figures, whereas 0.001300 has four significant figures. The quantity, 150.00, has five significant figures because the zeros to the right of the decimal point are significant, they are not holding the decimal place.

Significant Figures in Calculations

In the multiplication or division of quantities, the answer is rounded to the same number of significant figures as the quantity with the least number of significant figures. For example, (2.3456)(0.0200) = 0.046912 = 0.0469. The correct answer is rounded to three significant figures because 0.0200 has only three significant figures. Consider the following example.

$$[(1.30)(0.4532)(25.6)] /11 = 1.371136 = 1.4$$

In the division, the number with the least significant figures is 11 (two significant figures). The correct answer is therefore rounded to two significant figures.

In the addition or subtraction of quantities, the answer has the same number of digits after the decimal point as the quantity with the least number of digits after the decimal point. For example, 3.47 + 3.1 = 6.57 = 6.6, because the 7 in 6.57 is not significant.

Precision and Accuracy

Accuracy is defined as the extent to which a measured value agrees with the true value of the quantity measured. Precision is the reproducibility of a measurement. The errors in measurements are classified as either systematic or random. A **systematic error** causes an error in the same direction each time the measurement is made and can be due to the experimental method or a flaw in the equipment. For example, if a 25-mL volumetric pipette actually delivers 25.4 mL, the volume used in the calculations would always be 0.4 mL too high. Thus, a systematic error reduces the accuracy of the measurement, but the precision of the measurement can still be good. A systematic error can be corrected for by calibrating the equipment, in this case, the pipette.

When the same measurement is made a number of times, small variations in the measurement occur naturally. This is referred to as **random error**. Random error occurs because of the measuring process itself or minor variations in the quantity measured. Random errors reduce the precision of a measurement. For example, in this experiment you will weigh four pennies. Even though, the original pennies were supposed to be exactly the same size and composition, small defects in manufacturing, or wear and tear over the years, may contribute to random error. In random error, negative and positive deviations are equally likely to occur. By averaging a large number of measurements, the positive and negative deviations tend to cancel, thereby minimizing the error.

When a measurement is made several times, the mean value can be calculated as well as the average deviation from the mean. If the mass of four pennies were measured to be: 9.101 g, 9.234 g, 9.220 g and 9.123 g, the average mass (the mean value) would be:

$$\frac{9.101 + 9.234 + 9.220 + 9.123}{4} = 9.170 \text{ g}$$

Deviations from the mean are calculated as the absolute values of the difference between the measured values and the mean:

$$|9.101 - 9.170| = 0.069 \qquad\qquad |9.220 - 9.170| = 0.050$$
$$|9.234 - 9.170| = 0.064 \qquad\qquad |9.123 - 9.170| = 0.047$$

The average deviation from the mean is:

$$\frac{0.069 + 0.064 + 0.050 + 0.047}{4} = 0.058$$

The average mass reported includes the deviation from the mean, that is, 9.17 ± 0.06 g.

International System of Units (SI Units)

Any given measurement has units associated with them. Because there are multiple systems of units throughout the world, the scientific community has established a common system of units to use, called the International System of Units or SI units. This is a brief version of the metric system. Even though this has been established, the English system and the metric system are still used making it important to understand the conversions between these systems. Conversion factors are summarized in Table 4. The SI system and the metric system will be easier to use once you have memorized the prefixes.

Table 4. Conversion Factors for SI, Metric and English Units

Physical Quantity	SI Units	Common Metric Units	Conversions
Length	Meter (m)	Meter (m) Centimeter (cm)	1 m = 100 cm 1 m = 39.37 inch 1 inch = 2.54 cm
Volume	Cubic meter (m³)	Liter (L) Milliliter (mL)	1 L = 1000 cm³ 1 mL = 1 cm³ 1 L = 1.06 qt
Mass	Kilogram (kg)	Gram (g) Milligram (mg)	1 kg = 1000 g 1 kg = 2.205 lb. 1 lb. = 453.6 g
Temperature	Kelvin (K)	Degree Celsius (°C)	0 K = −273.15°C K = °C + 273.15
Energy	Joule (J)	Calorie (cal)	1 cal = 4.184 J 1 kJ = 1000 J

It is important to use dimensional analysis in carrying out conversions, as for example, the conversion of density from g/L to g/cm³:

$$\left(356\,\frac{g}{L}\right)\left(\frac{1\,L}{1000\,mL}\right)\left(\frac{1\,mL}{1\,cm^3}\right) = 0.356\,\frac{g}{cm^3}$$

SAFETY

WEAR SAFETY GLASSES

Take caution when using a mercury thermometer. If a thermometer is broken notify the instructor immediately.

Always wash your hands before leaving the laboratory.

Proper Care of Balance

1. Do not drop objects on the balance pan.

2. Gently place the object on the pan.

3. Do not weigh warm or hot objects; objects must be at room temperature.

4. Do not place chemicals directly on the pan; use weighing paper, a weighing boat or container.

5. Tare weight:
   a) After placing weighing paper or a container on the balance, briefly press the O/T, the On/Tare bar, to zero the balance. The balance should now read 0.000 g.

   b) Add sample to the weighing paper or container. The balance will now read the weight of the sample.

6. Remove the weighing paper containing sample.

7. Return balance to zero by briefly pressing the O/T bar. Leave the balance on.

8. Clean up any spilled material in the balance area immediately, using the brush provided. If material is spilled on the balance, turn the balance off by pressing the O/T bar until the display reads OFF, then clean up the material spilled.

PROCEDURE

Part 1. Laboratory Measuring Devices

Copy the following table into your lab notebook to record your data. Be sure to include units.

Apparatus	A	B	C	D
Name	100-mL graduated cylinder	10-mL graduated cylinder	50-mL burette	250-mL Erlenmeyer flask
Volume of Water				
Uncertainty in Measurement				

1. Observe and record the level of water in each piece of equipment, labeled A-D. Make sure your eyes are at the water level when reading the volume as shown in Figure 1. Do not have your eyes above or below the water level. When you read the water level in the burette, use the white card with the piece of black tape to help you see the meniscus more clearly. Your eyes should be level with the meniscus, and you should read the very bottom of the curve.

2. Determine and record the uncertainty for each piece of equipment (see Table 2, in the Principles section of this lab manual). For the Erlenmeyer flask, the % uncertainty is indicated on the flask.

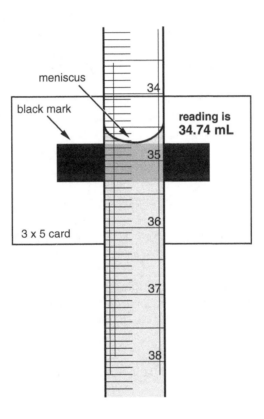

Figure 1. Proper eye position when reading the volume. Your eyes should be level with the meniscus, and you should read the very bottom of the curve.

Part 2. Using a Balance to Measure the Mass of Pennies

Copy the following table into your lab notebook to record your data. Be sure to include units.

Date	Mass	Mass	Mass	Mass	Average	Deviation
Pre-1982						
Post-1983						

In 1983 the composition of pennies was changed from 95% copper to 97.5% zinc coated with a thin layer of copper (2.5%). The size of the pennies remained the same.

1. Obtain four pre-1982 pennies and four post-1983 pennies.

2. Place a piece of weighing paper on the balance. To tare the weight, zero the balance by briefly pressing the O/T bar on the balance.

3. Place one penny on the weighing paper and record the mass and year of the penny in your notebook.

4. Repeat steps 2-3 for all of the pennies, one penny at a time.

5. Calculate the average mass (the mean value) for the copper pennies and the average mass of the zinc pennies. Calculate the average deviation from the mean in each case.

Part 3. Calibrate your 5-mL Pipette Using a Balance

1. In a beaker, obtain approximately 50 mL of deionized water (DI water), from the sink in the front of the room. There is only one deionized water tap in the lab; make sure you are using the correct one.

2. Weigh a clean, dry 125-mL Erlenmeyer flask. Be sure to zero the balance before weighing by briefly pressing the O/T bar.

3. Measure and record the temperature of the DI water.

4. To ensure the 5-mL volumetric pipette is clean, fill it with DI water above the 5-mL mark and let it drain out. If your pipette is clean, no water drops should be left behind on the inside walls of the pipette but the last drop will remain in the tip of the pipette. Your pipette is calibrated to deliver (TD), rather than to contain (TC). The last drop of liquid does not drain out of a TD pipette and should remain in the tip.

5. Using your 5-mL volumetric pipette, transfer exactly 5 mL of the water into the weighed flask. **NOTE:** Instructions on how to use a volumetric pipette will be demonstrated by your instructor and are given at the end of this section.

6. Weigh the water in the flask. Record the mass. Calculate the mass of the water.

7. Given the density of water at various temperatures (see Table 5), calculate the volume of water delivered from the pipette.

8. Repeat this measurement two more times. Calculate the mean and the deviation from the mean in the volume delivered by your 5-mL pipette.

Table 5. Density of Pure Water at Various Temperatures

Temperature (°C)	Density (g/mL)	Temperature (°C)	Density (g/mL)
15	0.999099	22	0.997770
16	0.998943	23	0.997538
17	0.998774	24	0.997296
18	0.998595	25	0.997044
19	0.998405	26	0.996783
20	0.998203	27	0.996512
21	0.997992	28	0.996232

Method for Using a Volumetric Pipette

The water is drawn into the pipette by applying a slight vacuum using a rubber squeeze bulb at the top of the pipette. Do not use your mouth to draw any liquid or solution into the pipette.

1. As shown in Figure 2, slip the squeeze bulb onto the very end of the pipette, just far enough to make an airtight connection.

2. Hold the pipette in the solution keeping the tip well below the surface of the solution.

3. Draw in a small amount of the solution to rinse the pipette, discard in waste beaker. Be careful not to draw the solution into the bulb.

4. Using the bulb, draw in enough of the solution so that the liquid level is above the calibration mark on the pipette.

5. Quickly but gently remove the bulb from the pipette and press your index finger on top of the pipette. Do not allow the liquid level to fall below the calibration mark. A slightly moistened finger may help control the flow of liquid.

■ EXPERIMENT 1

6. Keeping your finger securely on top of the pipette, remove the pipette from the solution.

7. Partially lift your finger off the pipette to drain some of the solution back into the beaker until the bottom of the meniscus aligns exactly with the calibration mark. At this point, quickly press your finger back on the pipette to stop the flow of liquid.

8. Touch the tip of the pipette to the inside of the beaker to transfer any hanging drops.

9. Move the pipette to the container into which you want to transfer the solution.

10. Lift your index finger off the pipette to allow the solution to drain into the container. Even after waiting a minute, some solution will remain in the tip of the pipette. Do not attempt to remove the small amount of solution remaining in the tip of a volumetric pipette. The pipette was calibrated to deliver the volume indicated excluding the small volume left in the tip.

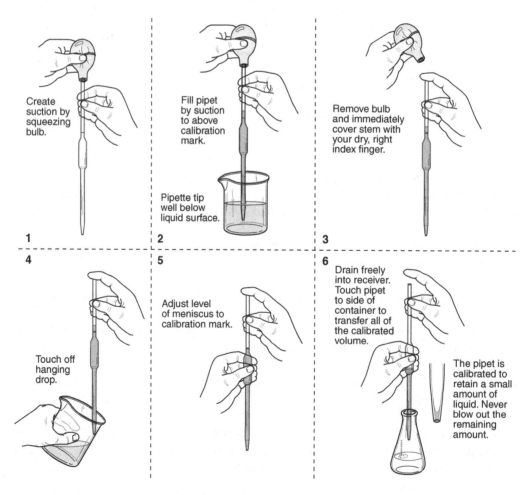

Figure 2. Method for using a volumetric pipette.

Part 4. Thermometer Calibration

In this part of the experiment, the accuracy of your thermometer will be determined by comparing the known freezing and boiling points of water to the observed values.

1. Place approximately 50 mL of ice in a 150-mL beaker and cover the ice with deionized water. Let the water/ice mixture sit for 15 minutes to allow it to come to equilibrium. In the mean time start boiling water (steps 3, 4 and 5).

2. Measure the temperature of the water using a thermometer. The temperature should be 0°C, theoretically.

3. Fill a 250 mL beaker half full of deionized water. Clamp a ring to a ring stand and place a piece of wire gauze on the ring. Place the beaker filled with water on the wire gauze.

4. Obtain a Bunsen burner and a piece of tubing from the back of the laboratory. Hook the tube to the Bunsen burner inlet and to the gas valve on the bench top labeled gas. Close the air inlet at the base of the Bunsen burner. With a match prepared to strike, turn the gas on at the valve. Strike the match and carefully place it next to the opening at the top of the Bunsen burner. Adjust the air inlet until a blue inner cone and a violet outer cone are visible.

5. Put the Bunsen burner under the beaker and heat the water to a boil. Record the temperature of the water using the thermometer. Make sure the thermometer is not touching the beaker when taking the measurement.

6. Obtain the atmospheric pressure from the teaching assistant.

7. The true freezing point of water is 0°C. However, the boiling point of water depends on the atmospheric pressure. It is 100°C at 760 mm Hg and decreases as the pressure decreases. Cooking your food at higher elevation takes longer because the boiling point of water is lower at higher elevation. Calculate the true boiling point of the water at the atmospheric pressure in the lab, as shown in the following example.

    Example:
    Determine the boiling point of water at 701.6 mm Hg.

    Boiling point correction   =   (760 mm Hg – atmospheric pressure) (0.037°C/mm)
    (760 mm Hg – 701.6 mm Hg) (0.037°C/mm) = 2.1°C

    True Boiling point of water at 701.6 mm Hg = 100.0°C – 2.1°C = 97.9°C

8. Using Excel on the computer in the lab, plot a line graph of the observed temperatures versus the true temperatures for the boiling and freezing points of water. This is your thermometer calibration line. If your thermometer reads 50°C, determine the true temperature from the graph.

■ EXPERIMENT 1

QUESTIONS

1. Express each of the following in scientific notation.
   a) 0.00435
   b) 143.6
   c) 1306

2. Express each of the following in decimal form.
   a) 2.3×10^{-5}
   b) -5.6×10^3
   c) 3.50×10^{-2}

3. Indicate the number of significant figures in each of the following.
   a) 700.00
   b) 25
   c) 0.024
   d) 0.0240
   e) 5.400×10^3

4. Express the answers of the following operations to the correct number of significant figures.
   a) 25.6×0.0782
   b) $112.8 - 57.43$
   c) $(17.54 + 39.5) / 65.89$
   d) $6.02 \times 10^{23} / 0.043$

5. The mass of a penny was measured six times. The following data was reported:
   9.314 g, 9.215 g, 9.323 g, 8.103 g, 9.278 g, and 9.344 g.

   a) Should any data be excluded in calculating the average mass of the penny?
   b) Calculate the average value of the mass of the penny, excluding unreasonable values.
   c) Calculate the average deviation from the mean.

6. What is the density of a cube that weighs 1.45 g and has sides, 15.2 cm in length? What is the density in units of g/mL and g/L?

7. In Part 2 of the lab, what was the average mass and deviation of the copper pennies (pre-1982) and zinc pennies (post-1982)? Is the difference in the average mass greater than the deviation? What does the difference in mass tell you about the relative density of copper versus zinc?

8. Explain the difference between precision and accuracy and between systematic and random errors.

LAB REPORT 1

For this experiment, the lab report should summarize the data and results, organized neatly in tables. Show all your work in doing the calculations and always include the correct number of significant figures and units. Include answers to the questions at the end of the lab. Include the duplicate copies of the original data recorded in your laboratory notebook.

PREPARATION FOR EXPERIMENT 2

Read Experiment 2 in the Lab Manual. Answer **PRE-LAB QUESTIONS** in your lab notebook. These are problems and questions, in the lab manual, which must be answered before the start of lab. The instructor will give students credit for completed Pre-Lab questions at the start of lab. Study for the quiz, which will be primarily on the first experiment as well as the PRE-LAB QUESTIONS from Experiment 2.

■ **EXPERIMENT 1**

Experiment **2**

2

Nomenclature and Reaction Stoichiometry

PURPOSE AND LEARNING OBJECTIVES

To understand basic nomenclature of compounds. To be able to write the name of an inorganic compound from its formula and the formula from its name.

PRINCIPLES

Metals and Non-Metals in the Periodic Table

Most of the elements in the periodic table are metallic, positioned on the left side of the bold line in Figure 1. Metallic elements tend to lose electrons, existing as positive ions in many compounds and in solution.

The non-metals include hydrogen and the elements in the upper right hand corner of the periodic table, on the right side of the bold line. Except for the noble gases, Group 8A, non-metals tend to have relatively high electronegativities. That is, non-metals have a strong attraction for electrons. As a result, non-metals tend to form negative ions in binary compounds with metals. All chemical compounds are electrically neutral.

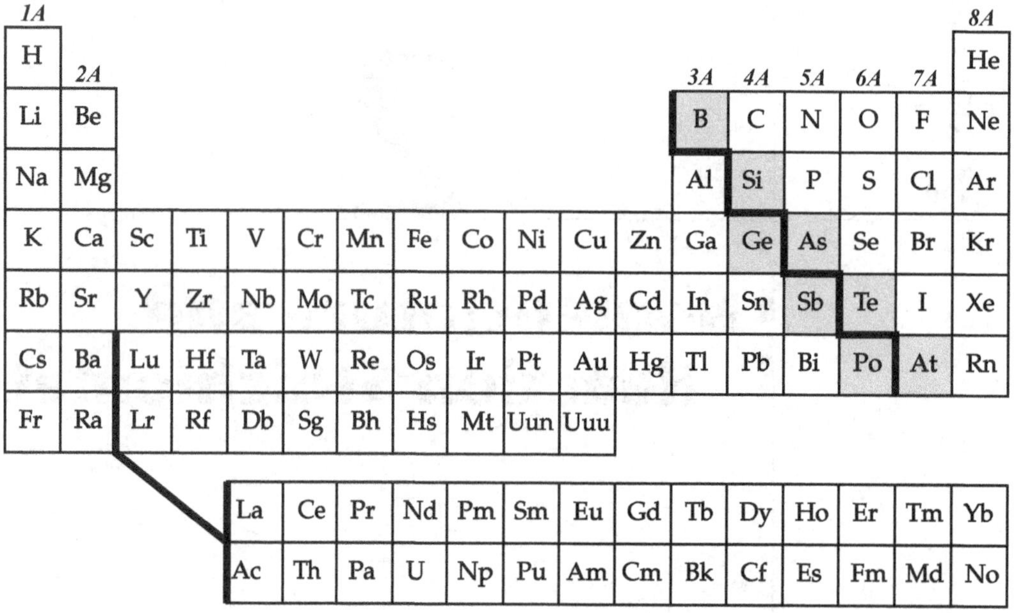

Figure 1. The periodic table. Non-metals are on the right of the bold line, and metals are on the left. The metalloids, also called semimetals, are directly adjacent to the bold line and are shaded.

CHEMICAL BONDING

Not all electrons in atoms participate in chemical bonding. Electrons appear to occupy a set of shells surrounding the nucleus: Inner shells have core electrons, which are not significantly involved in bonding between atoms. The outer-most partially filled shells have valence electrons, which participate in bonding. **A filled valence shell possesses great chemical stability.** As the atomic number increases, the number of electrons in the valence shell increases and is filled when a noble-gas element, He, Ne, Ar, Kr, Xe and Rn, is reached. The first additional electron, the outermost electron in the alkali metals, Li, Na, K, Rb, Cs, and Fr, is the first occupant of a new shell, which implies that alkali metals, Group 1A, each have one valence electron.

Lewis dot symbols show only valence electrons:

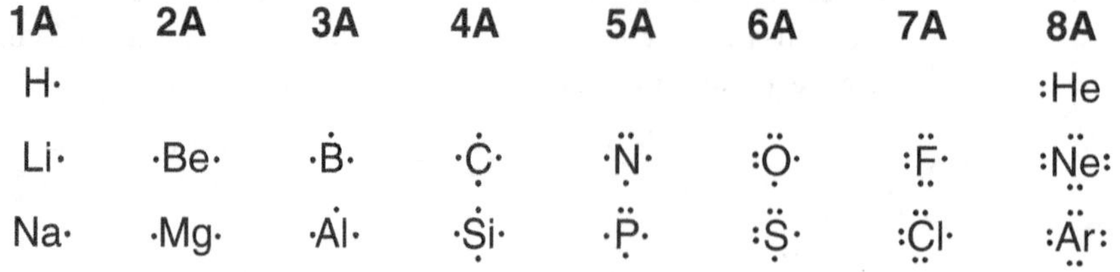

1A	2A	3A	4A	5A	6A	7A	8A
H·							:He
Li·	·Be·	·B·	·Ċ·	·N̈·	:Ö·	:F̈·	:N̈e:
Na·	·Mg·	·Äl·	·Si·	·P̈·	·S̈·	:C̈l·	:Är:

For the representative elements (Groups 1A through 8A), except for He, the number of valence electrons in the neutral atom is equal to the element's group number. Special stability results when an atom loses or gains electrons to make the outer shell electrons equal to the number of valence shell electrons in a noble gas.

The valence shell of hydrogen and helium are completed with two electrons. Elements in the second period generally follow the octet rule (with a maximum of eight electrons in their valance shell) with the exception of boron and beryllium, which can be electron deficient in their compounds (e.g. $BeCl_2$, BF_3). Elements in the third row and beyond can exceed the octet rule (valence shell expansion, e.g. SF_6).

Ionic and Covalent Bonding

Ionic Bond: An ionic bond is formed through the Coulomb force of attraction between ions of opposite charge. Chemical bonds between metal atoms and non-metal atoms tend to be ionic; the metal atoms tend to lose the number of electrons needed to give a noble gas configuration, and the non-metal atoms tend to gain the number of electrons needed to give a noble gas configuration. For example, in NaCl, Na gives up an electron and Cl gains an electron. Thus, an electron is transferred from Na to Cl to form an ionic bond, Na^+Cl^-. Compounds containing ionic bonds produce ions in aqueous solution, e.g. $NaCl(aq) \rightarrow Na+(aq) + Cl-(aq)$.

Covalent Bond: In covalent bonds two or more electrons are shared between two atoms. Chemical bonds between two non-metal atoms tend to be covalent. For example, in chlorine gas, Cl_2, both chlorine atoms want one electron so they share two electrons in a single bond, Cl–Cl. The single line represents two shared electrons. In oxygen gas, O_2, each oxygen atom wants two electrons so they share four electrons in a double bond, O=O. Non-metals tend to form covalent bonds with themselves (e.g. H_2, Cl_2, and O_2) and with other non-metals to form molecules (e.g. CO_2, CH_4 and H_2S) and stable polyatomic ions (e.g. SO_4^{2-}, NO^{3-}, NH^{4+}, and PO_4^{3}) as shown in Table 2. Covalent molecules generally do not dissociate to form ions in solution.

Table 1. Common Monatomic Cations And Anions (Memorize)

H^+	hydrogen	H^-	hydride
Li^+	lithium	F^-	fluoride
Na^+	sodium	Cl^-	chloride
K^+	potassium	Br^-	bromide
Cs^+	cesium	I^-	iodide
Mg^{2+}	magnesium	O^{2-}	oxide
Ca^{2+}	calcium	S^{2-}	sulfide
Ba^{2+}	barium	N^{3-}	nitride
Al^{3+}	aluminum	P^{3-}	phosphide

■ EXPERIMENT 2

Table 2. Common Polyatomic Ions (Memorize)

NH_4^+	ammonium	PO_4^{3-}	phosphate
H_3O^+	hydronium	HPO_4^{2-}	hydrogen phosphate
OH^-	hydroxide	$H_2PO_4^-$	dihydrogen phosphate
CN^-	cyanide		
SCN^-	thiocyanide	ClO^-	hypochlorite
		ClO_2^-	chlorite
NO_2^-	nitrite	ClO_3^-	chlorate
NO_3^-	nitrate	ClO_4^-	perchlorate
SO_3^{2-}	sulfite	MnO_4^-	permanganate
SO_4^{2-}	sulfate		
HSO_4^-	hydrogen sulfate (or bisulfate)	CrO_4^{2-}	chromate
		$Cr_2O_7^{2-}$	dichromate
CO_3^{2-}	carbonate		
HCO_3^-	hydrogen carbonate (or bicarbonate)	$C_2O_4^{2-}$	oxalate
CH_3COO^-	acetate	O_2^{2-}	peroxide

If you memorize the names and charges of all the ions ending in *-ate* then the suffixes and prefixes are changed in a systematic way to account for the number of oxygens in the ions:

-ite	corresponds to the ion with one fewer oxygen atom,
hypo- and *-ite*	with two fewer oxygen atoms,
per- and *-ate*	with one more oxygen atom than the ion ending in *-ate*

For example:

chlorate	ClO_3^-	
chlorite	ClO_2^-	
hypochlorite	ClO^-	least number of oxygens
perchlorate	ClO_4^-	greatest number of oxygens

NOTE:
1) adding or subtracting oxygen atoms does not change the charge on the ion
2) adding a hydrogen atom reduces the negative charge by one (e.g. sulfate, SO_4^{2-} and hydrogen sulfate HSO_4^-)

NAMING ACIDS

An acid is defined as a substance that produces hydrogen ions, H^+, in solution. For example, HCl dissociates to produce H^+ and Cl^- in aqueous solution. In oxyacids (e.g. HNO_3, H_2SO_4, and CH_3COOH), the hydrogen attached to an oxygen will dissociate to produce H^+ in aqueous solution as shown for acetic acid.

$$CH_3COOH \text{ (aq)} \quad \rightarrow \quad H^+ \text{ (aq)} + CH_3COO^- \text{ (aq)}$$

1) *Binary Acids*

Add *-ic* to the stem of the element (in place of *-ide* for the ion) and precede the stem by the prefix *hydro-*. For example, the stem of chlorine is chlor:

chloride ion (Cl^-) hydrochloric acid (HCl)

2) *Oxyacids*

Add *-ic* to the stem of the element if the anion ends in *-ate*
Add *-ous* to the stem of the element is the anion ends in *-ite*

For example, the stem of the element nitrogen is nitr:

nitrate ion (NO_3^-) nitric acid (HNO_3)
nitrite ion (NO_2^-) nitrous acid (HNO_2)

In cases where an element forms more than two oxyacids, the prefixes *per-* (for the largest number of oxygen atoms in the oxyacid) and *hypo-* (for the smallest number of oxygens) are used, just as for the oxyanions.

3) *Organic Acids*

The stems for the common organic acids are nonsystematic and must be memorized. The same relation as for oxoacids holds between the names of the ion and the acid. For example,

acetate ion (CH_3COO^-) acetic acid (CH_3COOH)

Table 3. Examples of acids.

Compound	Cation	Anion	Name
HF	H^+	F^-	hydroflouric acid
$HClO_4$	H^+	ClO_4^-	perchloric acid
H_3PO_4	H^+	$H_2PO_4^-$	phosphoric acid
H_2SO_4	H^+	HSO_4^-	sulfuric acid

NOTE: If the cation in the formula of a compound is H^+ and the anion is either a stable monatomic or polyatomic ion, than the compound is an acid.

■ EXPERIMENT 2

NAMING BINARY IONIC AND COVALENT COMPOUNDS
TYPE I:

Binary **ionic compounds** (a <u>metal</u> atom with a fixed charge bound to a <u>non-metal</u> atom) and ionic compounds containing polyatomic ions.

Metals which form only one type of cation, a positive ion with a fixed charge, include:

Group 1A: alkali metals generally form only singly charged cations:

Li^+, Na^+, K^+, Rb^+, Cs^+

Group 2A: alkaline earth metals generally form only doubly charged cations:

Be^{2+}, Mg^{2+}, Ca^{2+}, Sr^{2+}, Ba^{2+}

Group 3A: Boron is a non-metal, it makes covalent bonds with other non-metals. Al and Ga are metals; they tend to lose 3 electrons to form +3 cations:

Al^{3+}, Ga^{3+}

Name the cation first, using the element name: (e.g. Na^+ is named sodium)

Name the anion second, using the element stem and the suffix -*ide*
   (e.g. Cl^- is named chloride)

Table 4. Examples of Type I, Binary Ionic Compounds

Compound	Cation	Anion	Name
NaCl	Na^+	Cl^-	sodium chloride
Li_3N	Li+	N^{3-}	lithium nitride
NaH_2PO_4	Na^+	$H_2PO_4^-$	sodium dihydrogen phosphate
Na_2HPO_4	Na^+	HPO_4^{2-}	sodium hydrogen phosphate

TYPE II:

Binary **ionic compounds** (a metal atom bound to a non-metal atom)

Table 5. Metal atoms that form cations with variable charges.

Ion	Name	Alternative Name
Fe^{3+}	iron(III)	ferric
Fe^{2+}	iron(II)	ferrous
Cu^{2+}	copper(II)	cupric
Cu^+	copper(I)	cuprous

Ion	Name	Alternative Name
Co^{3+}	cobalt(III)	cobaltic
Co^{2+}	cobalt(II)	cobaltous
Pb^{4+}	lead(IV)	plumbic
Pb^{2+}	lead(II)	plumbous

The rules for naming type II ionic compounds are the same as for Type I compounds except that the charge of the metal ion must be specified using a roman numeral.

For example, $FeCl_2$ contains the Fe^{2+} ion and $FeCl_3$ contains the Fe^{3+} ion. The corresponding name indicates the charge on the metal ion.

$FeCl_2$ iron(II) chloride or ferrous chloride

$FeCl_3$ iron(III) chloride or ferric chloride

Exception: For Zn^{2+}, Cd^{2+}, and Ag^+ in compounds, no Roman numeral is required to specify the charge because Zn, Cd and Ag generally form only one type of ion with a fixed charge.

TYPE III:

Binary **covalent compounds** (two non-metal atoms bound)

Name the first element in the chemical formula first, using the element name.
Name the second element in formula as if it were an anion, element stem plus the suffix -ide.

Number of atoms must be indicated using the prefixes: *mono-, di-, tri-, tetra-, penta-, hexa-, hepta-, octa-*, etc. but *mono-* is never used to name the first element.

NO	nitrogen monoxide	CO	carbon monoxide
N_2O	dinitrogen monoxide	CO_2	carbon dioxide
N_2O_4	dinitrogen tetraoxide	NH_3	ammonia (or nitrogen trihydride)

■ EXPERIMENT 2

PRE-LAB QUESTIONS

1. Which of the following elements are metals?

    N   Cu   Sr   Se   Al   Br   Ne   H   V   Pb   Co   P

2. Which of the following elements are non-metals?

    O   Ga   Br   C   Zr   K   Ba   S   Ar   V   Hg   I

3. Give the definition of an ionic bond and a covalent bond?

4. Which of the following compounds are ionic? Explain why or why not.

    H_2O NO $CaCl_2$ Cl_2 NaCl H_2S KBr $Mg(OH)_2$

5. What is the charge on the ions formed by Group 1A metals and Group 2A metals? Explain why.

6. What is the charge on the ions formed by Group 7A non-metals? Explain why.

7. For each of the following elements, indicate the charge on the corresponding ion most likely formed in an ionic compound.

    Li   Ca   Cl   Cs   O   Al

8. Give the definition of an acid.

9. Which of the following compounds are acids?

    H_2S H_3PO_4 H_2 HBr $Zn(OH)_2$ LiH $HClO_4$

10. For each of the acids in question 9, write the dissociation reaction in aqueous solution.

11. Predict the formula for the compounds formed from each of the following pairs of elements.

    Ca and Cl   Al and O
    Li and N   Rb and S
    Ba and O   Li and F
    Na and O   Ag and Cl

2

**Nomenclature and
Reaction Stoichiometry**

Worksheet

Name

Section

Date

NOMENCLATURE (This section will be completed in lab section.)

Write the symbol and charge of the cation, the symbol and charge of the anion, and the formula for each of the following compounds.

	Cation	Anion	Formula
calcium phosphate	————	————	————————
potassium nitrate	————	————	————————
ammonium sulfate	————	————	————————
aluminum hydroxide	————	————	————————
rubidium peroxide	————	————	————————
lithium hydride	————	————	————————
calcium nitride	————	————	————————
ammonium nitrate	————	————	————————
nickel(III) sulfate	————	————	————————
barium nitrite	————	————	————————

■ EXPERIMENT 2

chromium(II) phosphate   _____ _____ _____

zinc sulfate   _____ _____ _____

lead(IV) acetate   _____ _____ _____

potassium permanganate   _____ _____ _____

carbonic acid   _____ _____ _____

ferric oxide   _____ _____ _____

silver iodide   _____ _____ _____

magnesium fluoride   _____ _____ _____

oxalic acid   _____ _____ _____

manganese(II) hydroxide   _____ _____ _____

potassium hydrogen phosphate   _____ _____ _____

calcium carbonate   _____ _____ _____

ammonium thiocyanide   _____ _____ _____

cobalt(III) nitrate   _____ _____ _____

NOMENCLATURE

Write the formula for each of the following compounds.

carbon tetrachloride _____   sodium hypochlorite _____

ammonia _____   dinitrogen trioxide _____

potassium dichromate _____   methane _____

carbon disulfide _____   lead(IV) oxide _____

hydrogen peroxide _____   ammonium sulfide _____

nitric acid _____   sulfuric acid _____

acetic acid _____   barium sulfate _____

hydrogen sulfide	_____	calcium oxalate	_____
nickel(II) phosphate	_____	oxalic acid	_____
hydrochloric acid	_____	sodium bicarbonate	_____
aluminum chloride	_____	aluminum hydroxide	_____
lithium nitrite	_____	silver acetate	_____
cobalt(III) oxide	_____	iron(III) hydroxide	_____
hydrofluoric acid	_____	magnesium nitrate	_____
gallium oxide	_____	silicon tetrachloride	_____
aluminum fluoride	_____	phosphoric acid	_____
silver chloride	_____	potassium dichromate	_____
aluminum sulfate	_____	perchloric acid	_____
nitrogen dioxide	_____	dinitrogen monoxide	_____
copper(I) sulfide	_____	zinc dichromate	_____
sodium sulfate	_____	nitrous acid	_____
dinitrogen tetroxide	_____	nickel(II) sulfite	_____
barium nitrate	_____	magnesium hydroxide	_____
potassium thiocyanide	_____	sodium oxalate	_____
carbon tetrachloride	_____	sodium hypochlorite	_____

NOMENCLATURE

Give the name for each of the following compounds.

$(NH_4)_2CO_3$	_____	$Zn(OH)_2$	_____
$CoCO_3$	_____	K_2SO_4	_____
Cr_2O_3	_____	H_2O_2	_____

■ **EXPERIMENT 2**

$Ni_3(PO_4)_2$ _____ N_2O_4 _____

HCl _____ H_2SO_4 _____

CH_3COOH _____ H_3PO_4 _____

HCN _____ HNO_3 _____

$Pb(CH_3COO)_2$ _____ P_2O_4 _____

$Ba(OH)_2$ _____ NO_2 _____

Na_2O _____ $Fe_2(SO_4)_3$ _____

$KClO_3$ _____ $Al(OH)_3$ _____

$CuHSO_4$ _____ Ca_3N_2 _____

$K_2C_2O_4$ _____ K_2O_2 _____

HNO_2 _____ H_2CO_3 _____

NH_4Cl _____ $CuSO_4$ _____

N_2F_4 _____ V_2O_5 _____

$(NH_4)_3PO_4$ _____ Li_3N _____

$Fe(OH)_3$ _____ $AgNO_3$ _____

$CaCl_2$ _____   FeO _____

KOH _____ SO_3 _____

Al_2O_3 _____ $Cu(NO_3)_2$ _____

H_2S _____ $HClO_4$ _____

NaOH _____ PbO_2 _____

NH_4OH _____ $H_2C_2O_4$ _____

AgCl _____ $NaHCO_3$ _____

CHEMICAL REACTIONS AND CHEMICAL EQUATIONS

Chemical reactions involve the reorganization of atoms in compounds. The atoms themselves remain the same. In a chemical reaction, atoms are neither created nor destroyed.

For example, we commonly burn natural gas for cooking and heating our homes. Natural gas is methane, with the molecular formula, CH_4, where one carbon is bound to four hydrogen atoms. Write the chemical reaction for the combustion of methane. What are the reactants and products? When you burn a substance, oxygen must be present. Methane reacts with oxygen to produce carbon dioxide and water as shown in the following chemical equation.

$$CH_4\ (g) + O_2\ (g)\ \rightarrow\ CO_2\ (g) + H_2O\ (g) \qquad\qquad \text{unbalanced equation}$$
$$\underbrace{\qquad\qquad}_{\text{reactants}} \qquad \underbrace{\qquad\qquad}_{\text{products}}$$

Mass is conserved in a chemical reaction. That is, all atoms that appear on the reactant side of the equation must be accounted for on the product side. The chemical equation for the reaction must be balanced to conserve mass. In balancing the reaction, the molecular formula of a given compound can not be changed. Coefficients in front of the molecular formulas are included as needed to balance the equation. It is generally easiest to start with the most complicated molecule in the reaction, the molecule with the greatest number of atoms.

Methane, CH_4

$$CH_4\ (g) + 2\ O_2\ (g)\ \rightarrow\ CO_2\ (g) + 2\ H_2O\ (g) \qquad\qquad \text{balanced equation}$$

The coefficient in front of each molecule indicates the relative numbers of reactants and products in the reaction. In the combustion of methane, 1 mole of CH_4 reacts with 2 moles of O_2 to produce 1 mole of CO_2 and 2 moles of H_2O.

In the balanced chemical equation no atoms are lost or gained. On the left side of the equation there are four hydrogen atoms, four oxygen atoms and one carbon atom. On the right side of the equation there are also four hydrogen atoms, four oxygen atoms and one carbon atom.

REACTION STOICHIOMETRY AND LIMITING REAGENT

When reacting substances are mixed in the exact proportions given by the chemical equation, all the reactants will be used up at the same time. However, if the reacting substances are mixed in a proportion different from that given by the chemical equation, one of the reactants is used up first, while some of the other reactants are left over. The reactant that is used up first is called the **limiting reagent**. Consider the reaction in which aluminum metal oxidizes in air to produce aluminum oxide, $Al_2O_3(s)$. $Al_2O_3(s)$ is a thin, tough, transparent coating that protects the aluminum from further oxidation.

$$4\ Al\ (s) + 3\ O_2\ (g)\ \rightarrow\ 2\ Al_2O_3\ (s)$$

If we have the exact proportion given by the chemical equation, that is, 4 moles of Al and 3 moles of O_2, both Al and O_2 will be used up simultaneously and 2 moles of Al_2O_3 (s) will be produced. The following questions involve reactant mixtures that differ from the proportions given by the chemical equation.

EXAMPLE QUESTIONS:
Consider the following reaction: $4\ Al\ (s) + 3\ O_2\ (g)\ \rightarrow\ 2\ Al_2O_3\ (s)$

1. a)   How many moles of O_2 are needed to react completely with 1 mole of Al?

To determine how many moles of O_2 are needed to react with 1 mole of Al, the stoichiometric coefficients given in the chemical equation are used as follows.

$$1\ \text{mol Al}\left(\frac{3\ \text{mol }O_2}{4\ \text{mol Al}}\right) = 0.75\ \text{mol }O_2$$

   b)   How many moles of Al_2O_3 will be produced when 1 mol of Al reacts with 0.75 mol of O_2? The reaction goes to completion. That is, the reaction continues until one or both reactants are used up.

$$1\ \text{mol Al}\left(\frac{2\ \text{mol }Al_2O_3}{4\ \text{mol Al}}\right) = 0.5\ \text{mol }Al_2O_3 \quad \text{or} \quad 0.75\ \text{mol }O_2\left(\frac{2\ \text{mol }Al_2O_3}{3\ \text{mol }O_2}\right) = 0.5\ \text{mol }Al_2O_3$$

Aluminum and the oxygen are used up at the same time, 0.5 moles of Al_2O_3 is produced.

2. How many grams of O_2 are needed to react with 100. g of Al?

The balanced chemical equation indicates that Al reacts with O_2 in the ratio of 4 moles of Al to 3 moles of O_2. First calculate the moles of Al in 100. g of Al. Then calculate the number of moles of O_2. From the moles of O_2 calculated, the grams of O_2 can be determined, shown as follows.

Reaction: $4\ Al\ (s) + 3\ O_2\ (g)\ \rightarrow\ 2\ Al_2O_3\ (s)$

First convert grams to moles! Then use the stoichiometric coefficients in the balanced equation to convert moles of Al to moles of O_2. The mass of O_2 is calculated using the molar mass of O_2.

$$100.\text{ g Al}\left(\frac{1\text{ mol Al}}{27.0\text{ g}}\right)=3.7\text{ mol Al}\left(\frac{3\text{ mol }O_2}{4\text{ mol Al}}\right)=2.8\text{ mol }O_2\left(\frac{32.0\text{ g}}{1\text{ mol }O_2}\right)=89.6\text{ g }O_2$$

or

$$100.\text{ g Al}\left(\frac{1\text{ mol Al}}{27.0\text{ g}}\right)\left(\frac{3\text{ mol }O_2}{4\text{ mol Al}}\right)\left(\frac{32.0\text{ g}}{1\text{ mol }O_2}\right)=89.6\text{ g }O_2$$

3. Determine the limiting reagent when 6 moles of Al are mixed with 5 moles of O_2. In other words, which reagent is used up first, Al or O_2?

$$6\text{ mol Al}\left(\frac{2\text{ mol }Al_2O_3}{4\text{ mol Al}}\right)=3\text{ mol }Al_2O_3\quad\text{or}\quad 5\text{ mol }O_2\left(\frac{2\text{ mol }Al_2O_3}{3\text{ mol }O_2}\right)=3.3\text{ mol }Al_2O_3$$

When all 6 moles of Al react, 3 moles of Al_2O_3 are produced. When all 5 moles of O_2 react, 3.3 moles of Al_2O_3 are produced. Can 3.3 moles of Al_2O_3 be produced? No, all the Al is used up when 3 moles of Al_2O_3 are produced. Al is the limiting reagent, it is used up first. How many moles of O_2 are left over?

$$6\text{ mol Al}\left(\frac{3\text{ mol }O_2}{4\text{ mol Al}}\right)=4.5\text{ mol }O_2\qquad 5\text{ mol }O_2-4.5\text{ mol }O_2=0.5\text{ mol }O_2$$

Thus, 6 moles of Al reacts with 4.5 moles of O_2 to produce 3 mol of Al_2O_3. When all 6 moles of Al are used up, 0.5 moles of O_2 still remain.

REACTION STOICHIOMETRY AND LIMITING REAGENT PROBLEMS

1. Balance each of the following reactions using integer coefficients.
    a) $NH_3+O_2\;\rightarrow\;N_2O_4+H_2O$
    b) $CaCl_2+Na_3PO_4\;\rightarrow\;Ca_3(PO_4)_2+NaCl$
    c) $Al+HCl\;\rightarrow\;H_2+AlCl_3$
    d) Write the balanced equation for the complete combustion of propanol, C_3H_8O.
    e) $H_2S+Fe(OH)_3\;\rightarrow\;Fe_2S_3+H_2O$

■ EXPERIMENT 2

2. The combustion of sugar produces carbon dioxide and water according to the following equation.

$$C_6H_{12}O_6 \text{ (s)} + 6\,O_2 \text{ (g)} \quad \rightarrow \quad 6\,CO_2 \text{ (g)} + 6\,H_2O \text{ (g)}$$

  a) Is this equation balanced?
  b) If 50 g of sugar is burned, how many moles of CO_2 will be produced?
  c) How many grams of sugar are needed to produce 26. g H_2O?
  d) How many moles of O_2(g) are needed to burn 50 g of sugar?

3. Consider the reaction: $4\,NH_3 + 7\,O_2 \quad \rightarrow \quad 4\,NO_2 + 6\,H_2O$
  a) How many grams of O_2 are required to burn 28.8 g of ammonia?
  b) How many grams of NO_2 will be produced from 28.8 g of ammonia?

4. Consider the reaction: $4\,NH_3 + 7\,O_2 \quad \rightarrow \quad 4\,NO_2 + 6\,H_2O$
  Identify the limiting reagent for each of the following reaction mixtures:
  a) 1 moles of NH_3 and 1 moles of O_2
  b) 3 moles of NH_3 and 5 moles of O_2
  c) 8 moles of NH_3 and 15 moles of O_2
  d) 0.5 moles of NH_3 and 0.8 moles of O_2
  e) 85 g of NH_3 and 192 g of O_2

5. How many grams of phosphoric acid will be produced when 135.0 g of P_4O_{10} is mixed with 90.0 g of water and the reaction goes until one of the reactants is completely used up?

$$P_4O_{10} + 6\,H_2O \quad \rightarrow \quad 4\,H_3PO_4$$

6. Sulfuric acid is produced when sulfur dioxide reacts with oxygen and water.

$$2\,SO_2 + O_2 + 2\,H_2O \quad \rightarrow \quad 2\,H_2SO_4$$

  If 300 g of SO_2 are mixed with 100 g of O_2 and 150 g of H_2O and the reaction goes until one of the reactants is completely used up, determine the following.

  a) Which is the limiting reagent?
  b) How many grams of sulfuric acid are produced?
  c) How many grams of each of the reactants, SO_2, O_2 and H_2O, are left over?

Experiment **3**

3

Analysis of Water

PURPOSE AND LEARNING OBJECTIVES

To use chemical and physical tests to determine the concentration and types of dissolved solids in tap water, ocean water and deionized water. To recognize and use terminology common to solutions. To provide an introduction to solubility rules for ionic compounds in water.

PRINCIPLES

High quality water is essential to the survival of all living plants and organisms. It not only provides the medium that is required for vital reactions to take place, but also moderates the temperatures on earth. The average consumption rate of water is very high relative to availability of high-quality water. If rate of use, waste and pollution of natural water supplies continues at the present rate, major shortages of quality water will be a world wide problem in less than 50 years. Both chemical and biological contaminants pollute our natural water supplies including surface and ground water. Even though tap water visually appears identical to deionized water, this experiment will show you that tap water contains many compounds that have been dissolved in the water as it comes to us from reservoirs and wells. Deionized water has been purified through reverse osmosis and by the passage through a membrane that retains ions or large molecules. The tests performed in this experiment will allow the determination of dissolved solids, ions and other contaminants in tap water and ocean water.

Common ions in ocean water include Cl^-, Na^+, SO_4^{2-}, Mg^{2+}, Ca^{2+}, K^+, HCO_3^-, Br^- and Sr^{2+}. In this experiment you will learn how to analyze for NO_3^-, Ca^{2+}, Mg^{2+}, Cl^-, SO_4^{2-} and Pb^{2+} ions in tap water, ocean water and deionized water. If ocean water is not available, choose another sample of water to be tested, such as creek or river water.

What is the source of Cl^- in our water supplies? To purify water, by eliminating harmful bacteria and viruses, an oxidizing agent stronger than O_2 must be used. Ozone, O_3 (g), and chlorine dioxide gas, $ClO_2\bullet$ (g), are commonly used to purify drinking water. $ClO_2\bullet$ oxidizes organic molecules by taking electrons from them producing Cl^- in the process.

Increasing levels of nitrate ions, NO_3^-, in drinking water is a concern especially in rural locations. The primary source of nitrate ions is runoff from agricultural lands into rivers. Excess nitrate ions in drinking water can cause respiratory failure particularly in newborn infants.

Solutions

A solution is a homogeneous mixture in which one or more substances are uniformly dispersed as separate atoms, molecules or ions throughout another substance. The air in the atmosphere is a solution of gases, and the ocean is a solution of water, salts, and many other dissolved compounds. The components in solution are referred to as the solvent and the solute. In general, the solvent is defined as the component that is present in greater amount. Solutions in which water is the solvent are called aqueous solutions. The ratio of solute to solvent is not fixed. In this experiment, for example, evaporating tap or ocean water by boiling the solution increases the solute to solvent ratio. Physical means, such as evaporation, crystallization or distillation, can be used to separate the solute from the solvent without changing their identities.

The concentration of a solution can be expressed in a number of ways including, molarity (M) and parts per million (ppm). The molarity of a substance is the number of moles of solute dissolved in one liter of solution.

$$\text{molarity} = M = \frac{\text{moles solute}}{\text{liter solution}}$$

The concentration of a dilute aqueous solution in parts per million is the milligrams of solute dissolved in one liter of solution at room temperature.

$$\text{parts per million} = \text{ppm} = \frac{\text{grams solute}}{10^6 \text{ grams solution}} = \frac{1000 \text{ mg}}{(1000)(1000 \text{ mL})} = \frac{\text{mg solute}}{\text{liters solution}}$$

In deriving this equation, the density of a dilute aqueous solution is assumed to be equal to the density of water (1 g/mL), that is, 1 g = 1 mL. In addition, the following conversion factors were used:

$$1 \text{ g} = 1000 \text{ mg} \qquad\qquad 1000 \text{ mL} = 1 \text{ L}$$

In this experiment you will measure the concentration of dissolved solids in a given volume of tap water and either ocean, lake or river water. By evaporating all the water and weighing the residue left in the beaker, the concentration of dissolved solids in parts per million (mg solute/ liters solution) will be determined.

Solubility of Ionic Compounds in Water

Solubility is defined as the amount of substance that dissolves in a given volume of solvent at a given temperature. One of the most valuable functions of water is its ability to dissolve a great variety of substances. How is water able to this? To answer this question, we must consider the structure of water. Water is a covalently bound molecule with bent geometry. In covalent compounds, the bonds between atoms are pairs of shared electrons. However, in covalent bonds such as the O–H bonds in water, the electrons are not shared equally because the oxygen has a greater attraction for electrons (greater electronegativity) than the hydrogen resulting in a polar bond. The shared electrons tend to spend more time closer to the oxygen than to either of the hydrogens, as indicated by the $2\delta^-$ on the oxygen and the δ^+ on each of the hydrogens (delta, δ, indicates a partial charge, less than one unit of charge). The polarity gives water its ability to dissolve many substances.

$$\underset{\delta^+ H \qquad\qquad H \delta^+}{\overset{2\delta^-}{\underset{}{O}}}$$

An ionic compound, such as Na^+–Cl^-, dissociates when dissolved in water due to the strong attractive forces between the dissociated ions and the polar water molecules. Solid NaCl dissolves in water to form aqueous Na^+ and Cl^- ions according to the following **dissolution reaction**.

$$NaCl \text{ (s)} \xrightarrow{\quad H_2O \text{ (l)} \quad} Na^+ \text{ (aq)} + Cl^- \text{ (aq)}$$

In this reaction, (aq) indicates that the ions are surrounded by water molecules.

The solubility of ionic compounds in water varies greatly. For example, even though sodium chloride is quite soluble in water (more than 10 g of NaCl (s) dissolves per liter of water), silver chloride is relatively insoluble (less than 0.1 g of AgCl (s) dissolves per liter of water). Thus, if a solution contains both Ag^+ and Cl^- ions, solid AgCl will appear in the solution, as shown in the following **precipitation reaction**.

$$Ag^+ (aq) + Cl^- (aq) \quad \rightarrow \quad AgCl (s)$$

In this reaction, $AgCl$ (s), referred to as the precipitate, is observed to be a white solid suspended in solution.

Relative solubilities of ionic compounds in water are listed in Appendix 1 of this Lab Manual. It is important to remember several basic solubility rules from this table. For example, salts containing either NO_3^- or CH_3COO^- are soluble. Salts containing Cl^-, Br^- and I^-, are soluble unless Ag^+, Pb^{2+} or Hg^{2+} are also present. SrF_2, BaF_2 and PbF_2 are listed as slightly soluble indicating 0.1 to 10 g of these salts dissolve per liter of water. Slightly soluble salts will produce cloudy solutions, whereas insoluble salts form precipitates which are visually solid. Also note that salts containing either NH_4^+ ions or Group I metal ions, Na^+, K^+, etc. are soluble.

CHEMICALS
Use a saturated $Ba(NO_3)_2$ solution (solubility 8.7 g/100 mL).

SAFETY
WEAR SAFETY GLASSES

Aqueous hydrochloric acid, HCl (aq), and sulfuric acid, H_2SO_4(aq), are both strong acids and will burn your skin and clothing if contact is made. If you spill acids on your skin, flush with water immediately.

If you spill concentrated H_2SO_4 on your skin, flush immediately with water and then pour sodium bicarbonate solution on the affected area to neutralize the acid, followed by more water.

Always wash your hands before leaving the laboratory.

PROCEDURE
There are two parts to this experiment, the physical analysis of water and the chemical analysis of water. For this experiment, you will work in pairs. In part 1, one third of the class will analyze ocean water, one third will analyze tap water and one third will analyze DI water. The data will be written on the board. Every student needs to record the data for ocean, tap, and DI water in their own lab notebooks. During the waiting periods (when the beakers are drying) begin part two of the experiment, again working in pairs.

Part 1. Analysis of water by physical changes
1. Clean a 400-mL beaker with soap and water, use deionized water (DI water) as the final rinse. Write your name on the beaker (use masking tape). Dry the beaker and place it in oven for complete drying, approximately 20 minutes in a hot oven, ~ 120°C. (While the beaker is drying, start part 2 of this experiment.)

2. Once the beaker is completely dry, avoid touching it with your hands, the oils from your skin can affect future measurements and the beaker will be hot. Use paper towels or beaker tongs to handle the beaker when it is hot and once it has cooled.

DO NOT TOUCH THE GLASSWARE, IT IS EXTREMELY HOT!

Remove the beaker from oven using beaker tongs or paper towels; fold the paper towels over the side of the beaker. Allow the beaker to cool to room temperature.

3. After the beaker is at room temperature, put in 2-3 boiling stones (chips). Weigh the beaker with boiling stones to the nearest thousandth of a gram (0.001g).

4. Using a graduated cylinder, measure 75.0 mL of ocean or tap water. Pour the water into the beaker and weigh the beaker with water and boiling stones.

5. Set up a Bunsen burner and ring stand with ring and wire gauze. Heat water. Allow the water to boil away gently. If the rate of boiling is too vigorous, lower the heat to avoid splattering.

6. When approximately 15 mL of the water is left, cover the beaker with a watch glass to avoid splattering. The watch glass is placed on the beaker, concave down.

7. Once all the water has evaporated, allow the beaker to cool down. If needed, rinse the watch glass with a small amount of DI water into the beaker (try to use less than 1 mL), and then evaporate the water. Observe and record the color of the residue left behind.

8. Once the beaker is at room temperature, weigh the beaker with the residue inside. Place the beaker back in the oven for 15 minutes. Cool to room temperature and re-weigh the beaker and its contents. The two weights should be within 3% of each other. If not, place the beaker back in the oven for another 15 minutes, cool to room temperature, and re-weigh.

9. Calculate the percent total solids in tap water and in ocean water. Also calculate the total solids dissolved in tap water and in ocean water in parts per million.

Part 2. Analysis of water by chemical change

1. Copy the following table in your lab notebook to record your observations. You will test tap water for NO_3^-, Ca^{2+}, Mg^{2+}, Cl^-, SO_4^{2-} and Pb^{2+} ions. If you observe a cloudy solution or a solid precipitate record it in the table below and indicate the color.

Water Sample	Test tube #1 NO_3^-	Test tube #2 NO_3^-	Test tube #3 Ca^{2+}/Mg^{2+}	Test tube #4 Cl^-	Test tube #5 SO_4^{2-}	Test tube #6 Pb^{2+}
Tap Water						

2. Clean a 250-mL beaker. Place 150 mL of tap water and 2-3 boiling stones in the beaker.

3. Using the Bunsen burner, gently boil the water down to approximately 25 mL. Allow to cool to room temperature.

4. Clean six medium-sized test tubes. The test tubes do not have to be dry. After the test tubes are washed and rinsed with DI water, simply shake out excess water. Mark the test tubes, #1 through #6.

5. Pour 2 mL of the cooled tap water sample into test tube #1.

6. If solids are present in the cooled tap water sample, add a few drops (~3) of dilute nitric acid, 6 M HNO_3, swirl beaker. If solids still remain add a few more drops of the acid and swirl.

7. Place approximately 2-3 mL of the solution into test tubes #2 through #6, save the remainder for additional testing if needed.

8. **Test for nitrate ion, NO_3^-.** Test tube #1 and #2.

   Note: Because HNO_3 was added to the solution in test tube #2, nitrate ions will be present. Thus, test tube #2 provides the opportunity for you to learn how to test for and observe the presence of NO_3^-. Once you are successful at testing for NO_3^-, test your water sample in test tube #1 for NO_3^-.

   Add 1 mL (~20 drops) of saturated iron(II) sulfate solution, $FeSO_4$ to test tube #2. In the hood, holding the test tube at a 45° angle with a test tube clamp, carefully add 2 mL (~40 drops) of concentrated sulfuric acid, 18 M H_2SO_4, allowing the acid to run down the side of the test tube. DO NOT MIX. If nitrate is present, there should be three separate layers: the bottom layer should be concentrated sulfuric acid, the middle layer should be a brown gaseous ring containing an iron(II) nitrosyl complex, $Fe(NO)^{2+}$, and the top should be the saturated iron(II) sulfate solution. If nitrate is not present in your solution, the brown ring will not form. You should observe the brown color in test tube #2. If not, discard contents in waste beaker and try again. Ask the teaching assistant for help if needed.

   Once you successfully observe NO_3^- in test tube #2, use the same procedure to test for NO_3^- in test tube #1.

   The reaction to form the nitrosyl complex is not straightforward and you are not expected to write an equation for this reaction.

9. **Test for calcium and magnesium ions, Ca^{2+} and Mg^{2+}.** Test tube #3.

    Add 1 M ammonium carbonate, $(NH_4)_2CO_3$, drop wise to test tube #3. After each drop, check for any precipitate. After you have added 5-10 drops, let the solution sit undisturbed for one minute. This precipitate may be difficult to see, so try holding the tube to the light. A cloudy solution indicates a precipitate is formed and that it is moderately soluble in aqueous solution. Do not add too much ammonium carbonate, this will cause the precipitate to redissolve back into the solution. Write the balanced reaction for the precipitation reactions.

10. **Test for chloride ion, Cl^-.** Test tube #4.

    a) Add 3 drops of 6 M nitric acid to test tube #4. Test with litmus paper to make sure the solution is acidic (put a drop of the solution on a piece of litmus paper using a glass rod).

    b) Add 5 drops of 0.05 M silver nitrate, $AgNO_3$. Does a precipitate appear? If not add 5 more drops of silver nitrate. Record your observations. Be sure to note the color of any solid in your observations. Write the balanced reaction for the precipitation reaction.

11. **Test for sulfate ion, SO_4^{2-}.** Test tube #5.

    Add 5 drops of saturated barium nitrate, $Ba(NO_3)_2$ solution to test tube #5. Record your observations, note the color of the precipitate formed. Write the balanced reaction for the precipitation reaction.

12. **Test for lead ion, Pb^{2+}.** Test tube #6.

    Add 5 drops of 6 M HCl to test tube #6. If a precipitate does not appear, add 5 more drops of the hydrochloric acid. If after 10 drops of acid no precipitate appears, then the amount of lead in your sample solution is too small to be detected by this type of analysis. This test can detect 100 ppm lead. Write the balanced reaction for the precipitation reaction.

WASTE DISPOSAL
Dispose of all waste in the appropriately labeled waste bottle in the hood.

PRE-LAB QUESTIONS
1. a) Molarity (M) is a unit of concentration. What are the units that make the concentration unit, molarity?
    b) What are the units that make up the concentration unit, parts per million (ppm)?

2. Calculate the molarity of each of the following solutions.
    a) 25.0 g of sodium hydroxide in 150.0 mL solution
    b) 10.0 g of hydrogen chloride in 200.0 mL solution

■ EXPERIMENT 3

3. How many moles of solute are present in 300.0 mL of a 6.0 M HCl?

4. How many grams of solute are present in 1.6 L of 3.0 M NaOH?

5. What is the concentration of dissolved solids in parts per million of the following solutions?
    a) 5.0 g of the pesticide, DDT, in 200.0 g water
    b) 45.0 g of NaCl in 200.0 mL solution

6. Which solution do you expect to contain the least amount of dissolved solids: Santa Barbara tap water, deionized water, or ocean water?

7. In Part 1 of this experiment, how will you determine the total dissolved solids in tap or ocean water? **NOTE**: You can bring in a sample of water that you would like to analyze. Water from a lake, river or pond near agricultural lands may be interesting to test.

8. When you weigh the beaker in Part 1, why must it be at room temperature?

9. In Part 2 of this experiment why will you boil down 150 mL of water to 25 mL of water?

10. In testing for NO_3^- in test tube #2, if NO_3^- is observed does that mean NO_3^- was originally in the water sample? Why do you test for NO_3^- in test tube #2?

DISCUSSION QUESTIONS

Briefly discuss the experimental results and the methods used to obtain them; include balanced equations for precipitation reactions observed. In discussing the results or methods, use general terms only, do not refer to specific test tube numbers or parts of the experiment. The reader should be able to understand your discussion without having to refer back to the lab procedure. Compare the concentration of dissolved solids found in ocean (or other samples of water) and tap water in this experiment to the maximum allowable contaminant level of 1000 ppm mandated by the Environmental Protection Agency (EPA). Are your values reasonable? Discuss the possible sources of error in determining the concentration of dissolved solids in the water samples. Compare the concentrations of dissolved solids found in ocean water and in tap water. Are the results consistent with what you expected? What ions did you detect in tap water? Were nitrate ions present in the tap water sample?

REVIEW QUESTIONS

1. Deionized water is available in the laboratory to do chemistry experiments throughout this year. In general, is it better to use deionized water or tap water in chemistry experiments? Explain why.

2. Why are some substances allowed in drinking water?

3. In Part 1 of the experiment, why was it important to reheat and reweigh the beakers containing the residue?

4. Write the molecular formulas for the products and balance each of the following reactions. Circle the products, which are likely to form a precipitate in solution (use the table of solubilities, Appendix 1 in this lab manual).

$AgNO_3 + BaCl_2 \rightarrow$ silver chloride and barium nitrate
$(NH_4)_2CO_3 + CaCl_2 \rightarrow$ ammonium chloride and calcium carbonate
$KCl + H_2S \rightarrow$ potassium sulfide and hydrochloric acid
$Mg + H_3PO_4 \rightarrow$ magnesium phosphate and hydrogen gas
$KOH + H_2SO_4 \rightarrow$ potassium sulfate and water
$FeBr_3 + NH_4OH \rightarrow$ iron (III) hydroxide and ammonium bromide

5. In 1990, the Environmental Protection Agency (EPA) set the maximum allowable nitrate ion concentration in water at 1.0 mg/L. Calculate the molarity of nitrate ion at this concentration.

■ EXPERIMENT 3

Experiment **4**

4

Determination of a Chemical Formula

PURPOSE AND LEARNING OBJECTIVES

To observe the reactivity of metals with water and acid. To introduce acid-base titration as a method to determine the molecular formula of a compound.

PRINCIPLES

Reactivity of Metals

Elements in the periodic table are generally classified as metals, non-metals or metalloids. Metals are substances having characteristic malleability, ductility, luster, and high electrical and thermal conductivity. Non-metals lack metallic properties and metalloids are semi-metals. Most of the elements in the periodic table are metals. Metallic properties of elements increase as we proceed down a given group in the periodic table and decrease across each of the rows from left to right. Most of the non-metals are in the upper right hand corner of the periodic table to the right of the bold line.

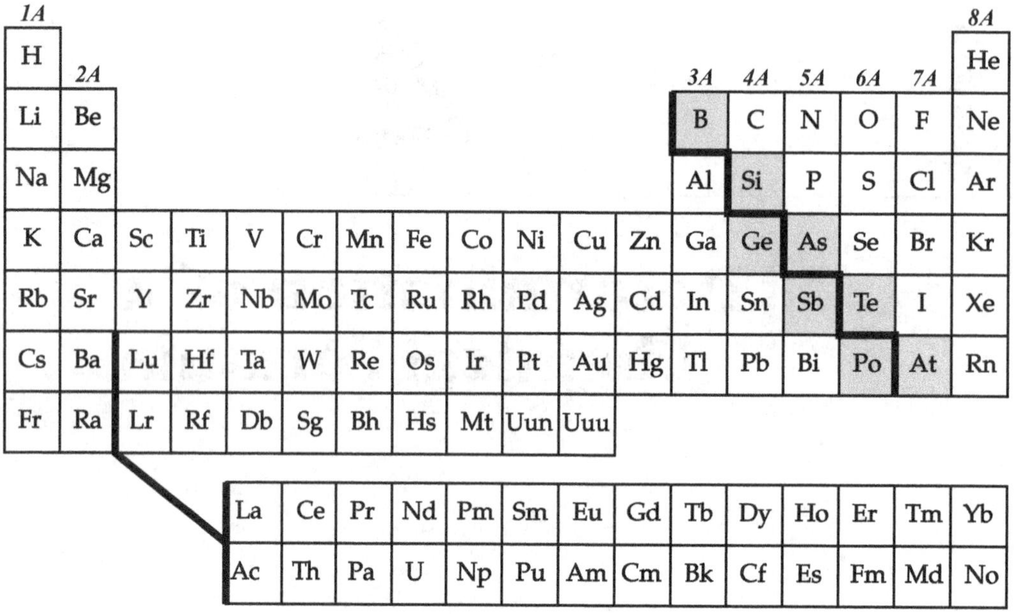

Figure 1. The periodic table. Non-metals are on the right of the bold line, and metals are on the left. The metalloids are directly adjacent to the bold line and are shaded.

Metals tend to lose electrons to form cations. For example, the alkali metals in Group 1A tend to lose one electron and the alkaline earth metals in Group 2A tend to lose two electrons to attain noble gas electronic configurations. Non-metals tend to gain electrons to form anions. The halogens in Group 7A, for example, tend to gain one electron to attain an electronic configuration like that of a noble gas. The alkali metals in Group 1A and the alkaline earth metals in Group 2A are therefore very reactive with non-metals.

In this laboratory you will observe the reactions of zinc and calcium with water and hydrochloric acid. The reaction of either of these metals with hydrochloric acid or water produces hydrogen gas. These reactions can be written in three forms: the molecular equation, the total ionic equation and the net ionic equation shown for calcium and hydrochloric acid as follows.

Molecular Equation: $\quad Ca\ (s) + 2\ HCl\ (aq) \quad \rightarrow \quad CaCl_2\ (aq) + H_2\ (g)$

Total Ionic Equation: $\quad Ca\ (s) + 2\ H^+\ (aq) + 2\ Cl^-\ (aq) \quad \rightarrow \quad Ca^{2+}\ (aq) + 2\ Cl^-\ (aq) + H_2\ (g)$

Net Ionic Equation: $\quad Ca\ (s) + 2\ H^+\ (aq) \quad \rightarrow \quad Ca^{2+}\ (aq) + H_2\ (g)$

The net ionic equation is the simplest way to show which species take part in the reaction. The chloride ions which appear on both sides of the total ionic equation, are spectator ions, they do not participate in the reaction and therefore cancel.

The reactions of zinc and calcium with water and hydrochloric acid are classified as oxidation-reduction reactions (redox reactions). In these reactions the metal is oxidized, losing two electrons. In general, the oxidation of a metal, M, involves the loss of one or more electrons as shown in the following equation, where n represents the number of electrons lost.

$$M \rightarrow M^{n+} + n\ e^- \qquad\qquad \text{(oxidation, loss of electrons)}$$

Oxidation is accompanied by reduction, a gain of electrons. The two electrons lost by the calcium are gained by the hydrogen ions to produce neutral molecular hydrogen, H_2.

Determination of a molecular formula by titration

In the reaction of calcium and water to produce hydrogen gas and calcium hydroxide, you can predict the molecular formula of calcium hydroxide based on the charge of the calcium ion and the hydroxide ion. In this experiment, you will determine the molecular formula of calcium hydroxide by an acid-base titration and show your prediction is correct.

Calcium hydroxide is a base. According to Arrhenius, a base is defined as a substance that, when dissolved in water, increases the concentration of the hydroxide ion, OH^-, relative to that in pure water. An acid is defined as a substance that, when dissolved in water, increases the concentration of the hydrogen ion, H^+, relative to that in pure water. The reaction of an acid with a base produces a salt and water, a process known as neutralization. For example, the reaction of hydrochloric acid with sodium hydroxide produces sodium chloride and water.

$$\text{HCl (aq)} + \text{NaOH (aq)} \rightarrow \text{NaCl (aq)} + H_2O \text{ (l)}$$
$$\quad\text{Acid}\qquad\quad\text{Base}\qquad\qquad\quad\text{Salt}\qquad\quad\text{Water}$$

This reaction can also be written as the total net ionic equation to show which species are present in solution and the net ionic equation, which clearly shows the neutralization reaction.

Total Ionic Equation: $H^+ \text{(aq)} + Cl^- \text{(aq)} + Na^+ \text{(aq)} + OH^- \text{(aq)} \rightarrow Na^+ \text{(aq)} + Cl^- \text{(aq)} + H_2O \text{ (l)}$

Net Ionic Equation: $H^+ \text{(aq)} + OH^- \text{(aq)} \rightarrow H_2O \text{ (l)}$

When the concentration of H^+ is greater than the concentration of OH^-, the solution is acidic. When the concentration of H^+ is less than the concentration of OH^-, the solution is basic. When the concentration of H^+ is equal to the concentration of OH^-, the solution is neutral. Square brackets indicate concentration.

$[H^+]$ > $[OH^-]$ acidic solution
$[H^+]$ < $[OH^-]$ basic solution
$[H^+]$ = $[OH^-]$ neutral solution

A titration is used to determine the concentration of an acid or a base. If the concentration of either the acid or the base is known, the concentration of the other can then be determined. The solution of known concentration is added to a solution of unknown concentration until the equivalence point (or end-point) is reached. At this point the number of moles of hydroxide ions is equal to the number of moles of hydrogen ions.

At the end-point: moles of H^+ = moles of OH^-

The completion of reaction is shown by a change in some physical property, such as a change in color. In colorless reactions an indicator is used to signal the end-point. An indicator is a substance, which changes color dramatically with one drop of additional titrant. Phenolphthalein is an indicator which is colorless in acidic solution and violet in basic solution. Thymol blue is another indicator which is blue in basic solution and turns yellow in acidic solution.

Calcium metal reacts with water to produce calcium hydroxide that dissociates to produce Ca^{2+} (aq) and OH^- (aq) according to the following equations.

$$Ca\ (s) + H_2O\ (l) \quad \rightarrow \quad Ca(OH)_n$$
$$Ca(OH)_n \quad \rightleftharpoons \quad Ca^{2+}\ (aq)\ + n\ OH^-\ (aq)$$

In this equation n is the number of moles of OH^- produced. The solution is titrated with HCl of known concentration and reacts with OH^- (aq) in the solution according to the following net ionic equation.

$$H^+\ (aq) + OH^-\ (aq) \quad \rightarrow \quad H_2O\ (l)$$

By weighing a sample of Ca(s), the moles of Ca(s) can be calculated. From the titration data the moles of OH^- (aq) produced from the calcium hydroxide is determined. As a result, the mole ratio of Ca to OH can be calculated.

SAFETY
WEAR SAFETY GLASSES

Aqueous hydrochloric acid, HCl (aq), is a strong acid and will burn your skin and clothing if contact is made. If you spill chemicals on your skin, flush with water immediately. Hydrogen gas is a colorless, flammable gas. Use forceps or tongs to handle calcium metal. It is corrosive and irritating to skin.

MATERIALS

The calcium metal pieces are approximately 50 mg each stored in petroleum ether to avoid oxidation of calcium to produce a relatively insoluble calcium oxide coating, CaO (s).

PROCEDURE

Part 1. Reaction of Zinc and Calcium with dilute HCl and Water

1. Copy the table on the following page into your lab notebook. Record your observations.

2. Place approximately 2 mL of 6 M HCl in a clean, small test tube. Using a spatula, add a small amount of mossy zinc to the test tube. Place another test tube over the first at a slight angle to allow for air displace-ment. Working rapidly, have another student bring a match close to the mouth of the test tubes. What do you expect to happen? Record your observations. Is heat produced or absorbed in this reaction?

Reactants	Observations
Zn + 6 M HCl	
Ca + 0.02 M HCl	
Zn + water	
Ca + water	

3. Place 2 mL of very dilute HCl, 0.02 M, in a clean, small test tube. Using tweezers or forceps, place a small piece of calcium metal in the dilute HCl and repeat the collection and igni-tion of the gas evolved from the reaction. Always use forceps or tongs to handle calcium metal. It is corrosive and irritating to your skin. Record all your observations. What does the difference in the molarities of the HCl used in these reactions, tell you about the rela-tive reactivity of the two metals? Which metal do you expect to be more reactive with water?

4. Fill two small test tubes with 3 mL of deionized (DI) water. Add a small amount of mossy zinc to one test tube and a small piece of calcium metal to the other. Record your observa-tions. Add two drops of 0.1% phenolphthalein indicator to the test tube containing cal-cium metal. Record the color of the solution. Is the solution acidic or basic?

5. If any unreacted metal remains, add 6 M HCl until it has completely reacted.

6. All waste is disposed of in the appropriately labeled waste container located in the hood.

Part 2. Titration of the Product of the Reaction of Calcium in Water

1. Weigh two approximately 50-mg samples of calcium metal to the nearest 0.001 g. Be sure to use weighing paper and tare the balance. The calcium is stored in petroleum ether to keep it from oxidizing in air. The petroleum ether evaporates very quickly and the calcium can be weighed immediately after removing it from the petroleum ether.

2. Copy the table on the following page into your lab notebook and record the mass of each calcium sample.

Data	Trial 1	Trial 2	Trial 3 (if needed)
Mass of calcium			
Initial volume in the burette			
Final volume in the burette			
Volume of HCl used			
Molarity of HCl			
Molarity of H^+			
Moles of H^+ used to titrate sample			
Moles of OH^- neutralized			
Moles of calcium			
Mole ratio of OH^- to Ca			
Round the ratio to the nearest integer			
Experimental chemical formula			

3. Place each sample into its own clearly labeled 250-mL Erlenmeyer flask (indicate the mass of the calcium sample on the label). Add 150 mL of DI water to each flask. Swirl the flasks until the calcium has completely reacted.

4. Set up a clean, 50-mL burette using a burette clamp and a ring stand. Pour approximately 50 mL of 0.30 M HCl into a clean beaker. Rinse the burette with 5 mL of 0.30 M HCl. Be sure to run some of the acid out of the bottom and the top of the burette into a waste beaker to ensure the burette is sufficiently rinsed.

5. Pour the remainder of the 0.30 M HCl acid into the burette. Titrate a few milliliters into a waste beaker making sure that there are no air bubbles in the tip of the burette. Use a piece of white paper to accurately read the starting point of the HCl in the burette, read the bottom of the meniscus at eye level. Record the initial volume.

6. Add 10 drops of 0.1% thymol blue indicator to one of the 250-mL Erlenmeyer flasks. Titrate the flask by slowly adding acid to it until the blue color changes to yellow. Be sure to swirl the flask with each addition of acid. Once the solution turns yellow, read and record the final volume of the burette at the end point. The difference between the initial and final volumes is the amount of acid added to the flask. Will the second flask need more or less acid than the first? Why?

7. Repeat step 5 with the second Erlenmeyer flask. Make sure the volumes of acids used are recorded with the respective mass of each calcium metal sample.

8. Determine the molecular formula of calcium hydroxide for each of the trials. Do a third trial if you find significant discrepancy between the first two trials.

WASTE DISPOSAL
When all titrations are complete, neutralize the flasks with sodium bicarbonate. After foaming stops dispose of all solutions in the appropriately labeled waste bottle in the hood.

PRE-LAB QUESTIONS
1. In forming compounds does a calcium atom gain or lose electrons? How many electrons? What is the charge on the hydroxide ion? What would you predict for the chemical formula of calcium hydroxide? Does the calcium hydroxide compound have a charge?

2. The alkali metals and alkaline earth metals (Group 1A and 2A) are known to react vigorously with water and acid, both reactions produce hydrogen gas as shown for sodium metal. Balance the equations below:

$$Na\ (s) + H_2O\ (l)\ \ \rightarrow\ \ NaOH\ (aq) + H_2\ (g)$$

$$Na\ (s) + HCl\ (aq)\ \ \rightarrow\ \ NaCl\ (aq) + H_2\ (g)$$

3. How many moles of H_2 will be produced if 15.0 g of Na reacts completely with excess HCl?

4. In this experiment a sample of calcium reacts with water to produce calcium hydroxide and hydrogen gas.
    a) The solution is titrated with HCl. Write the net ionic reaction that occurs.
    b) How will you know when the reaction is complete?

5. A solution contains thymol blue indicator. For each of the following, indicate if the solution is acidic, basic or neutral and the color of the solution.

a) $[H^+]$ > $[OH^-]$

b) $[H^+]$ < $[OH^-]$

c) $[H^+]$ = $[OH^-]$

6. Complete and balance each of the following reactions in aqueous solution, show both the molecular equation and the net ionic equation.

$$HCl + KOH \rightarrow$$

$$HCl + Ba(OH)_2 \rightarrow$$

DISCUSSION QUESTIONS

Discuss the reactions observed including the relative reactivity of the metals, the production of a gas, combustion of the gas evolved, production or consumption of heat, and observed changes in color. Include balanced equations for each reaction discussed. Also include the molecular, total ionic and net ionic equations for hydrochloric acid reacting with calcium hydroxide. In determining the molecular formula for calcium hydroxide, before rounding to the nearest integer, was the hydroxide to calcium ratio high or low with respect to the theoretical ratio? Discuss possible sources of error, and the affect the calcium, hydroxide mole ratio, would it be too high or too low? Compare the trials and discuss which you feel is the more accurate value and why.

REVIEW QUESTIONS

1. Give the molecular formula of aluminum hydroxide. How many equivalents of HCl will react with aluminum hydroxide?

2. Give the molecular formula for sodium hydroxide. How many equivalents of HCl will react with sodium hydroxide?

3. If some of the calcium metal remains unreacted when you start the titration, the calcium will react with hydrochloric acid to produce hydrogen gas.

$$Ca\ (s) + 2\ HCl\ (aq) \rightarrow CaCl_2\ (aq) + H_2\ (g)$$

Would this cause error in the titration? If so, would more or less HCl be required? How would this effect the molecular formula for calcium hydroxide?

4. Sodium bicarbonate ($NaHCO_3$) is used to neutralize acids to form sodium chloride, a salt, carbon dioxide gas, and water. Normally sodium bicarbonate is added until the fizzing ceases, at which point no more CO_2 (g) is produced.

$$NaHCO_3 \text{ (s)} + HCl \text{ (aq)} \quad \rightarrow \quad NaCl \text{ (aq)} + CO_2 \text{ (g)} + H_2O \text{ (l)}$$

If 100 mL of 6 M HCl is spilled on a lab bench what is the minimum mass of sodium bicarbonate that must be used to neutralize the acid?

■ EXPERIMENT 4

Experiment **5**

5

The Molar Volume of Gases

PURPOSE
To determine the molar volume of a gas. To learn how to quantitatively measure the volumes of gases and calculate the molar volume of a gas at standard temperature and pressure using the ideal gas law and Dalton's law of partial pressures.

PRINCIPLES
Molar Volume of an Ideal Gas
The **molar volume** is defined as the volume of one mole of a substance, or the volume per mole of substance, V/n. The molar volume of a gas varies with temperature and pressure as the gas expands and compresses. We can calculate the molar volume of a gas from its density and molar mass at a given temperature and pressure.

$$\frac{V}{n} = \frac{\text{molar mass (g / mol)}}{\text{density (g / L)}} = \text{molar volume (L / mol)}$$

Table 1. Molar Volumes of Gases at 0°C and 1 atm

Gas	Density (g/L)	Molar Mass (g/mol)	Molar Volume (L/mol)
CO	1.250	28.010	22.406
N_2	1.250	28.013	22.403
He	0.178	4.003	22.429
H_2	0.0899	2.016	22.429
CO_2	1.977	44.010	22.262
HCl	1.639	36.461	22.244
O_2	1.429	31.999	22.392

Table 1 clearly shows that for a variety of gases, at standard temperature and pressure (STP), the molar volume is very near 22.4 L/mol. In other words, at 0°C and 1 atm, one mole of a gas occupies approximately 22.4 L. Two moles of gas would occupy 44.8 L. This is known as **Avogadro's Law**: For a gas at constant temperature and pressure the volume is directly proportional to the number of moles of gas, n.

$$V \alpha n \qquad \text{(fixed pressure and fixed temperature)}$$

The relationship between molar volume and pressure and temperature are described in Boyle's law and Charles' law as follows.

Boyle's Law: The volume of a fixed quantity of gas at a fixed temperature is inversely proportional to pressure. As the volume increases the pressure decreases.

$$P \alpha (1/V) \qquad \text{(fixed temperature and fixed amount of gas)}$$

Charles' Law: For a fixed quantity of gas at constant pressure, the volume increases as the temperature increases. A plot of volume versus temperature is a straight line and the intercept of this plot, when T is measured in °C, is –273.15°C. This is why absolute zero of temperature is defined as 0 K = –273.15°C. T (in Kelvin) = T (in °C) + 273.15

$$V \alpha T \qquad \text{(fixed pressure and fixed amount of gas)}$$

Combining the gas laws of Boyle, Charles and Avogadro, the ideal gas law is derived. The general equation given for the ideal gas law, is an empirical law which holds approximately for all gases near atmospheric pressure and becomes increasingly accurate at low pressures.

$$PV = nRT \qquad\qquad \text{Ideal Gas Law}$$

The temperature, T, is the absolute temperature in units of Kelvin. R is the universal gas constant that has the same value for all gases. R can be estimated from the observation that one mole of any gas at 0°C and 1 atm occupies approximately 22.4 L.

$$R = \frac{PV}{nT} = \frac{(1.0\text{ atm})(22.4\text{ L})}{(1\text{ mol})(273\text{ K})} = 0.08206\ \frac{\text{L atm}}{\text{mol K}}$$

The numerical value of R depends on the units chosen for pressure and volume. Commonly used values of the gas constant, obtained through simple unit conversions, include the following:

$R = 0.08206$ L atm mol^{-1} K^{-1} $\qquad\qquad$ $R = 1.987$ cal mol^{-1} K^{-1}

$R = 8.314$ J mol^{-1} K^{-1} $\qquad\qquad$ $R = 8.314$ kg m^2 sec^{-2} mol^{-1} K^{-1}

In this experiment you will determine the molar volume of oxygen and hydrogen at standard temperature and pressure (STP; 0°C and 1 atm) and compare these values to the molar volume of 22.414 L/mol for an ideal gas at STP. To determine the molar volume of oxygen, the decomposition reaction of hydrogen peroxide, H_2O_2, to produce water and oxygen will be used.

$$2\,H_2O_2\,(l) \xrightarrow{\text{catalyst}} 2\,H_2O\,(l)\ +\ O_2\,(g)$$

This reaction is slow and a catalyst is needed to speed up the reaction. The catalyst used in this experiment is $FeCl_3$, it speeds up the reaction without being consumed in the reaction itself. Because mass is always conserved in a reaction, the difference between the weight of reactants before the reaction takes place and the weight of products after the reaction goes to completion equals the mass of oxygen gas evolved. By measuring the volume of O_2 produced at a known temperature and pressure, we can calculate the molar volume of O_2 in L/mol (the volume of O_2 divided by the moles of O_2 produced).

To determine the molar volume of hydrogen, the reaction of magnesium with excess hydrochloric acid to produce hydrogen gas, will be used.

$$Mg(s) + 2\,HCl\,(aq)\ \rightarrow\ MgCl_2\,(aq) + H_2\,(g)$$

By weighing a piece of magnesium metal and letting it completely react, the number of moles of hydrogen gas produced can be calculated directly from the reaction stoichiometry. By measuring the volume of H_2 produced at a known temperature and pressure, we can calculate the molar volume of H_2 in L/mol (the volume of H_2 divided by the moles of H_2 produced).

The volume of oxygen gas and hydrogen gas produced in these reactions, corresponds to the volume of water displaced by each gas. We must take into account that when any gas in a closed container is collected over liquid water, or is exposed to water, the water contributes to the total vapor pressure. Water evaporates until a saturated vapor results, that is, until opposing rates of evaporation and condensation of water molecules at the liquid surface reach a balance. According to Dalton's law of partial pressures, each gas exerts its own pressure regardless of the presence of other gases. For example, in the collection of oxygen gas the total pressure is the sum of the partial pressure of oxygen and water.

$$P_{TOTAL} = P_{O_2} + P_{H_2O}$$

Thus, to determine the pressure of oxygen gas, a correction for the vapor pressure of water (P_{H_2O}) must be made.

$$P_{O_2} = P_{TOTAL} - P_{H_2O}$$

The state of a gas is defined by its pressure, volume, temperature and the number of moles. For the change in state from P_1, V_1, T_1, n_1 to P_2, V_2, T_2, n_2 the following equations hold:

$$\frac{P_1V_1}{n_1T_1} = \frac{P_2V_2}{n_2T_2}$$

$$\frac{P_1V_1}{T_1} = \frac{P_2V_2}{T_2} \quad \text{at constant n}$$

This equation can be rearranged to: $\quad V_2 = V_1\left(\frac{P_1}{P_2}\right)\left(\frac{T_2}{T_1}\right)$ at constant n

Thus, if we measure the volume of a gas to be V_1, at temperature T_1, and pressure P_1, the volume of the gas (V_2) can be calculated at any other temperature (T_2) and pressure (P_2). In this experiment, you will measure the volume of oxygen and hydrogen at the experimental temperature and pressure and you will then calculate the volume of each gas at STP (0°C and 1 atm).

EQUIPMENT
Extra small test tubes, 10 × 75 mm, are supplied for the $FeCl_3$ catalyst. These test tubes must be returned after class.

SAFETY
WEAR SAFETY GLASSES

Aqueous hydrochloric acid, HCl (aq), is a strong acid and will burn your skin and clothing if contact is made. If you spill chemicals on your skin, flush with water immediately.

PROCEDURE
Part 1. Production of Oxygen Gas

1. Assemble the apparatus as shown in Figure 1. Clean the glassware with soap and water, use deionized water (DI water) as the final rinse. For flask B use a 500-mL Erlenmeyer flask or a 500-mL filter flask. You may have one in your drawer. If not, borrow one from the stock room. Remove the yellow side arm from the filter flask and put a cork in the hole on the side of the flask. Corks are provided in a bin along with the rubber stoppers and hoses.

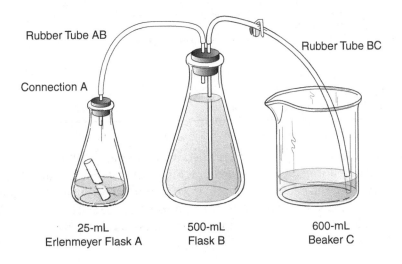

Figure 1. Note the position of the clamp, it is near the top of flask B.

2. Measure 20 mL of 3% H_2O_2 solution in a graduated cylinder and pour it into a 250-mL Erlenmeyer flask (flask A in the Figure). Measure and pour approximately 4.5 mL of 3M $FeCl_3$ into a 10 × 75 mm test tube (a very small test tube provided for this experiment). Holding flask A at an angle, carefully slide the test tube into the flask or lower the test tube with a pair of tongs.

3. Weigh flask A and its contents. Copy the table below into your lab notebook to record the data.

Data: Decomposition of H_2O_2 using $FeCl_3$ as a catalyst	
Mass of flask A and its contents before reaction	
Mass of flask A and its contents after reaction	
Temperature of the gas in flask A (The temperature of the solution in flask A)	
Temperature of the gas in flask B (The temperature of the solution in flask B)	
Average temperature of the gas	
Volume of oxygen gas collected	
Barometric pressure	
Water vapor pressure at the average temperature of the gas (see Appendix 1, interpolate the value)	

4. Fill the 500-mL Erlenmeyer flask B to the neck with tap water. Fill the 600-mL beaker C about one-third full with tap water. Disconnect the rubber stopper at point A and attach a pipette bulb. With the pinch clamp open, force air into rubber tube AB by squeezing the pipette bulb, forcing water from flask B into the beaker C. Raise and lower beaker C to move water back and forth through rubber tube BC to remove all air bubbles. With water half-way up the neck of flask B, reconnect the stopper at point A.

5. With the pinch clamp open, test the apparatus for leaks, as follows. Raise beaker C as high as possible without removing tubing from the beaker. The water level in flask B should move a little and then remain fixed. If the water level continues to change, a leak is present. Do not proceed until the leak is fixed.

6. Equalize the pressures inside and outside flask B by raising the beaker until the water level in the beaker and in flask B are the same. While one student holds the beaker to keep the water levels the same, another student closes the pinch clamp, positioned near the stopper on flask B. Pour out all the water in beaker C. Replace the tube in the beaker and open the pinch clamp. A little water will flow out and should be retained in the beaker.

7. Tip flask A carefully so that the $FeCl_3$ catalyst spills out of the test tube into the hydrogen peroxide solution (avoid getting the solution on the stopper). Note and record any changes that you see. As the oxygen is released, water is forced from flask B into beaker C. Feel the bottom of flask A. Is heat released or absorbed in the reaction? Note the level of the water in beaker C. When the reaction stops, and the water level remains constant, you can assume the decomposition of the hydrogen peroxide is complete.

8. Raise beaker C until the water levels in flask B and beaker C are equal, at which point another student closes the pinch clamp on tube BC. Measure the volume of oxygen produced by carefully pouring the water in beaker C into a graduated cylinder. Record the volume of water displaced by the oxygen gas.

9. To measure the temperature of the gas produced in the reaction, loosen the stopper on flask A and insert a thermometer into the solution. Measure and record the temperature of the solution in flask A. Similarly, measure and record the temperature of the solution in flask B. The average of these two temperatures represents the temperature of the oxygen gas.

10. Disconnect flask A at point A and weigh and record the flask and its contents.

11. Obtain the barometric pressure from your instructor. You can also obtain the value on the web: http://www.weather.com/weather/us/cities.html

    For the local barometric pressure enter the name of the city or the zip code.

12. All waste is disposed of in the appropriately labeled waste container located in the hood.

Part 2. Production of Hydrogen Gas

1. Set up the apparatus as in part 1. Clean the glassware with soap and water, use DI water as the final rinse.

2. Weigh an 8-cm piece of magnesium and place it into a 250-mL Erlenmeyer flask. Pour 4.5 mL of 3 M HCl into a small, 10×75 mm, test tube. Holding flask A at an angle, carefully slide the test tube into the flask or lower it using a pair of tongs without spilling any of the contents.

3. Copy the following table into your lab notebook to record the data.

Data: Reaction of Mg (s) with HCl	
Mass of magnesium metal	
Temperature of the gas in flask A (The temperature of the solution in flask A)	
Temperature of the gas in flask B (The temperature of the solution in flask B)	
Average temperature of the gas	
Volume of hydrogen gas collected	
Barometric pressure	
Water vapor pressure at the average temperature of the gas (see Appendix 1, interpolate the value)	

4. Repeat steps 4-11 of Part 1. Note in step 7, when flask A is tipped the HCl spills out of the test tube into the flask containing the Mg (s). The reaction is complete when all the magnesium disappears. The reaction produces hydrogen gas. When the temperature of the gas in flask A is measured, tip the flask to submerge the tip of the thermometer in the HCl solution.

WASTE DISPOSAL
Dispose of all waste in the appropriately labeled waste container in the hood.

CALCULATIONS
Part 1. The molar volume of oxygen.
Make a table (as shown) in your lab notebook to do calculations.

Data	Calculations
Mass of oxygen	
Moles of oxygen	
Average temperature of gas (absolute, K)	
Pressure of oxygen, P_{O_2}	
Volume of O_2 at STP (calculate this from your data)	
Molar volume of O_2 at STP (L/mol)	

Part 2. The molar volume of hydrogen.

Make a table (as shown) in your lab notebook to do calculations.

Data	Calculations
Mass of magnesium	
Moles of hydrogen	
Average temperature of gas (absolute, K)	
Pressure of hydrogen, P_{H_2}	
Volume of H_2 at STP (calculate this from your data)	
Molar volume of H_2 at STP (L/mol)	

PRE-LAB QUESTIONS

1. The density of ammonia, NH_3, is 0.76 g/L at STP. Calculate the molar volume of ammonia at STP. Hint: What are the units of molar volume? Once you know the units you want, you can easily see how to get from g/L to the units you want.

2. What is the volume of one mole of oxygen at STP?

3. What is the volume of 48.1 g of CH_4 at STP?

4. In Part 1, you will determine the molar volume of O_2 produced in the decomposition of hydrogen peroxide.

$$2\ H_2O_2\ (l) \xrightarrow{\text{catalyst}} 2\ H_2O\ (l) + O_2\ (g)$$

    a) How will you determine the mass and number of moles of oxygen produced?
    b) How will you determine the volume of oxygen produced?

5. In Part 1, you will determine the volume of oxygen gas produced at the experimental temperature and pressure. In the collection of oxygen gas over liquid water, the total pressure is the sum of the partial pressure of oxygen and water.

$$P_{TOTAL} = P_{O_2} + P_{H_2O}$$

Thus, to determine the pressure of oxygen gas, you subtract the vapor pressure of water (P_{H_2O}) from the total pressure (P_{TOTAL}).

$$P_{O_2} = P_{TOTAL} - P_{H_2O}$$

How do you determine P_{TOTAL} in this equation? Why must you equalize the pressure inside and outside flask B to determine P_{TOTAL}?

6. Calculate the partial pressure of water at 21.6°C by interpolation from the vapor pressure table in Appendix 2 of this Lab Manual.

7. If you collect hydrogen over water (by water displacement) at 767.0 torr total pressure and 22.3°C, what is the partial pressure of the hydrogen?

8. In Part 2, you will determine the molar volume of H_2 produced the reaction of magnesium with excess hydrochloric acid to produce hydrogen gas, will be used.

$$Mg(s) + 2\ HCl\ (aq) \quad \rightarrow \quad MgCl_2\ (aq) + H_2\ (g)$$

   a) How will you determine the number of moles of hydrogen produced?
   b) How will you determine the volume of hydrogen produced?

9. If the volume of hydrogen is 110 mL, at 750 torr and 20°C, what is the volume at STP? Organize the information given:

   $V_1 = 110$ mL $V_2 = ?$
   $P_1 = 750$ torr $P_2 = 1$ atm = 760 torr
   $T_1 = 20°C + 273 = 293$ K $T_2 = 0°C = 273$ K

How do you solve for V_2? It is best to solve for V_2 in terms of variables first then substitute in the numbers.

$$V_2 = V_1 \left(\frac{P_1}{P_2} \right) \left(\frac{T_2}{T_1} \right)$$

Note that the temperature must be in units of Kelvin.

DISCUSSION QUESTIONS

Briefly discuss what was measured in this experiment and the general method used (include reactions where appropriate). Compare your experimental value for the molar volume of H_2 and O_2 at STP to the expected value. What is the expected value? Under the conditions of this experiment, would you expect both H_2 and O_2 gases to behave ideally? Explain why or why not. Discuss the main sources of error in this experiment. Discuss whether or not this is a reliable method for measuring the molar volume of a gas.

REVIEW QUESTIONS

1. Explain the function of $FeCl_3$ in the decomposition of H_2O_2? If we would have used 5.0 mL of 3 M $FeCl_3$ rather than 4.5 mL of 3 M $FeCl_3$, would it have made any difference in the amount of oxygen gas collected? Explain why or why not.

2. In this experiment, some oxygen gas and hydrogen gas will dissolve in water. How will this effect the molar volume calculated? Would the molar volume be too high or too low?

3. If 0.49 g of a gas occupies 275 mL at 26°C and 1.10 atm, calculate the molar mass of the gas.

4. The density of a gas is 0.940 g/L at 25°C and 360 torr. Calculate the molar mass of the gas.

5. The density of dry air is 1.2929 g/L at STP. Calculate the average molar mass of air. Is this a reasonable value? Explain why or why not.

6. What is an ideal gas?

7. Under what conditions do real gases behave most like ideal gases?

8. The molar volume for CO_2 and HCl are 22.262 L/mol and 22.244 L/mol, respectively. Why are these molar volumes slightly less than the ideal molar volume, 22.4 L/mol?

9. Hydrogen gas can be produced from the reaction of calcium hydride and water.

   $$CaH_2 \text{ (s)} + 2\ H_2O \text{ (l)} \rightarrow 2\ H_2 \text{ (g)} + Ca(OH)_2 \text{ (aq)}$$

   How many grams of calcium hydride are needed to produce 1.0 L of hydrogen gas, collected over water at 26°C and 760 torr total pressure.

■ EXPERIMENT 5

Experiment **6**

6

Thermochemistry

PURPOSE AND LEARNING OBJECTIVES

To develop an understanding of temperature, heat, and heat capacity. To calibrate a simple calorimeter which is used to measure the specific heat of a metal, the heat of solution, and the heat of neutralization.

PRINCIPLES

The first law of thermodynamics states that energy must be conserved. Energy can be converted from one form into another, but can not be created or destroyed. Conservation of energy is as fundamental to chemical processes as the laws of conservation of mass and charge. These laws are not derived but are drawn from an immense number of observations of the way matter behaves. A chemical reaction generally involves breaking bonds and making new bonds. Energy is required to break bonds and energy is released when bonds are formed. In a chemical reaction, if energy is released the reaction is **exothermic** ($\Delta H < 0$) and if energy is absorbed the reaction is **endothermic** ($\Delta H > 0$). In this experiment, the heat of solution will be measured for the dissolution of a salt in aqueous solution and the heat of neutralization will be measured for acid-base reactions.

In a reaction, the energy absorbed or released is in the form of heat. The magnitude of heat flow in a reaction is measured using a thermally insulated container called a **calorimeter**. Ideally, no energy will be lost from the calorimeter to its surroundings. Consider the neutralization reaction for a strong acid reacting with a strong base.

$$H^+ (aq) + OH^- (aq) \rightarrow H_2O (l) + heat$$

The solution and the calorimeter will absorb the heat released by the reaction. The amount of heat absorbed by the solution, q, depends on the mass of the solution, m, its specific heat capacity, c_s, and change in temperature, ΔT.

$$q = m\, c_s\, \Delta T$$

The specific heat capacity is defined as the amount of heat required to raise the temperature of one gram of substance by one degree under constant pressure conditions. The heat released by the reaction is exactly equal to the heat absorbed by the solution and the calorimeter.

$$q_{reaction} = -(q_{solution} + q_{calorimeter})$$

$$q_{reaction} = -(m\, c_s\, \Delta T + C_{cal}\Delta T)$$

where C_{cal} is the heat capacity of the calorimeter in units of $J\ K^{-1}$. In order to calculate the heat of reaction, C_{cal} must be determined. The heat released in a reaction depends on the number of moles of reactant consumed. When two moles of acid react with two moles of base to produce two moles of water, the heat released will be twice as much as when one mole of acid and base is consumed in the reaction.

In this experiment, in addition to measuring heats of reaction, the specific heat capacity of an unknown metal will be determined. The specific and molar heat capacities of a number of metals are shown in Table 1. If the specific heat capacity of an unknown metal is measured, the metal can be identified using the data in this table.

The molar heat capacities are nearly constant for all the metals, with an average value of approximately 25 J mol^{-1} K^{-1}. This was discovered by Pierre Dulong and Alexis Petit in 1819 and is referred to as the **Law of Dulong and Petit**. Even though they did not understand the reason for this, they used this observation to estimate the atomic masses of metals. In 1907 Albert Einstein published a theory explaining the observed molar heat capacities of metals. The metal atoms are treated as oscillators, vibrating in three dimensions. Einstein showed that as the temperature approaches absolute zero (zero degrees Kelvin) the molar heat capacity reduces to 3R, where R is the universal gas constant, R = 8.314 J mol^{-1} K^{-1}. Thus, his theory predicts an average molar heat capacity of 24.9 J mol^{-1} K^{-1}.

Table 1. Specific Heat Capacities and Molar Heat capacities of various metals

Metal	Specific Heat Capacity (J K^{-1} g^{-1})	Molar Heat Capacity (J mol^{-1} k^{-1})
Li	3.561	24.77
Mg	1.024	24.89
Al	0.903	24.35
Fe	0.449	25.10
Ni	0.444	26.07
Zn	0.389	25.40
Cu	0.385	24.44
Ag	0.235	25.35
Au	0.129	25.42
Pb	0.128	26.44

In measuring heat capacities, only differences in temperature are considered. The numerical difference in temperature is the same on the Celsius and Kelvin scales. For example, if the initial temperature is measured to be 20°C and the final temperature 45°C, $\Delta T = 25°C = 25$ K, shown as follows.

$$\Delta T = T_{final} - T_{initial} = 45°C - 20°C = 25°C$$

or

$$\Delta T = T_{final} - T_{initial} = 318 \text{ K} - 293 \text{ K} = 25 \text{ K}$$

The specific heat capacity of water is 4.184 J°C^{-1}g^{-1} or 4.184 JK^{-1}g^{-1}. Water has an unusually high heat capacity and boiling point because of a network of hydrogen bonds formed between the water molecules. Thus, a small amount of water can absorb a relatively large amount of heat. As a result, large bodies of water, oceans and lakes, moderate the temperature on earth. It also makes water a convenient coolant for many devices, including engines, vacuum pumps and lasers.

■ EXPERIMENT 6

SAFETY
WEAR SAFETY GLASSES

HCl is a strong acid and NaOH is a strong base. In case of contact, rinse thoroughly with water. Clean up spills immediately.

PROCEDURE
This experiment will be performed in pairs. It is important to stay consistent when taking measurements. Have one partner read the thermometer throughout a given part of the lab.

Part 1. The Heat Capacity of the Calorimeter
1. Construct the Styrofoam cup calorimeter shown in Figure 1. Obtain two Styrofoam cups and a lid. Place one cup inside the other and put the lid on.

2. Obtain a 0.1˚C thermometer. Be careful using the mercury thermometer. The thermometer runs through the center of a cork, held by a clamp, attached to a ring-stand. Align the thermometer so it goes through the center of the lid, into the cups.

    NOTE: The thermometer must slide easily through the cork, if not, exchange this thermometer for another.

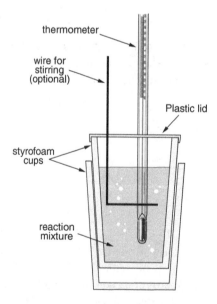

Figure 1. A Styrofoam cup calorimeter.

3. Chill approximately 60 mL of DI water in an ice bath to about 10˚C.

4. Heat another 60 mL of DI water to between 60-80˚C using a Bunsen burner.

5. Using the 100-mL graduated cylinder, add exactly 50.0 mL of chilled water to the calorimeter. The lid should be on the cup with the thermometer sticking through the lid. Swirl the cup and record the temperature every 30 seconds for 4 minutes, until the temperature is constant. At this point the temperature of the chilled water and the calorimeter have come to equilibrium.

6. When the heated water is between 60-80°C, measure 50.0 mL of the hot water in a graduated cylinder and record its temperature.

7. Quickly add the heated water to the chilled water in the calorimeter.

8. Swirl the cup and begin taking measurements every 15 seconds for 4 minutes. The temperature will rise and then decrease.

Calculate the Heat Capacity of the Calorimeter

1. Use Excel on the computer to graph the temperature of the calorimeter water (°C) on the y-axis and the time (seconds) on the x-axis, as shown in Figure 2.

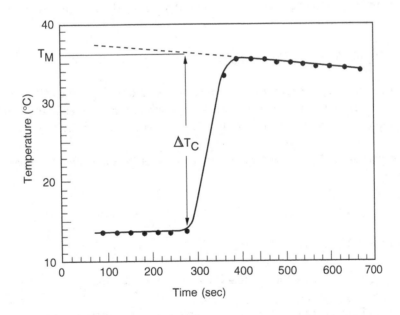

Figure 2. The temperature of the water in the calorimeter is measured as a function of time. Initially the temperature of the cold water is measured. When hot water is added, the temperature is observed to increase. As the hot and cold water mix some heat is lost to the calorimeter so the maximum temperature measured is not as high as it would be if no heat were lost. To obtain the maximum temperature of the solution, T_M, the data must be extrapolated back to the time the solutions were mixed.

2. Determine the maximum temperature, T_M, from your graph.

3. Use the maximum temperature, T_M to calculate the decrease in temperature of the hot water, ΔT_H.

$$\Delta T_H = T_M - T_H$$

4. Use T_M to calculate the increase in temperature of the cold water, ΔT_C.

$$\Delta T_C = T_M - T_C$$

5. The amount of heat lost by the hot water, q_H, is calculated from its mass, m_H, specific heat, c_s, and ΔT_H.

$$q_H = (m_H)(c_s)(\Delta T_H)$$

The specific heat of water, $c_s = 4.184$ J K^{-1} g^{-1}. The density of water is 1 g/mL.

6. The total amount of heat gained by the cold water and by the calorimeter, q_C, is calculated as the sum of the two.

$$q_C = (m_C)(c_s)(\Delta T_C) + C_{cal}(\Delta T_C)$$

The first quantity represents the heat gained by the cold water in the calorimeter and the second quantity represents the heat gained by the cup, thermometer, and stirrer. The symbol C_{cal} represents the heat capacity of the calorimeter in units of J K^{-1}.

7. The heat gained by the cold water and the calorimeter is exactly equal to heat lost by the hot water.

$$q_C = -q_H$$

$$(m_C)(c_s)(\Delta T_C) + C_{cal}(\Delta T_C) = -(m_H)(c_s)(\Delta T_H)$$

Use this equation, to solve for the heat capacity of the calorimeter, C_{cal}.

8. Repeat the calibration to make sure you are able to obtain consistent results.

9. Show your graphs and calculations to your instructor before proceeding to Part 2.

Part 2. Heat Capacity of an Unknown Metal

1. Fill a 250-mL beaker with approximately 200 mL of DI water. Allow the water to come to room temperature.

2. Set up a Bunsen burner and ring stand with a ring and wire gauze.

3. Weigh a sample of approximately 80 grams of the unknown metal to the nearest 0.01 g. **The metal must be thoroughly dry.** Put the metal sample in a large labeled test tube and loosely stopper the test tube.

4. Fill a 600-mL beaker two thirds full with water.

5. Immerse the test tube in the 600-mL beaker. Heat the water in the beaker to a boil using the Bunsen burner.

6. Once the water is boiling, the test tube must be left for at least 15 minutes to ensure the temperature of the metal reaches equilibrium with the temperature of the water.

7. While keeping an eye on the boiling water, do Part 3.

8. After completing Part 3, clean and dry the calorimeter.

9. Measure 50.0 mL of room temperature DI water.

10. Pour the water into the calorimeter. Stir the water and record the temperature until a consistent temperature is reached.

11. Record the temperature of the boiling water with the test tube containing the metal in it.

12. Using a folded paper towel, take the test tube with the unknown metal out of the boiling water. Quickly and carefully pour the metal into the calorimeter. **Make sure no hot water is added to the calorimeter.**

13. Stir the water in the calorimeter and record the temperature every 30 seconds for about 3 minutes or until the temperature remains constant.

14. Decant most of the water out of the calorimeter. Pour the metal onto a paper towel, dry the metal and put it into the appropriately labeled beaker in the hood. The metal must be completely dry before it can be reused.

Calculate the Heat Capacity of the Unknown Metal and Identify the Metal

1. Use Excel on the computer to graph the temperature of the calorimeter water (˚C) on the y-axis and the time (seconds) on the x-axis, analogous to the graph shown in Part 1.

■ **EXPERIMENT 6**

2. Determine T_M and calculate the temperature increase of the water, ΔT_C, and the temperature decrease in the metal, ΔT_H.

3. Using the heat capacity of the calorimeter, C_{cal}, determined in Part 1, calculate the heat gained by the water and the calorimeter.

$$q_C = (m_C)(c_s)(\Delta T_C) + C_{cal}(\Delta T_C)$$

4. The heat lost by the metal equals the heat gained by the water and calorimeter

$$-q_m = q_C$$

$$-(m)(c_{metal})(\Delta T_H) = (m_C)(c_s)(\Delta T_C) + C_{cal}(\Delta T_C)$$

Calculate the specific heat for the unknown metal, c_{metal}. Include units. From the table of specific heats of metals, identify your metal.

5. According to the Law of Dulong and Petit, the molar heat capacity of a metal, c_p, is equal to the specific heat of the metal, c_{metal}, times its molar mass, M.

$$c_p = (c_{metal})(M)$$

It was shown that $c_p \approx 25$ JK^{-1}mol^{-1} for most metals. Using your experimental value for the specific heat and $c_p = 25$ JK^{-1}mol^{-1}, obtain the atomic mass of the unknown metal in the table below.

Specific Heat Capacity of the unknown metal	Metal	Calculated Atomic Mass of the Metal	Actual Atomic Mass of the Metal

Part 3. The Heat of Solution

1. Use the calorimeter calibrated in Part 1. Drain the water and dry the calorimeter.

2. Add 50.0 mL of room temperature DI water to the calorimeter and put on the lid. Let the water sit in the calorimeter 3-4 minutes to allow the water and the calorimeter come to an equilibrium temperature. Record the temperature of the water.

3. Weigh two grams of NH_4NO_3 using weighing paper, to the nearest 0.001 g.

4. Quickly add the ammonium nitrate to the calorimeter. Swirl the cup and record the temperature every 15 seconds for 5 minutes.

5. Drain the ammonium nitrate solution from the calorimeter into the appropriately labeled waste bottle in the hood. Rinse the calorimeter with DI water and dry it.

Calculate the Heat of Solution

1. Write the balanced equation for the reaction.

2. Use Excel to graph your data. In your graph you must include the temperature measurements of the water before the ammonium nitrate was added.

3. Calculate the change in temperature, $\Delta T = T_{final} - T_{initial}$.

4. Calculate the heat of solution, q. Assume the solution has a density of 1.00 g/mL and a specific heat of 4.184 $JK^{-1}g^{-1}$.

$$q = -(C_{cal}\Delta T + m_{solution}C_s\Delta T)$$

5. Calculate the molar heat of solution, $\Delta H_{solution}$.

$$\Delta H_{solution} = \frac{q}{moles\ of\ NH_4NO_3}$$

6. Calculate ΔH of reaction from the thermodynamic data given as follows.

	NH_4NO_3 (s)	$\rightarrow$	NH_4^+ (aq)	+	NO_3^- (aq)
ΔH_f° (kJ/mol)	−365.6		−132		−205

How does the calculated value of ΔH compare with your experimental value?

	NH_4NO_3 (s) + H_2O (l)
Net Ionic Reaction	
ΔT	
q	
Experimental $\Delta H_{solution}$	
Calculated $\Delta H_{solution}$	

Part 4. The Heat of Neutralization

1. Using a graduated cylinder, add 50.0 mL of 3.0 M NaOH to the calorimeter. Cover it with the lid and let the NaOH solution sit for 4 minutes. Record the temperature.

2. Measure 50.0 mL of 3.0 M HCl in a clean graduated cylinder. Record the temperature. The temperature of the HCl and NaOH solutions should be the same (within 0.2°C). If the temperatures are not the same, adjust the temperature of the HCl by running warm or cold tap water on the outside of the graduated cylinder.

3. Quickly but carefully add the HCl to the calorimeter. Put the lid on. Stir the solution and record the temperature every 15 seconds for 4 minutes.

4. Pour the waste into the appropriately labeled waste container in the hood. Clean and dry the calorimeter.

5. Repeat the measurement (steps 1-5) using acetic acid, 3 M CH_3COOH, instead of HCl.

Calculate the Heat of Neutralization

1. Write the balanced net ionic equation for HCl reacting with NaOH. HCl is a strong acid and NaOH is a strong base. Both dissociate completely in aqueous solution.

2. Graph the data and determine T_M. In your graph you must include the temperature measurements of the 50 mL NaOH in the calorimeter before the HCl was added.

3. Calculate the change in temperature of the solution and the heat of neutralization, q.

$$\Delta T = T_{final} - T_{initial} = T_M - T_{initial}$$
$$q = - (C_{cal}\Delta T + m_{solution}C_s\Delta T)$$

In this equation, $m_{solution}$ is the mass of the solution (total volume): 50 mL 3 M HCl plus 50 mL 3 M NaOH. Assume all solutions have a density of 1.00 g/mL and a specific heat of 4.184 J $K^{-1}g^{-1}$.

4. Calculate the molar heat of neutralization, $\Delta H_{neutralization}$.

$$\Delta H_{neutralization} = \frac{q}{\text{moles of } H_2O \text{ produced}}$$

The molar heat of neutralization is the heat released per mole of H_2O produced in the reaction. To calculate the number of moles of H_2O produced, the limiting reagent must be determined.

$$H^+ + OH^- \rightarrow H_2O$$

5. Calculate the molar heat of neutralization for CH_3COOH reacting with NaOH.

    CH_3COOH is a weak acid and does not like to give up a proton, H^+, in aqueous solution. However, the OH- is a strong base and will take the H+ from CH_3COOH until the reaction has gone to completion. The net ionic reaction for CH_3COOH reacting with NaOH is as follows.

    $$CH_3COOH + OH^- \rightarrow CH_3COO^- + H_2O$$

6. Calculate ΔH for each of the following reactions from the thermodynamic data given.

	H^+ (aq) +	OH^- (aq)	→	H_2O (l)
ΔH_f° (kJ/mol)	0	–230.0		–285.83

	CH_3COOH (aq) +	OH^- (aq)	→	CH_3COO^- (aq) +	H_2O(l)
ΔH_f° (kJ/mol)	–485.76	–230.0		–486.01	–285.83

    How do the calculated values of ΔH compare with your experimental values?

	HCl + NaOH	**CH_3COOH + NaOH**
Net Ionic Reaction		
ΔT		
q		
Experimental ΔH$_{neutralization}$		
Calculated ΔH$_{neutralization}$		

PRE-LAB QUESTIONS

1. Define specific heat capacity. Why is the specific heat capacity of water unusually high?

2. How much heat is required to raise the temperature of 50.0 g of water from 35°C to 55°C? Be sure to include units.

3. If 50.0 mL of 10.0°C water is added to 40.0 mL of 65.0°C, calculate the final temperature of the mixture assuming no heat is lost to the surroundings, including the container. Is your answer reasonable?

4. In Part 1 of this experiment, you will determine the heat capacity of the calorimeter. The styrofoam cup calorimeter is shown Figure 1. A typical heat capacity of this type of calorimeter is between 20 and 50 J/K.
   a) What is the heat capacity of the calorimeter due to?
   b) Why do we use two Styrofoam cups?
   c) After the hot water is mixed with the cold water, why should the lid be placed on the cup when the temperature measurements are made? Will the heat capacity of the calorimeter be higher of lower with the lid off?
   d) Some students who stirred too vigorously ended up with a negative heat capacity for their calorimeter. These students continued to do the experiment and determined the heat capacity of a metal and heats of reaction, using the negative heat capacity for the calorimeter. Explain why a negative heat capacity was obtained and if the results for the remainder of the experiment could possibly be reasonable.

   NOTE: Please RETURN the thermometers, lids and Styrofoam cups but discard lids with rips or holes in it. The stockroom has more lids and cups if needed.

5. In a calorimeter, 50.0 mL of 60.0°C water is added to 50 mL of 14.0°C water. If the maximum temperature, T_M, was determined to be 36.0°C, calculate the heat capacity of the calorimeter, C_{cal}.

6. In Part 2 of this experiment you will measure the heat capacity for a metal. The metal must be thoroughly dry. The metal is inside a test tube and the test tube is placed in a hot water bath for 20 minutes to heat the metal. Why do you need to wait 20 minutes? How does the metal get to the temperature of the water bath? In other words, how is the heat transferred from the water to the metal on a molecular level?

7. In Part 3 of this experiment, you will measure the heat of reaction for the dissolution of NH_4NO_3 (s).

   $$NH_4NO_3 \text{ (s)} \quad \rightarrow \quad NH_4^+ \text{ (aq)} + NO_3^- \text{ (aq)}$$

   Some dissolution reactions are endothermic and some are exothermic. W here does the heat come from?

8. In Part 4 of this experiment, you will measure the heat of neutralization reactions.
   a) Write the net ionic equation for HCl reacting with NaOH.
   b) Write the net ionic equation for CH_3COOH reacting with NaOH.
   c) For neutralization reactions, where does the heat come from?

DISCUSSION QUESTIONS

Are you confident in the identification of your unknown metal? How does the atomic mass of the metal calculated using the Law of Dulong and Petit compare with the actual atomic mass? What are the greatest sources of error in this experiment? Is the dissolution of NH_4NO_3 exothermic or endothermic? How does the calculated value of ΔH compare to your experimental value of ΔH for the dissolution of NH_4NO_3? Is the acid-base neutralization reaction exothermic or endothermic? How do the calculated values of $\Delta H_{neutralization}$ compare to your experimental values of $\Delta H_{neutralization}$? Explain why your values may be high or low and discuss possible sources of error?

QUESTIONS

1. In this experiment, how would the value of the atomic mass of the metal calculated be affected if the hot metal sample cooled off before it was transferred to the water in the calorimeter? Would it be too high or too low? Explain your answer.

2. In this experiment, if the hot metal sample was wet, before it was transferred to the water in the calorimeter, how would this effect the experimental heat capacity of the metal? Explain your answer in terms of the specific heat of water relative to that of the metal you used in this experiment.

3. A 10.0 g piece of metal at 100°C is transferred to a calorimeter containing 50.0 mL of water initially at 23.0°C. Calculate the specific heat capacity of the metal if the heat capacity of the calorimeter, C_{cal}, is 25.0 J/K. The final temperature, T_{final}, is 25.6°C.

4. The heat of combustion for a sample of coal is 23.0 kJ/g. What quantity of coal (in grams) must be burned to heat 500.0 g of water from 20.0°C to 95.0°C. The specific heat capacity of water is 4.184 $J°C^{-1}g^{-1}$. Is your answer reasonable?

5. The combustion of carbon monoxide is exothermic.

$$CO \text{ (g)} + \text{1/2 } O_2 \text{ (g)} \rightarrow CO_2 \text{ (g)} \qquad \Delta H = -283.0 \text{ kJ}$$

Determine ΔH for each of the following reactions.

a) $2\,CO \text{ (g)} + O_2 \text{ (g)} \rightarrow 2\,CO_2 \text{ (g)}$

b) $2\,CO_2 \text{ (g)} \rightarrow 2\,CO \text{ (g)} + O_2 \text{ (g)}$

6. Consider the following reaction.

$$H_2 \text{ (g)} + 2\,CO \text{ (g)} \rightarrow H_2O_2 \text{ (l)} + 2\,C \text{ (s)} \qquad \Delta H = +33.3 \text{ kJ}$$

Calculate the enthalpy change when 5 mole of CO is consumed.

■ EXPERIMENT 6

Experiment **7**

7

Reaction Enthalpies and Hess's Law

PURPOSE AND LEARNING OBJECTIVES
To measure the change in enthalpy of two reactions and apply Hess's law to determine the change in enthalpy of a third reaction.

PRINCIPLES
Most chemical and physical changes that occur in nature either consume or produce heat. For example, heat is consumed when snow melts or when water evaporates. Heat is produced when we burn fuel or when we burn up carbohydrates.

In this experiment you will measure the heat flow for chemical reactions using a calorimeter. The measured heat flow is quantitatively expressed as the change in enthalpy of the reaction, ΔH. A reaction that releases heat is **exothermic** and ΔH is negative. A reaction that absorbs heat is **endothermic** and ΔH is positive.

The **standard enthalpy** of a reaction ΔH^0 is defined to be the enthalpy change when all reactants and products are in their standard state. For a gas the standard state corresponds to a pressure of 1 atm. For a species in solution, the standard state corresponds to 1 M concentration and 1 atm of external pressure. For an element or compound the standard state is the most stable state in which the element exists under conditions of 1 atm and a specified temperature.

The **standard enthalpy of formation**, ΔH_f^0 of a compound is the enthalpy change for the reaction that produces one mole of the compound from its elements in their standard state. Reactions (1) and (4) below correspond to the heat of formation of MgO (s) and H_2O (l), respectively.

For the reaction: $aA + bB \rightarrow cC + dD$

$$\Delta H^0 = [c\ \Delta H_f^0\ (C) + d\ \Delta H_f^0\ (D)] - [a\ \Delta H_f^0\ (A) + b\ \Delta H_f^0\ (B)]$$

The purpose of this experiment is to determine the enthalpy of formation for MgO(s) which corresponds to the formation of one mole of MgO from its elements in their standard state.

$$(1)\quad Mg\ (s) + {}^1/_2\ O_2\ (g) \rightarrow MgO\ (s) \qquad\qquad \Delta H_1 = \Delta H_f = ?$$

The enthalpy change for this reaction is difficult to measure directly. However, according to **Hess's law,** if two or more chemical equations are added to give another chemical equation, the corresponding enthalpies of reaction are added. Enthalpy is a state function. The calculated ΔH for a reaction is independent of how many steps are taken to get from reactants to products. It can be calculated in one step or in a series of steps. Thus, ΔH_f of MgO can be obtained indirectly by measuring the change in enthalpy for reactions (2) and (3), and using Hess's law to determine ΔH_f of MgO.

$$(2)\quad Mg\ (s) + 2\ HCl\ (aq) \rightarrow MgCl_2\ (aq) + H_2\ (g) \qquad\qquad \Delta H_2 = ?$$

$$(3)\quad MgO\ (s) + 2\ HCl\ (aq) \rightarrow MgCl_2\ (aq) + H_2O\ (l) \qquad\qquad \Delta H_3 = ?$$

$$(4)\quad H_2\ (g) + {}^1/_2\ O_2\ (g) \rightarrow H_2O\ (l) \qquad\qquad \Delta H_4 = -286\ kJ$$

In this experiment, ΔH_2 and ΔH_3 will be determined. These measurements in addition to the heat of formation of water, ΔH_4, will be used to calculate the heat of formation of MgO (s).

SAFETY
WEAR SAFETY GLASSES

HCl is a strong acid which can cause burns. In case of contact, rinse thoroughly with water. Clean up spills immediately. Magnesium metal and H_2 gas are flammable. In Part 2 of this experiment you will measure the heat of reaction of magnesium metal and hydrochloric acid, producing H_2 gas. No open flames should be anywhere near where you are running this reaction.

PROCEDURE
This experiment will be performed in pairs. It is important to stay consistent when taking measurements. Have one partner read the thermometer throughout a given part of the lab.

Preparation for Part 2

1. In a 500-mL Erlenmeyer flask, prepare 230 mL of 2 M HCl by diluting 6 M HCl with DI water. Check your calculations with the TA before you make the solution. Measure the DI water and the 6 M HCl using the large graduated cylinder. Put the water in the flask first, then slowly add the 6 M HCl. Mix thoroughly.

2. Label the flask.

3. While the 2 M HCl equilibrates to room temperature, do Part 1.

Part 1. The Heat Capacity of the Calorimeter

1. Construct the Styrofoam cup calorimeter shown in Figure 1. Obtain two Styrofoam cups and a lid. Place one cup inside the other and put the lid on.

2. Obtain a 0.1°C thermometer. Be careful using the mercury thermometer. The thermometer runs through the center of a cork and the cork must be secured to a ring-stand using a clamp. Align the thermometer so it goes through the center of the lid, into the cups. **WARNING**: If the thermometer does not slide easily through the cork, do not apply excessive force, use lubrication. Notify the instructor and get a new thermometer and cork. The stockroom has a lubricant to fix the problem.

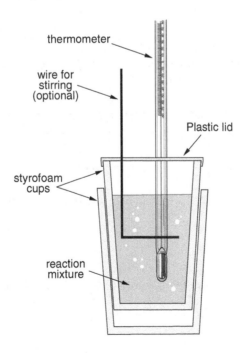

Figure 1. A Styrofoam cup calorimeter.

3. Chill approximately 80-100 mL of DI water in an ice bath to about 5-10°C.

4. Heat another 80-100 mL of DI water to between 60-80°C using a Bunsen burner.

5. Rinse a 100-mL graduated cylinder with about 20 mL of cold DI water.

6. Using the 100-mL graduated cylinder add exactly 50.0 mL of chilled water to the calorimeter. The lid should be on the cup with the thermometer sticking through the lid. Gently swirl the water in the cup and RECORD the temperature every 30 seconds for 4 minutes, until the temperature is constant. At this point the temperature of the chilled water and the calorimeter have come to equilibrium.

7. When the heated water is between 60-80°C, rinse a 100-mL graduated cylinder with about 20 mL of hot DI water.

8. Measure 50.0 mL of the hot water in the graduated cylinder and record its temperature.

9. Quickly add the heated water to the chilled water in the calorimeter.

10. Swirl the solution inside the Styrofoam cups and begin taking measurements every 15 seconds for 4 minutes. Record the temperature. The temperature will rise and then decrease.

Calculate the Heat Capacity of the Calorimeter

You MUST calibrate the calorimeter twice before you do this experiment. You can not use last week's calibration data.

1. Use Excel on the computer to graph the temperature of the calorimeter water (°C) on the y-axis and the time (seconds) on the x-axis, as shown in Figure 2.

2. Determine the maximum temperature, T_M, from your graph.

3. Use the maximum temperature, T_M to calculate the decrease in temperature of the hot water, ΔT_H.

$$\Delta T_H = T_M - T_H$$

4. Use T_M to calculate the increase in temperature of the cold water, ΔT_C.

$$\Delta T_C = T_M - T_C$$

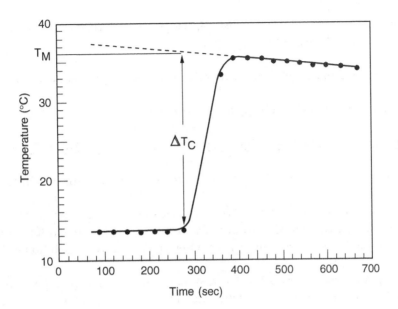

Figure 2. The temperature of the water in the calorimeter is measured as a function of time. Initially the temperature of the cold water is measured. When hot water is added, the temperature is observed to increase. As the hot and cold water mix, some heat is lost to the calorimeter so the maximum temperature measured is not as high as it would be if no heat were lost. To obtain the maximum temperature of the solution, T_M, the data must be extrapolated back to the time the solutions were mixed.

5. The amount of heat lost by the hot water, q_H, is calculated from its mass, m_H, specific heat, c_s, and ΔT_H.

$$q_H = (m_H)(c_s)(\Delta T_H)$$

The specific heat of water, $c_s = 4.184 \text{ J K}^{-1} \text{ g}^{-1}$. The density of water is 1 g/mL.

6. The total amount of heat gained by the cold water and by the calorimeter, q_C, is calculated as the sum of the two.

$$q_C = (m_C)(c_s)(\Delta T_C) + C_{cal}(\Delta T_C)$$

The first quantity represents the heat gained by the cold water in the calorimeter and the second quantity represents the heat gained by the cup, thermometer, and stirrer. The symbol C_{cal} represents the heat capacity of the calorimeter in units of J K^{-1}.

7. The heat gained by the cold water and the calorimeter is exactly equal to heat lost by the hot water.

$$q_C = -q_H$$

$$(m_C)(c_s)(\Delta T_C) + C_{cal}(\Delta T_C) = -(m_H)(c_s)(\Delta T_H)$$

Use this equation, to solve for the heat capacity of the calorimeter, C_{cal}. If C_{cal} is not between 10 and 50 J/K, repeat the calibration.

8. Show your graph and calculations to your instructor before proceeding to Part 2.

Part 2. Measure the Change in Enthalpy for the Reaction:

$$Mg\ (s)\ +\ 2\ HCl\ (aq)\ \rightarrow\ MgCl_2\ (aq)\ +\ H_2\ (g) \qquad \Delta H_2\ =\ ?$$

1. Use the calorimeter calibrated in Part 1. Drain the water and dry the calorimeter.

2. Add 100.0 mL of room temperature 2 M HCl to the calorimeter and put on the lid. Let the solution sit in the calorimeter 3 - 4 minutes to allow the solution and the calorimeter to come to an equilibrium temperature. Record the temperature of the solution every minute.

3. Using weighing paper, weigh 0.2 to 0.3 grams of magnesium ribbon to the nearest 0.001 g. Record the mass. The magnesium ribbon should be cut into small pieces (0.5 to 1 cm in length).

4. Add the magnesium pieces, all at once, to the calorimeter. Quickly put the lid back on the calorimeter. Stir (or swirl) the solution and record the temperature every 30 seconds for 5 minutes.

5. Drain the solution from the calorimeter into the appropriately labeled waste bottle in the hood. Rinse the calorimeter with DI water and dry it.

6. Repeat this measurement with a new sample of magnesium.

Calculate the Change in Enthalpy for the Reaction of Mg(s) and HCl.
1. Use Excel to graph your data. In your graph, be sure to include the temperature measurements of the HCl in the calorimeter before the magnesium was added. Determine the final temperature from your graph (the same method as used to determine the maximum temperature in Part 1 of this experiment).

2. Calculate the change in temperature.

$$\Delta T\ =\ T_{final}\ -\ T_{initial}$$

3. Calculate the heat of reaction, q. Assume the solution has a density of 1.03 g/mL and a specific heat of 4.0 J K^{-1} g^{-1}.

$$q\ =\ -\ (C_{cal}\Delta T\ +\ m_{solution}C_S\Delta T\ )$$

4. Calculate the change in enthalpy, ΔH_2.

$$\Delta H_2 = \frac{q}{\text{moles of Mg}}$$

5. In pre-lab question 4b, ΔH_2 for the following reaction was calculated.

$$Mg(s) + 2\,H^+(aq) \rightarrow Mg^{2+}(aq) + H_2\,(g)$$

How does the calculated value of ΔH_2 compare with your experimental value?

Data	Run 1	Run 2
Mass of Mg (s)		
ΔT		
q		
Experimental ΔH_2 (from your data)		
Average Experimental ΔH_2 (run 1 and run 2) include the average deviation from the mean		
Calculated ΔH_2 (See pre-lab question, 4b)		

Part 3. The Change in Enthalpy for the Reaction:

$$MgO\ (s)\ +\ 2\,HCl\ (aq)\ \rightarrow\ MgCl_2\ (aq)\ +\ H_2O\ (l) \qquad \Delta H_3 = ?$$

1. Rinse and dry the calorimeter.

2. Using a graduated cylinder, add 100.0 mL of 6.0 M HCl to the calorimeter. Cover it with the lid and let the HCl solution sit for 4 minutes. Record the temperature every minute.

3. Using a 100-mL beaker, weigh 0.6 to 0.7 grams of MgO (s). Obtain the mass of the beaker with the MgO sample to the nearest 0.001 g. After the MgO is added to the HCl, obtain the mass of the "empty" beaker. The amount of MgO transferred to the calorimeter in each run will be the difference between the two masses. Any MgO left in the beaker will be accounted for.

4. Add the MgO (s), all at once, to the calorimeter. Quickly put the lid on the calorimeter. Swirl the solution and record the temperature every 15 seconds for 5 minutes.

5. Drain the solution from the calorimeter into the appropriately labeled waste bottle in the hood. Rinse the calorimeter with DI water and dry it.

6. Repeat this measurement with a new sample of MgO.

Calculate the Change in Enthalpy for the Reaction of MgO(s) and HCl.

1. Use Excel to graph your data. Determine the final temperature from your graph (the same method as used to determine the maximum temperature in Part 1 of this experiment).

2. Calculate the change in temperature, $\Delta T = T_{final} - T_{initial}$.

3. Calculate the heat of reaction, q. Assume the solution has a density of 1.03 g/mL and a specific heat of 4.0 J K^{-1} g^{-1}.

$$q = -(C_{cal}\Delta T + m_{solution}C_s\Delta T)$$

4. Calculate the change in enthalpy, ΔH_3.

$$\Delta H_3 = \frac{q}{\text{moles of Mg}}$$

5. Calculate ΔH_3 of reaction from the thermodynamic data given in Pre-Lab question 5b.

$$MgO \text{ (s)} + 2 H^+(aq) \rightarrow Mg^{2+}(aq) + H_2O \text{ (l)}$$

How does the calculated value of ΔH_3 compare with your experimental value?

Data	Run 1	Run 2
Mass of 100-mL beaker plus MgO (s)		
Mass of "empty" 100-mL beaker (after MgO (s) was added to the calorimeter)		
Mass of MgO (s)		
ΔT		
q		
Experimental ΔH_3 (from your data)		
Average Experimental ΔH_3 (run 1 and run 2) include the average deviation from the mean		
Calculated ΔH_3 (See pre-lab question, 5b)		

Calculate the Heat of Formation of MgO (s)

1. Calculate ΔH_f for MgO(s) using your average ΔH_2 and ΔH_3 values. Write the equations for reactions (2) - (4) and the corresponding changes in enthalpy. Show how these reactions add up to yield reaction (1) and how the changes in enthalpy add up to yield the heat of formation of MgO, that is, $\Delta H_1 = \Delta H_2 + \Delta H_3 + \Delta H_4$. Remember that if you reverse reactions, the sign of ΔH is reversed.

2. For MgO(s), $\Delta H_f° = -601.8$ kJ/mol. Determine the relative percent error in your measurement.

PRE-LAB QUESTIONS

1. What volume of 6.0 M HCl do you need to make 230 mL of 2.0 M HCl?

2. Define the standard enthalpy of formation, $\Delta H_f°$.

3. Write the equation for the formation of 1 mole of each of the following compounds from its elements in their standard states. Indicate the corresponding standard enthalpy of formation, $\Delta H_f°$.
   a) MgO (s)
   b) CO (g)
   c) H_2O (l)

■ EXPERIMENT 7

4. In Part 2 of this experiment you will measure the change in enthalpy for magnesium metal reacting with aqueous hydrochloric acid to produce aqueous magnesium chloride and hydrogen gas.

$$Mg\ (s)\ +\ 2\ HCl\ (aq)\quad \rightarrow\quad MgCl_2\ (aq)\ +\ H_2\ (g)$$

a) Write the net ionic reaction. Identify any spectator ions. Why are spectator ions not included in the net ionic reaction?

b) Calculate ΔH for this reaction from the following heats of formation.

	ΔH_f° (kJ /mol)
Mg (s)	0
H^+ (aq)	0
H_2 (g)	0
Mg^{2+}(aq)	–467

c) Is it important that the concentration of HCl is exactly 2.0 M? If a 0.25 g sample of magnesium metal is used would 1.9 M HCl or 2.1 M HCl work just as well? Will the heat of reaction measured be the same for all three concentrations? Explain why or why not?

5. a) Write the balanced net ionic reaction of magnesium oxide reacting with aqueous hydrochloric acid to produce aqueous magnesium chloride and water.

b) For the net ionic equation in part a, calculate the heat of the reaction, ΔH, from the following data.

	ΔH_f° (kJ/mol)
MgO (s)	–602
H^+ (aq)	0
H_2O (l)	–286
Mg^{2+}(aq)	–467

6. State Hess's law.

7. Given the following data:

$$2\ NH_3\ (g)\quad \rightarrow\quad N_2\ (g)\ +\ 3\ H_2\ (g)\qquad\qquad \Delta H^0\ =\ 92\ kJ$$
$$2\ H_2\ (g)\ +\ O_2\ (g)\quad \rightarrow\quad 2\ H_2O\ (g)\qquad\qquad \Delta H^0\ =\ -\ 484\ kJ$$

Calculate ΔH^0 for the reaction
$$2\ N_2\ (g)\ +\ 6\ H_2O\ (g)\quad \rightarrow\quad 3\ O_2\ (g)\ +\ 4\ NH_3\ (g)$$

DISCUSSION QUESTIONS

What method was used to measure what? What was the heat capacity of your calorimeter? Is this a reasonable value. What were the experimental ΔH values (including the average deviation) determined for Mg reacting with HCl and MgO reacting with HCl. Are these reactions exothermic or endothermic? How does the calculated value of ΔH compare to your experimental value? Explain why your values may be high or low and discuss possible sources of error? What was the experimental value for the enthalpy of formation of MgO. How did this compare with the actual enthalpy of formation of MgO? Were you able to verify Hess's law? How would you improve this experiment?

QUESTIONS

1. Magnesium ribbon oxidizes in air to produce a thin, dull, MgO coating. How will this effect the change in enthalpy measured for the reaction of Mg and HCl? Would the heat of reaction measured for the oxidized magnesium be more or less exothermic than pure magnesium metal?

2. Over time, MgO (s) can absorb water. If your MgO sample were hydrated, how would this effect your data? Would the ΔH_3 determined be more or less negative?

3. When I did this experiment I found that the heat of reaction, measured for MgO reacting with HCl, increased with increasing HCl concentration. The heat released in this reaction was significantly higher when 6.0 M HCl was used then when 2.0 M HCl was used. The heat released using 6.0 M was in better agreement with the actual value. Explain why this effect may be observed.

3. For which one of the following is ΔH_f° equal to zero?
   a) CO_2 (g)
   b) HCl (g)
   c) He (g)
   d) C (g)

4. Using the ΔH_f° values given, calculate ΔH° for the combustion of carbon disulfide.

   $$CS_2 \text{ (l)} + 3\,O_2 \text{ (g)} \rightarrow CO_2 \text{ (g)} + 2\,SO_2 \text{ (g)}$$

	ΔH_f° (kJ/mol)
CS_2 (l)	89.7
CO_2 (g)	– 393.5
SO_2 (g)	– 297.0

5. Given the following data:

   $$Cu_2O \text{ (s)} + \tfrac{1}{2}\,O_2 \text{ (g)} \rightarrow 2\,CuO \text{ (s)} \qquad \Delta H^\circ = -144 \text{ kJ}$$
   $$Cu_2O \text{ (s)} \rightarrow Cu \text{ (s)} + CuO \text{ (s)} \qquad \Delta H^\circ = +11 \text{ kJ}$$

   Calculate the standard enthalpy of formation, ΔH_f°, of CuO (s). Hint: Look up the definition of standard enthalpy of formation then write the reaction for the standard enthalpy of formation of CuO (s).

■ EXPERIMENT 7

Experiment 8

8

Atomic Spectroscopy

PURPOSE AND LEARNING OBJECTIVES

In this experiment, you will employ spectroscopic methods to explore the light emitted by several different atomic sources including mercury, hydrogen and a number of metal atoms (Li, Na, K, Ca, Sr and Ba) heated in a flame. This experiment provides an introduction to the relationship between atomic line spectra and atomic structure.

PRINCIPLES

From the time of birth we experience a world in which we sense the influence of a variety of forms of energy. The interaction of energy with living systems – animals, plants and even microorganisms – is fundamental to life as we understand it. Most organisms are sensitive to the amount of energy transferred during these interactions through sensory mechanisms that include sensitivity to both temperature and color. In fact the two are closely related to one another through our experience with very hot objects. Molten metals illustrate this relationship. As we heat a piece of iron it glows red, then orange, then yellow and finally white. We associate white-hot objects with a higher temperature than those that appear red to our eye. Quantitatively, this led to the development of Planck's blackbody radiation law that associates the distribution of light energies from a radiant object, such as molten metal, to the temperature. The metal atoms in a hot piece of iron oscillate with a distribution of frequencies, υ, and radiate energy in "packets" or "quanta" of magnitude, $h\upsilon$. From the association of energy, in the form of temperature, to color, scientists such as Planck and Einstein formulated the quantitative relationships between wavelength and energy for electromagnetic radiation. Through these developments, scientists came to understand that the interaction of radiation with matter at the molecular level is associated with a particle-like property of electromagnetic radiation, and this particle was given the name of a photon. This concept in conjunction with prior under-standings of radiation that associated it with wave properties led to the initial understanding that matter, just like energy, can display both particle and wave properties.

The perception of color by our eyes is due to our ability to discriminate wavelengths of light in a very small region of the electromagnetic spectrum referred to as the visible region. This re-gion extends from about 400 nm to 750 nm. Our vision is not capable of separating colors from a light source that radiates with a wide range of visible radiation. For example, light that con-tains wavelengths from the entire range of visible radiation appears to our vision as white. However, many natural phenomena lead to separation of different wavelengths which our eye or other radiation sensors can then identify, as for example the interaction of white light from the sun with finely divided droplets of moisture to form a rainbow. The area of science that focuses attention upon processes that separate different radiation wavelengths and then iden-tifies these wavelengths is referred to as spectroscopy – indeed, the first spectroscopy occurred with the first observations of rainbows, so it is truly an ancient discipline. It is interesting to note that this ancient discipline led to key contributions towards some of the greatest scientific discoveries known to chemistry and physics. Nobel prizes associated with names such as Bohr, Einstein, Planck, Schroedinger and Heisenberg were in part due to observations based upon spectroscopic methods.

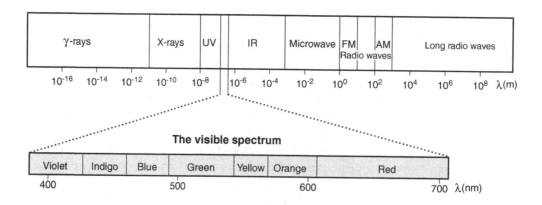

Figure 1. Electromagnetic Spectrum. The visible spectrum is only a small portion of the electromagnetic spectrum.

In this experiment we will employ spectroscopic methods to explore the light emitted by several different atomic sources including mercury vapor, hydrogen gas as well as a number of metal atoms (Li, Na, K, Ca, Sr and Ba). It is interesting to note that the light that radiates from these sources can best be understood in terms of the photon, or particle concept. The photon relates its wavelength to differences in energy levels of the atom or molecule from which it originates. However, the basic measurement techniques used to determine the wavelength of this radiation is best understood in terms of the interaction of the wave character of this light with a diffraction grating. The manifestation of dual wave and particle properties of light is commonplace in the natural world, and extension of this concept to matter in the form of atoms and molecules led to our present understanding of the nature of matter.

The wave nature of electromagnetic radiation can be described in terms of the relationship between the frequency, wavelength and speed of a sinusoidal wave. Frequency (υ) is defined as the number of oscillations of the wave per second whereas the wavelength (λ) gives the distance between peak amplitudes of the wave. These are related by the speed of light (c),

$$c = \lambda \upsilon$$

where $c = 3.00 \times 10^8$ m/s. The particle nature of light when it interacts with matter relates the energy absorbed or lost by the atom or molecule during the interaction. The particle property of light is described by the equation

$$E = h\upsilon$$

where E is energy in joules (J), υ is the frequency of the radiation in Hz or sec^{-1}, and h is Planck's constant ($h = 6.63 \times 10^{-34} J \bullet s$). Combining these two equations leads to a useful relationship, which illustrates the inverse proportionality of energy and wavelength.

$$E = \frac{hc}{\lambda}$$

Thus, gamma-rays, X-rays, and UV radiation, which have relatively short wavelengths, are high in energy. Atmospheric gases, such as oxygen and nitrogen, protect us from very high energy gamma rays, X-rays and vacuum UV radiation, whereas a thin ozone layer provides protection from UV radiation in the range of 220-320 nm. Microwaves and radiowaves have relatively long wavelengths – a form of low energy radiation. These long wavelength radiations are useful in communications (radar and AM/FM radio) and the use of microwaves has become commonplace in cooking applications.

Ordinary white light from the sun contains wavelengths from the entire range of visible radiation. When white light is passed through a prism or diffraction grating it produces a continuous band spectrum, like a rainbow. However, when atoms are sufficiently excited, either in flames or electrical discharges, and the light emitted is passed through a prism, a spectrum with discrete parallel lines is observed. Each element has a unique line spectrum. What does a line

■ EXPERIMENT 8

spectrum signify? Bohr proposed a model for the hydrogen atom to explain its line spectrum. By assuming that the electron in the hydrogen atom could only have certain values of angular momentum, Bohr found that ΔE, the difference in the energy levels calculated, were consistent with the hydrogen atom emission spectrum.

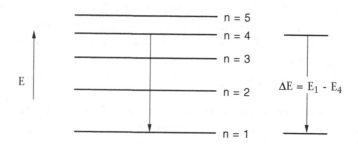

When an excited hydrogen atom is formed in an electrical discharge, the electron absorbs energy by making a transition from the lowest energy state (the ground state, n=1) to one of several higher energy states (excited states, n=2,3,4,5....). The electron in an excited hydrogen atom has excess energy. When the electron returns to a lower energy state it emits light that corresponds to the energy difference between the two states, E_{final} and $E_{initial}$.

$$\Delta E = E_{final} - E_{initial} = h\nu = \frac{hc}{\lambda}$$

The electron emits a quantum of energy (a photon, of energy $h\nu$) equivalent to ΔE when making a transition to a lower energy state. If the electron is in the n = 1 level, it is as close to the nucleus as possible and corresponds to the lowest energy state of the hydrogen atom. If the electron makes a transition from the n = 4 energy state to the ground state, we can experimentally determine the wavelength of the light emitted using a spectroscope and then calculate the energy difference. In this way, information about the atomic structure of hydrogen is obtained from its line spectrum.

According to the Bohr model, the difference in the energy levels for hydrogen absorption or emission spectrum is calculated as follows:

emission of a photon: $\Delta E < 0$
absorption of a photon: $\Delta E > 0$

$$\Delta E = E_{final} - E_{initial} = -(2.18 \times 10^{-18} J)\left(\frac{1}{n_{final}^2} - \frac{1}{n_{initial}^2}\right) \quad \text{where n = 1, 2, 3, 4 ... } \infty$$

Converting units from Joules to kJ/mol yields the following equation.

$$\Delta E = E_{final} - E_{initial} = -\left(1312 \frac{kJ}{mol}\right)\left(\frac{1}{n_{final}^2} - \frac{1}{n_{initial}^2}\right) \qquad \text{where n = 1, 2, 3, 4 ... } \infty$$

$$|\Delta E| = E_{photon} = h\upsilon = 1 \text{ quantum of energy}$$

The absolute value of ΔE corresponds to the photon energy. From the photon energy, the frequency and wavelength can be calculated. The photon energy, frequency and wavelength are all greater than zero.

SAFETY
WEAR SAFETY GLASSES!!!

The safety glasses will absorb some of the ultraviolet light emitted from the lamps. Do not look directly at the lamps. Lamps should be in the hood, the hood sash blocks UV. Please do not touch the hydrogen lamp. If there is a problem notify the instructor immediately. Vaporized barium is toxic and must be done in the hood. Set up a Bunsen burner in the hood for the students to use.

PROCEDURE
There are three parts to this experiment. First, you will calibrate the spectroscope using the mercury lines from the fluorescent lights in the room. By plotting the wavelength versus the spectroscope scale reading, you obtain a calibration line, which allows you to determine the wavelength for any spectroscope scale reading. Second, you will measure the hydrogen line spectrum, and use the calibration line from Part 1 to determine the wavelengths observed. In the third part, you will heat salts of various alkali metals and alkaline earth metals, in a flame to observe the color of light emitted directly, and with the spectroscope. For this experiment, you will work in pairs. Both students will observe each of the mercury and hydrogen lamps as well as the metal atoms. Each partner needs to observe and record all the data in their own lab notebooks.

Part 1. Spectroscope Calibration
1. Sign out a spectroscope for you and your partner.

2. Look through the spectroscope at the light coming in through the windows or from the natural light lamps in the hood. Record your observations.

3. Look through the spectroscope at the overhead lights in the lab. Record the position on the scale where the violet, blue, green and yellow lines are observed. These lines are due to mercury and can be used to calibrate the spectroscope. The red line is due to another gas mixed in with the mercury vapor to give the light a softer more natural glow.

4. Copy the following table into your lab notebook and record the spectroscope scale reading for each of the mercury lines observed in the fluorescent lights.

Mercury Lines

Color of Emission	Wavelength (nm)	Spectroscope Scale Reading
Violet	404.7	
Blue	435.8	
Green	546.1	
Yellow	579.0	

5. Make a calibration graph by plotting the wavelength on the x-axis and the spectroscope scale readings on the y-axis. Draw a straight line through the points. Determine the corrected wavelength using this calibration graph for the remainder of this experiment.

Part 2. Emission Spectrum of Hydrogen

1. The hydrogen lamp is in the hood with the sash down to protect you from UV radiation. Do not touch the lamp; the high voltage discharge needed to produce the excited hydrogen atoms can be dangerous. With the spectroscope in hand, stand a few feet away from the hood and observe the spectrum. It may be difficult to see at first. Move the spectroscope around until you observe sharp lines, all in focus. Record the color of each emission line and the scale reading.

2. Determine the wavelength for each of the emission lines using the calibration graph from Part 1.

3. Copy the table above into your lab notebook. Record the observed wavelengths and compare them to accepted values of the wavelength. Calculate the percent error in the observed line spectra.

Hydrogen Line Spectrum

Color of Emission	Scale Reading	Observed Wavelength (nm)	Accepted Wavelength (nm)
			410
			434
			486
			656

4. The transitions observed in the visible region correspond to the Balmer series where $n_{initial} >$ 2 and $n_{final} = 2$. Using the equation given for the hydrogen atom absorption or emission spectrum,

$$\Delta E = E_{final} - E_{initial} = -(2.18 \times 10^{-18}) \left(\frac{1}{n_{final}^2} - \frac{1}{n_{initial}^2} \right) \text{ where } n = 1, 2, 3, 4 \dots \infty$$

determine which energy transition $(n_{initial} \rightarrow n_{final})$ each of the observed lines represents. Given that the energy levels, n_{final} and $n_{initial}$, are integers and that $n_{final} = 2$, trial and error will allow you to determine the transitions. Be sure to convert kJ/mol to kJ using Avogadro's number.

Part 3. Emission Spectra from Alkali and Alkaline Earth Metals

1. Set up a Bunsen burner. This will be used as the excitation source of the metal atoms.

2. Obtain an 8 inch piece of nichrome wire. Curl one end of the wire into a few loops, ranging from 0.5 to 1 cm in diameter.

3. Put approximately 3 to 5 mL 6 M HCl into a small, labeled test tube.

4. Put 3 to 5 mL of each of the 0.5 M metal salt solutions, $CaCl_2$, NaCl, SrCl, $BaCl_2$, LiCl and KCl into small, labeled test tubes.

5. Dip the looped end of the nichrome wire into 6 M HCl. Heat the wire over the hottest part of the flame until no visible color is produced from the nichrome wire. Repeat this cleaning process as needed and every time you switch to a new metal salt solution.

6. Dip the looped section of the nichrome wire into the solution and put it into the hottest part of the flame. Record the color observed directly without the use of the spectroscope. If a drop of solution is trapped in the loop of the nichrome wire, the intensity and duration of the emission will increase. Repeat and observe the line spectrum for each of the metal atoms. Some are easier to see then others. Record the color and scale reading for each of the lines. Each partner needs to observe the line spectra and record the data.

7. Repeat steps 4 - 5 for NaCl, $CaCl_2$, LiCl, $SrCl_2$, $BaCl_2$, and KCl. The $BaCl_2$ will be vaporized in the hood.

PRE-LAB QUESTIONS

1. Draw a wave which has a frequency, $\upsilon = 2$ cycles/sec. Indicate the distance that represents a wavelength, λ. Frequency units are expressed in several ways. For example, $\upsilon = 2$ cycles/sec = 2 Herz = 2 Hz = 2 sec^{-1}.

2. The electromagnetic spectrum is shown in Figure 1. It includes γ-rays, x-rays, UV, Visible, Infrared, Microwaves and Radio Waves.

   a) Write the equations that relate energy, E, and wavelength, λ, and energy, E, and frequency, v.
   b) Which rays in the electromagnetic spectrum have the highest energy, shortest wavelength and highest frequency?
   c) Which rays in the electromagnetic spectrum have the lowest energy, longest wavelength and lowest frequency?

3. The visible spectrum is shown in Figure 1.

   a) What range in wavelengths does the visible spectrum correspond to?
   b) What color of light is highest in energy?
   c) As you heat a piece of iron it glows. As the temperature increases colors change from red to orange to yellow to white (very hot). Explain how and why the color changes as the temperature changes.

4. When ordinary light passes through a prism, a continuous band spectrum is observed (like a rainbow). When the light, emitted by electronically excited atoms, passes through a prism, discreet lines are observed. What does the line spectrum signify?

5. The electron in a hydrogen atom can be in the lowest energy state (the ground state, n = 1) or in one of several higher energy states (excited states, n = 2,3,4,5... ∞).

   a) In which state is the electron closest to the nucleus?
   b) In the hydrogen atom when an electron makes a transition from n = 2 to n=4, is energy emitted or absorbed by the electron?
   c) When an electron makes a transition from an excited state to a lower energy state, it emits light with an energy that corresponds to the energy difference between the two states.

   $$\Delta E = E_{final} - E_{initial} = hv = \frac{hc}{\lambda}$$

   In this equation,   h = Planck's constant = 6.626×10^{-34} J s
                        c = speed of light = 3.00×10^8 m/s.

   Consider the electronic transitions: n =5 to n = 2 and n = 3 to n = 2. For which transition, will the light emitted have the longer wavelength? Figure this out by looking at the equation without using a calculator. You do not need to calculate ΔE.

d) For the hydrogen atom, calculate the frequency and wavelength of light emitted for an electronic transition from n = 5 to n = 2.

e) If the energy of light emitted is 3.37×10^{-19} Joules, what is its wavelength and color?

6. In Part 1 of this experiment you will calibrate the spectroscope. How and why will you do this?

7. In Part 2 of this experiment you will measure the hydrogen line spectrum. Would you be able to observe the n = 6 to n = 2 transition with the spectroscope? Explain why or why not.

8. In Part 3 of this experiment you will observe the emission spectra from alkali metals and alkaline earth metals by heating salt solutions in a flame. The frequency of light emitted by magnesium is 1.05×10^{15} Hz, what color, if any would be observed in a flame?

DISCUSSION QUESTIONS

Briefly discuss what was measured in this experiment and the general method used. Discuss the observed wavelengths from the hydrogen spectrum in comparison to the accepted values. How accurate were they? Discuss any possible sources of errors and the effect on your results. What energy transitions were associated with the observed wavelengths? Discuss the emission spectra observed for the metal atoms. Could you observe the line spectrum for all of the metals?

REVIEW QUESTIONS

1. What is the purpose of the slit in the spectroscope?

2. In the hydrogen atom, for which transition is the emission line observed at shorter wavelength, n = 4 to n = 2 or n = 5 to n = 1? Show the equation needed to figure this out. Consider the relative size of ΔE to determine the relative wavelength. There is no need to calculate ΔE.

3. Suppose that hydrogen atoms are prepared in the n = 2 energy level. Calculate the wavelength of light emitted by these excited atoms when returning to the ground state.

4. The strength of common bonds in living organisms range from 300 to 500 kJ/mol. For example, single carbon-carbon bonds in organic molecules have energies of about 348 kJ/mol (that is, the energy required to break a single carbon-carbon bond is 348 kJ/mol). Calculate the minimum wavelength of light needed to break the C–C bond. Could UV lamps be used to break the C–C bond?

5. In the emission spectrum of hydrogen, the transitions observed in this experiment are in the visible region corresponding to the Balmer series. In other series, including Lyman, Paschen, Bracket and Pfund emission lines are present in different regions of the electromagnetic spectrum. Calculate the wavelength of the n=4 to n=1 and the n=4 to n=3 transitions. Indicate in which regions of the electromagnetic spectrum these transitions would occur.

■ EXPERIMENT 8

Experiment **9**

9

Determination of Avogadro's Number

PURPOSE AND LEARNING OBJECTIVES

Avogadro's number will be determined by measuring the area of a monolayer of a known volume of oleic acid on the surface of water. Types of intermolecular forces and their effect on boiling points, surface tension and solubility will be explored.

PRINCIPLES

In 1808 John Dalton published his atomic theory of matter. He postulated that all matter is made of atoms, and that atoms of a given chemical element are identical in mass and in all other properties. He also postulated that atoms retain their identities in chemical reactions and that compounds formed from a combination of atoms of unlike elements do so in small whole-number ratios. What Dalton did not realize, was that many elements such as hydrogen, oxygen, and the halogens exist as diatomic molecules in their stable states. Consequently, Dalton was doubtful about Joseph Gay-Lussac's data when he found that in combining equal volumes of hydrogen and chlorine gas, twice the volume of hydrogen chloride gas was formed. If, as Dalton believed, hydrogen and chlorine were monatomic gases, one volume of hydrogen would react with one volume of chlorine to produce only one volume of hydrogen chloride, not two.

$$H + Cl \rightarrow HCl$$

Neither Dalton or Gay-Lussac understood this result. Amedeo Avogadro, however, explained this data by assuming that hydrogen and chlorine were diatomic gases. In this case, one volume of hydrogen gas reacts with one volume of chlorine gas to produce two volumes of hydrogen chloride, as was observed in the experiment.

$$H_2 + Cl_2 \rightarrow 2 HCl$$

In 1811, Avogadro published the hypothesis that, equal volumes of different gases, held at the same pressure and temperature, contain equal numbers of particles. Avogadro was not able to determine how many atoms or molecules were in a given volume of gas. However, several estimates of Avogadro's number were made using a variety of experiments. The values ranged from 5.4 to 6.0×10^{23} particles/mol. It wasn't until 1915, when Robert Millikan determined the charge of the electron (e) that a more accurate value of Avogadro's number was obtained. Dividing Farra-day's constant (F), the charge represented by one mole of electrons, by the charge of the electron yields the number of particles per mole, $N_A = F/e$. Presently, Avogadro's number (N_A) is defined as the number of atoms in exactly 12 grams of ^{12}C, which is equal to 6.022137×10^{23} atoms/mol.

In this experiment, Avogadro's number will be determined by measuring the area of a film of oleic acid, of known volume, on the surface of water. From the known volume of oleic acid, and the area it covers on the water, the thickness (or height) of the acid film can be calculated. Assuming the oleic acid forms a single layer of molecules on the surface of water (a monolayer), with the acid molecules arranged as shown in Figure 1, the number of molecules present in the film can be calculated. From the known molar mass and density of oleic acid, the number of molecules present in one mole of acid is calculated. Using this simple technique, values on the order of 1 to 10×10^{23} molecules/mol are obtained.

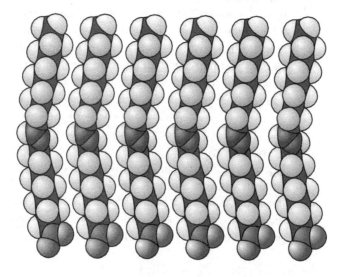

Figure 1. Oleic acid molecules, $C_{18}H_{34}O_2$, packed on-end on the surface of water. The polar carboxyl group (–COOH) is located at the bottom of the oleic acid where it interacts with the polar water molecules.

One of the most important concepts in understanding this experiment is the role of intermolecular forces. Because attractive forces exist between molecules, a gas can be condensed to form a liquid or a solid. Intermolecular forces for a given substance include: 1) Ion-Ion; the Coulomb force of attraction between ionic molecules, 2) Dipole-Dipole; the force of attraction between polar molecules, and 3) Induced Dipole-Induced Dipole; the force of attraction between non-polar molecules, referred to as either London Dispersion Forces (LDF) or van der Waal Forces.

For the dipole-dipole force a distinction is made between polar molecules which form hydrogen bonds and those which do not. Hydrogen bonding occurs only if molecules have a hydrogen atom bound to nitrogen, oxygen or fluorine atoms (all highly electronegative). For polar molecules, such as H_2O, CH_3OH, NH_3, NH_2NH_2, and HF, hydrogen bonding is the dominant intermolecular force and is generally stronger than the dipole-dipole force for polar molecules such as HCl or SO_2, for example. From the trend in boiling points of hydrides, the boiling point of water without hydrogen bonds would be approximately –123°C. Thus, without hydrogen bonds water would be a gas at room temperature and life as we know it would not be possible!

Read the discussion on intermolecular forces in your text. The general trend in intermolecular force strength is as follows:

Ion-Ion	>	Hydrogen-Bonding	>	Dipole-Dipole	>	LDF (van der Waal forces)
(ionic)		(H bound to N,O,F)		(polar molecules)		(induced dipole forces)

NOTE: Even though LDF is generally considered a weak intermolecular force, it increases with size and polarizability of molecules. For large molecules, with large surface areas, LDF can be quite large giving rise to relatively high boiling points. For example, the non-polar hydrocarbon, $C_{25}H_{52}$, is a solid at room temperature. Its boiling point is 400°C. Even though the dominant intermolecular force for $C_{25}H_{52}$ is LDF, the boiling point of $C_{25}H_{52}$ is much higher than that for H_2O where hydrogen bonding is the dominant intermolecular force.

Why does water form beads on a waxed surface? The tendency for any liquid to form beads on a surface is due to intermolecular forces. When a liquid is in contact with air, the molecules near the surface of the liquid feel a net force of attraction inward minimizing its surface area. The resulting spherical shape represents the minimum surface area for a given volume. The resistance of a liquid to increase its surface area is called surface tension. Surface tension increases with the strength of the intermolecular force. The surface tension of water is particularly strong due to the strong network of hydrogen bonds between the water molecules. This is important in this experiment to provide the convex surface needed to allow the oleic acid to spread into a monolayer.

The polarity of water is also important in this experiment. The oleic acid molecule, $C_{18}H_{34}O_2$, is a long chain of carbon atoms with a carboxyl group (–COOH) at the end.

$$CH_3\text{-}CH_2\text{-}CH_2\text{-}CH_2\text{-}CH_2\text{-}CH_2\text{-}CH_2\text{-}CH_2\text{-}CH=CH\text{-}CH_2\text{-}CH_2\text{-}CH_2\text{-}CH_2\text{-}CH_2\text{-}CH_2\text{-}CH_2\text{-}COOH$$

Because polar molecules attract each other, the polar –COOH group of the oleic acid is attracted to the polar water molecules. The long chain of carbon atoms in the oleic acid is non-polar and repels water (like an oil does). Due to the long non-polar chain in oleic acid, the collective intermolecular forces, LDF, are strong. The resulting on-end stacking of oleic acid molecules on the surface of water is as shown in Figure 1.

SAFETY
WEAR SAFETY GLASSES

NO OPEN FLAMES DURING THIS LAB. Pentane is a volatile, flammable solvent! Lycopodium powder is also highly flammable. Do not use either pentane or Lycopodium powder near open flames.

PROCEDURE
1. Obtain four medium-large size test tubes provided for this experiment. Clean the test tubes with soap and water, use DI water as the final rinse. Mark the test tubes #1 through #4.

2. Use a graduated cylinder to place 10 mL of pentane in each of the four test tubes. If you overshoot pour excess pentane into a waste beaker. Never pour chemicals back into reagent bottles. Immediately stopper each of the test tubes to reduce evaporation.

3. To the first test tube add exactly 1.0 mL of oleic acid using a 1.0-mL syringe. Mix the solution by gently swirling the test tube.

4. Rinse the syringe with pentane. Transfer 1 mL of the solution in test tube #1 to test tube #2 using the syringe. Mix the solution by gently swirling the test tube.

5. Transfer 1 mL of the solution in test tube #2 to test tube #3. Mix the solution.

6. Transfer 1 mL of the solution in test tube #3 to test tube #4. Mix the solution.

7. Clean a large watch glass, 14 cm in diameter. Grease the edge of the watch glass with vacuum grease by running your finger around the entire circumference. Place the watch glass on a rubber-coated ring provided for this experiment (located in the hood).

8. Put approximately 500 mL of water in a 600-mL beaker and add 2 to 3 drops of 6 M HCl to prevent reaction of the oleic acid with any basic impurity in the water.

9. Fill the watch glass with water until the water level is just above the edge (add as much water as possible without spilling water over the edge). Note the convex surface of the water. **A convex surface is necessary for the oleic acid to spread in a monolayer film on the surface.** Insufficient water will result in a slight concave surface causing the oleic acid to pool in the center.

10. Clean the surface of the water using a glass rod. Hold the glass rod horizontal to the watch glass and sweep over the water. Some water will spill over the edge of the watch glass. **Add some water to make** sure you have a convex surface.

11. Add one small drop of motor oil to the surface of the water. The oil spreads out as a film over the surface. Lightly dust the oil with Lycopodium powder to make it easier to see the oleic acid film as it spreads on the surface of water.

12. Use the syringe to transfer exactly 0.05 mL of the most dilute oleic acid solution (from test tube #4) onto the water surface (0.05 mL = 2 drops from the syringe). The pentane evaporates as the oleic acid film spreads out over the surface, outlined by a ring of oil and dust. If the oleic acid film reaches the edge of the watch glass, the experiment must be repeated. Clean the surface of the water with a glass rod before repeating the experiment. Hold the glass rod horizontal to the watch glass and sweep over the water. Some water will spill over the edge of the watch glass. **Add some water to make** sure you have a convex surface.

13. Support a sheet of glass (9 to 10 inches square) over the watch glass using the corks provided (located in the hood). Quickly and accurately outline the shape of the oleic acid film using an overhead pen.

14. Trace the shape of the oleic acid film on a clean piece of graph paper. You can hold the glass up to the light to improve visibility in tracing the outlined area onto the piece of graph paper.

15. Cut out the oleic acid film shape and a 5-cm by 5-cm area of the same graph paper. Weigh both pieces of paper to the nearest 0.001 g. From these two weights calculate the surface area covered by the oleic acid. Attach the graph paper, showing the outline of the oleic acid, onto the report for this experiment.

16. Clean the surface of the water and repeat the measurement at least twice. Calculate Avogadro's number before you leave the lab. The value obtained should be in the 1 to 10×10^{23} molecules/mol range.

CALCULATIONS

1. In test tube #1, the volume of oleic acid in the solution is 1 mL in 11 mL of solution. Three successive dilutions were made. The final volume of oleic acid per milliliter of solution in test tube #4 is calculated as follows.

$$\left(\frac{1 \text{ mL oleic acid}}{11 \text{ mL solution}}\right)\left(\frac{1}{11}\right)\left(\frac{1}{11}\right)\left(\frac{1}{11}\right) = 7 \times 10^{-5} \frac{\text{mL oleic acid}}{\text{mL solution}}$$

Calculate the volume of oleic acid in 0.05 mL of this solution, that is, the volume of oleic acid in the film.

■ EXPERIMENT 9

2. From the volume of oleic acid in the film and the area of the film, calculate the thickness or height, h, of the acid film.

3. In this experiment the oleic acid molecules are assumed to form a monolayer. Figure 1 represents the actual packing of the oleic acid molecules calculated using a molecular modeling program. Thus, the relative width and depth of the individual molecules can be determined relative to the height directly from the figure. The volume of space occupied by one oleic acid molecule includes space between molecules.

$$V = (height)\ (width)\ (depth)$$

$$V = (h)\left(\frac{h}{4.5}\right)\left(\frac{h}{4.5}\right) = \frac{h^3}{20}$$

4. From the molar mass of oleic acid, $C_{18}H_{34}O_2$, 282.5 g/mol, its density, 0.895 g/mL, and the volume per molecule determined, calculate the number of molecules per mole, which is Avogadro's number.

PRE-LAB QUESTIONS

1. Consider the following molecules: BF_3, SO_2, CCl_4 and $CHCl_3$.
   a) Draw the Lewis structures and indicate the molecular geometry of each molecule.
   b) Indicate the polarity of each of the bonds in BF_3, SO_2, CCl_4 and $CHCl_3$ and state whether the molecule is polar or non-polar.
   c) Indicate the dominant intermolecular force for each substance.

2. Indicate the dominant intermolecular force for each of the following substances.
   a) H_2O
   b) HCl
   c) NH_4Cl
   d) N_2
   e) CH_4

3. Natural gas, methane, is used in many homes and in the laboratory. Propane is also a common source of fuel. As the size of the alkane increases so does the boiling point. Methane, ethane, propane, and butane are all gases at room temperature. Pentane, however, is a liquid at room temperature. All these gases are highly combustible, and even though pentane is a liquid, it is highly volatile and flammable. Rationalize the relative boiling points observed for the straight chain alkanes in terms of intermolecular forces.

Straight-Chain Alkane		Boiling Point (°C)
methane	CH_4	– 167.7
ethane	C_2H_6	– 88.6
propane	C_3H_8	– 42.1
butane	C_4H_{10}	– 0.5
pentane	C_5H_{12}	36.1

4. In this experiment, the volume of oleic acid in the solution is 1 mL in 10 mL of pentane. Three successive dilutions are made. Pentane is a volatile liquid and therefore evaporates rapidly.

   a) If the solutions are not stoppered immediately, discuss the resulting errors in the concentration of the oleic acid and in Avogadro's number calculated? Would Avogadro's number be higher of lower than the actual value?

   b) Why do we use pentane? Could we use water instead? Explain why or why not.

   c) Why don't we use a solvent, less volatile than pentane? In what part of this experiment is it necessary for the solvent to volatile?

5. Discuss the nature of both attractive and repulsive forces between water and oleic acid. Explain the on-end stacking of oleic acid molecules on the surface of water is as shown in Figure 1?

6. If the water surface is concave rather than convex, what is the affect on the size of the area of the oleic acid film?

DISCUSSION QUESTIONS

Compare the value of Avogadro's number obtained to the actual value. Discuss all the possible sources of error in this experiment. Several assumptions were made in determining Avogadro's number. State the assumptions and justify their validity. Try to account for the difference between your value and the accepted value of Avogadro's number.

REVIEW QUESTIONS

1. Discuss the forces of attraction between oleic acid molecules? Which is the dominant force?

2. Why does oleic acid dissolve in pentane? What is the dominant intermolecular force between oleic acid and pentane?

3. For 1.0 L of water at room temperature, calculate the total number of possible hydrogen bonds among the water molecules. The density of water is 1.0 g/mL.

■ **EXPERIMENT 9**

10

Colligative Properties: Freezing Point Depression

PURPOSE AND LEARNING OBJECTIVES

To determine the freezing point of a pure solvent and the freezing point depression of a solution as a function of solute concentration. To define molality and understand the importance of molality in colligative properties.

PRINCIPLES

Recall that a solution is a homogeneous mixture in which one or more substances is uniformly dispersed as separate atoms, molecules or ions throughout another substance. The components in solution are referred to as the solvent and the solute. In general, the solvent is defined as the component, which is present in greater amount.

The concentration of a solution can be expressed in a number of ways including, molarity (M) and molality (m). The molarity of a substance is the number of moles of solute dissolved in one liter of solution.

$$\text{molarity} = M = \frac{\text{moles solute}}{\text{liter solution}}$$

When working with colligative properties we are concerned with the number of solute particles relative to solvent particles. Thus, the molality of a substance is defined as the number of moles of solute dissolved in one kilogram of solvent.

$$\text{molality} = m = \frac{\text{moles solute}}{\text{kg solvent}}$$

The addition of a solute to a solvent can change some of the physical properties of the solution relative to those of the pure solvent in important ways. For example, at 1.0 atm pressure, water freezes at 0°C. When a substance is dissolved in water, the resulting aqueous solution freezes at a lower temperature, below 0°C. This is why an aqueous solution of ethylene glycol is used as antifreeze in car radiators. Relative to pure water, the solution has a lower freezing point and a higher boiling point. Thus, not only does it protect the cooling system from freezing in cold weather; it also allows us to run the engine hotter before it boils over.

Freezing point depression, boiling point elevation, vapor-pressure lowering and **osmotic pressure** all depend on the number of solute particles in solution and not on the nature of the solute. These are termed colligative properties of solution (colligative stems from the Latin word *colligar*, which means to collect together). **Colligative properties** of solution are due to the collective effect of the number of solute particles in solution. The number of solute particles corresponds to the total number of ions and/or molecules in solution. In this experiment you will measure the freezing point depression of a solution as a function of solute concentration.

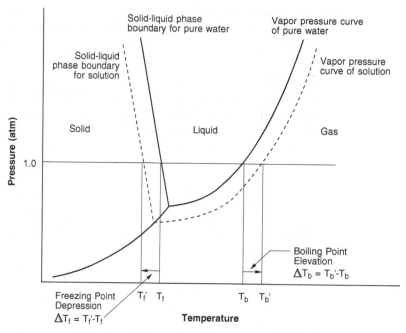

Figure 1. The solid curves represent the phase diagram for pure water. The addition of a non-volatile solute lowers the vapor pressure (illustrated with the dashed curves) causing boiling point elevation and freezing point depression.

The addition of a non-volatile solute to a volatile solvent results in a solution with a lower vapor pressure relative to that of the pure solvent. The greater the solute concentration, the lower the vapor pressure of the solution. This decrease in vapor pressure gives rise to boiling point elevation. The boiling point of a liquid is the temperature at which its vapor pressure equals atmospheric pressure. Boiling point elevation occurs because the reduced vapor pressure of the solvent above the solution requires that the solution be heated to a higher temperature to produce a vapor pressure equal to atmospheric pressure. This gives rise to an increase in the boiling point of the solution relative to the pure solvent. This phenomenon is shown in the phase diagram in Figure 1. The solid lines represent the phase diagram for pure water, and the vapor pressure curve of the solution is dashed. The boiling point elevation is indicated as $\Delta T_b = T_b' - T_b$, where T_b is the boiling point of the pure water and T_b' is the boiling point of the solution. Also shown is the solid-liquid phase boundary of pure water (solid line) and that of a dilute solution (dashed line). The freezing point depression is shown to be $\Delta T_f = T_f' - T_f$, where T_f is the freezing point of pure water and T_f' is the freezing point of the solution.

The basis for the colligative properties of dilute solutions is stated mathematically by **Raoult's Law**. The vapor pressure of the solvent above the solution, P_1, is equal to the mole fraction of the solvent, X_1, times the vapor pressure of the pure solvent, P_1^o.

$$P_1 = X_1\, P_1^{\,o} \qquad\qquad\qquad X_1 = \frac{n_1}{n_1 + n_2}$$

In the expression for the mole fraction, n_1 is the number of moles of solvent and n_2 is the number of moles of solute. This shows that vapor pressure lowering is due to the relative numbers of solute and solvent particles.

For dilute solutions the freezing point depression and boiling point elevation are directly proportional to the molality, m.

$$\Delta T_f = -\, i\, K_f m \qquad\qquad\qquad \Delta T_b = i\, K_b\, m$$

The proportionality constants, K_f and K_b are the freezing point depression constant and the boiling point elevation constant, respectively. These constants are determined for a given solvent by measuring ΔT_f and ΔT_b for dilute solutions of known molality. Values of K_f and K_b for a few solvents are listed in Table 17.5, Pg. 811 in your text. The magnitude of ΔT_f and ΔT_b depends on the number of particles in solution. In the above equations, the factor i, accounts for the moles of particles formed when electrolytes dissociate to form ions in solution. For example,

$C_6H_{12}O_6$ (aq) $\rightarrow$ non-electrolyte, no ions formed $\qquad$ i = 1

$NaCl$ (aq) $\rightarrow$ Na^+ (aq) + Cl^- (aq) i = 2

$CaCl_2$ (aq) $\rightarrow$ Ca^+ (aq) + 2 Cl^- (aq) $\qquad\qquad$ i = 3

Which of the following aqueous solutions will result in the greatest freezing point depression, ΔT_f, and greatest boiling point elevation, ΔT_b?

1 m NaCl   1 m CaCl$_2$ 1 m glucose (C$_6$H$_{12}$O$_6$)

To answer this question we must consider the fact that NaCl and CaCl$_2$ are both strong electrolytes and are therefore assumed to dissociate completely in water to form ions in solution. Glucose, however, is a covalently bound molecule, it is a non-electrolyte and does not dissociate to form ions in aqueous solution. The individual glucose molecules stay intact. Of the three aqueous solutions, 1 m CaCl$_2$ has the greatest number of moles of particles in solution because it dissociates to produce 3 moles of particles per kilogram of water, i = 3, and therefore results in the greatest ΔT_f and ΔT_b. The 1 m NaCl solution dissociates to produce 2 moles of particles per kilogram of water, i = 2, and thus results in a greater ΔT_f and ΔT_b than 1 m glucose which does not dissociate, i = 1.

SAFETY
WEAR SAFETY GLASSES

PROCEDURE
You will work with a partner. One person keeps track of the time and records the data, while the other person reads the temperature and stirs. Before leaving the lab, both partners need to record all the data into their own lab notebooks. Each person will graph and analyze their data independently.

Part 1. Freezing Point of Pure Benzophenone
1. Clean and dry a large test tube. Use an Erlenmeyer flask to support the test tube in an upright position.

2. Use a weighing boat to weigh approximately 10.0 g of benzophenone to the nearest 0.01 g. Transfer the benzophenone to the test tube.

3. Set up a Bunsen burner and ring-stand with a ring clamp and wire mesh to support a 600-mL beaker. Fill the beaker two-thirds full with deionized water.

4. Clamp the test tube to the ring-stand so that it is immersed in the water bath but does not touch the bottom of the beaker. Carefully insert a tenth degree (0.1°C) thermometer and a wire stirrer into the test tube. Suspend the thermometer so that it does not touch the sides or the bottom of the test tube when reading the temperature. The wire stirrer has a loop at the end, which encircles the thermometer. Heat the water to approximately 50°C, stir it using a glass stirring rod. When the benzophenone has completely melted, remove the flame (to avoid overheating, remove the flame when the benzophenone is approximately 45°C, the temperature will continue to rise a few degrees without further heating). Stir the water and the benzophenone.

In this part of the experiment, <u>the test tube containing the benzophenone must be left in the hot water bath</u> as it cools, otherwise it cools too quickly and there won't be enough data to plot the cooling curve.

5. When the temperature of the melted benzophenone is 50°C and not rising, start recording the temperature every thirty seconds (if the temperature is still rising, start recording when it has cooled to 50°C). Make sure to stir both the water bath and the benzophenone between readings.

6. Note the temperature and time when the crystals first appear in the benzophenone and continue taking temperature readings for another 7 minutes.

Part 2. Freezing Point of a Benzophenone and Cyclohexanone Solution

1. Use a 1 mL syringe to transfer 1.0 mL of cyclohexanone to the benzophenone.

2. Heat the water bath until the benzophenone melts. Stir the solution with the wire stirrer.

3. Turn off the gas and carefully remove the water bath. In this part of the experiment, <u>the hot water bath must be removed</u> otherwise the benzophenone cools much too slowly.

4. Measure and record the temperature every 15 seconds. Stir the solution.

5. Note the temperature when the crystals first appear in the solution and continue taking temperature readings for another 3 minutes.

6. Use a weighing boat to weigh approximately 5.0 g benzophenone to the nearest 0.01 g. Add the benzophenone to the test tube.

7. Heat the water bath until the benzophenone melts. Stir the solution with the wire stirrer.

8. Turn off the gas and carefully remove the water bath.

9. Measure and record the temperature every 15 seconds.

10. Note the temperature and time when the crystals first appear in the solution and continue taking temperature readings for another 3 minutes.

WASTE DISPOSAL
Dispose of all waste in the labeled waste bottle in the hood.

■ EXPERIMENT 10

CALCULATIONS

Part 1.

1. Plot the data obtained in Part 1 with the temperature on the y-axis and the time on the x-axis. Clearly label each axis, including the units. This is the freezing point curve for pure benzophenone. Indicate the point at which crystals first appeared.

2. You may observe a dip in the temperature as crystals begin to form due to supercooling. Determine the freezing point of benzophenone. Calculate the percent error in the value of the freezing point determined if the actual value is 47.8°C.

Part 2.

1. Plot the two sets of data obtained in Part 2 with the temperature on the y-axis and the time on the x-axis. Clearly label each axis, including the units. Indicate the point at which crystals first appeared.

2. Determine the freezing point of each of the benzophenone/cyclohexanone solutions.

3. Calculate the freezing point depression constant, K_f, for each of the solutions. The density of cyclohexanone is 0.948 g/ml. Calculate the average value of K_f and indicate the deviation.

PRE-LAB QUESTIONS

1. Distinguish between solute, solvent and solution.

2. What are the units of molarity and molality?

3. The phase diagram for water is shown below. Label the axis and the regions where water is a gas, a liquid and a solid. Indicate where the triple point is located and define the triple point.

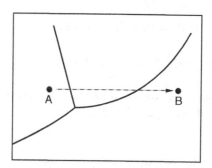

COLLIGATIVE PROPERTIES: FREEZING POINT DEPRESSION ■

a) What do the solid lines in the phase diagram represent? What phase changes occur in going from point A to point B?

b) Is the triple point for water, above or below 1 atm pressure?

c) According to the phase diagram above, starting at point A, what phase change occurs if the pressure is increased and the temperature remains constant?

d) If NaCl is added to water, the vapor pressure of the resulting solution is reduced relative to that of pure water. Draw the vapor pressure curve of the solution on the phase diagram and show the effect on the boiling point and the freezing point.

4. What is a non-volatile solute? What is a volatile solute?

5. Why is the vapor pressure of a solution containing a non-volatile solute lower than the pure solvent? If the solution consists of a solvent and a volatile solute, would anything be different in the drawing? Discuss any differences.

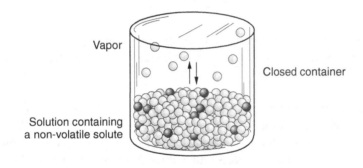

Vapor

Closed container

Solution containing a non-volatile solute

6. If $\Delta T_f = -iK_f m$ and $\Delta T_b = iK_b m$, then i is used to remind you to determine the total number of dissolved particles in solution. What is i for each of the following?

a) glucose ($C_6H_{12}O_6$)

b) Na_2SO_4

c) $(NH_4)_3PO_4$

7. If a 1.0 m solution of glucose ($C_6H_{12}O_6$), Na_2SO_4 and $(NH_4)_3PO_4$, is made, which one will have the lowest vapor pressure, highest boiling point and lowest freezing point?

8. In Part 1 of this experiment you will determine the freezing point of benzophenone. Benzophenone is a solid at room temperature and is completely dissolved at 50°C. By letting the liquid cool and measuring the temperature as a function of time, the freezing point, T_f, of benzophenone is obtained.

■ **EXPERIMENT 10**

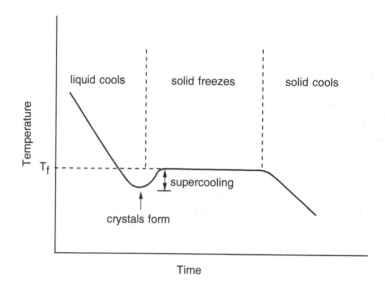

For pure benzophenone the temperature drops only a few degrees. Crystals form and the temperature goes back up and then remains constant. The dip in the curve is due to super-cooling. What is supercooling?

9. In Part 2 of this experiment, cyclohexanone is added to the benzophenone. You will be able to smell the cyclohexanone.
    a) Does this indicate that cyclohexanone is a non-volatile or volatile solute?
    b) Would the freezing point depression be different for a volatile than for a non-volatile solute? Explain how it would be different.

10. Consider the structures for benzophenone and cyclohexanone shown as follows.

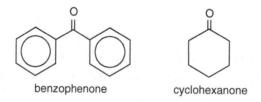

benzophenone   cyclohexanone

    a) Are all the atoms in the same plane in the benzophenone?
    b) Are all the atoms in the same plane in the cyclohexanone?
    c) What are the dominant intermolecular forces in each substance?
    d) Explain why benzophenone is a solid at room temperature and why cyclohexanone is at liquid at room temperature.

e)   Determine the molecular formula for benzophenone and cyclohexanone. Search for the structures of these compounds on the following website:

http://webbook.nist.gov/chemistry/

Search by name, for benzophenone and cyclohexanone. It will give you the molecular formula, the structure and a lot of other information.

11. The cooling curves for a pure solvent and a solution are shown in the figure below. It shows how the freezing point of a solution must be determined by extrapolation of the cooling curve. Extrapolation is necessary because unlike the pure solvent, as the solution freezes, the freezing point drops continuously. Why doesn't the solution reach a constant temperature like the pure solvent?

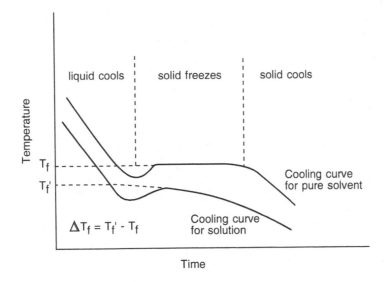

Clearly, supercooling produces an ambiguity in the freezing point and should be minimized. Stirring the solution helps to minimize supercooling.

DISCUSSION QUESTIONS

Briefly summarize the experimental results and the methods used to obtain them. Discuss the observed freezing point depression as a function of solute concentration. Was the solute cyclohexanone non-volatile? How can you tell? If it is volatile how would this affect the freezing point of the solution? Compare the value of K_f determined for benzophenone with the actual value of 8.7 K kg mol^{-1}. Discuss the possible sources of error in this experiment. Are both K_f values high or are both low? Are there any systematic errors in this experiment?

QUESTIONS

1. How many grams of ethylene glycol, $C_2H_4(OH)_2$, are needed per kilogram of water to protect radiator fluid against freezing down to −10°C?

2. For benzene, C_6H_6, the freezing point constant, K_f, is 4.9 K kg mol^{-1} and its normal freezing point is 5.5°C. What is the freezing point of a solution containing 100.0 g of benzene and 20.0 g of naphthanlene ($C_{10}H_8$)?

3. When 5.0 g of an unknown substance is dissolved in 100.0 g of water, the freezing point of the solution decreases by 1.5°C. What is the molar mass of the unknown substance if the compound does not dissociate to form ions in solution, that is, $i = 1$?

4. If 2.00 moles of a substance is dissolved in 1.00 kg of water, the freezing point of the solution decreases by 7.44°C. Does this substance dissociate to form ions in solution? Explain why.

5. Calculate the freezing point of a 0.2 m $CaCl_2$ aqueous solution, assuming it dissociates completely to form ions in solution.

Experiment 11

11

Kinetics: The Rate of a Chemical Reaction

PURPOSE AND LEARNING OBJECTIVES

To measure the rate and determine the rate law for reaction of peroxydisulfate, $S_2O_8^{2-}$, with iodide, I^-.

$$S_2O_8^{2-} + 2\,I^- \;\rightarrow\; I_2 + 2\,SO_4^{2-}$$

PRINCIPLES

Rates of reaction range from very slow to extremely fast. For example, the rusting of iron is reasonably slow, whereas the decomposition of explosives, such as trinitrotoluene (TNT), is extremely fast. The rate of a given reaction depends on the conditions in which the reaction takes place. Sugar oxidizes rapidly in a flame, slowly in living cells and not at all if left sitting out exposed to air. Why are the rates of some reactions slow and others extremely fast? How does temperature, effect a reaction and how does a catalyst increase the rate of a reaction? Understanding reaction rates helps us control them. For example, TNT can be stored and used safely as an explosive because we know it will not decompose until it is ignited; refrigeration of foods allows us to slow down food spoilage; catalytic converters in cars increase the rate at which pollutants are converted to harmless gases. These are all examples in which we control the reaction conditions.

In order for a reaction to occur, reactants must come into direct contact. However, even when direct contact is made, collisions may not be reactive. For example, the reaction between hydrogen and oxygen gas to produce water is exothermic, but the two gases will not react at room temperature and pressure.

$$2\,H_2\,(g) + O_2\,(g) \rightarrow 2\,H_2O\,(l) \qquad\qquad \Delta H° = -571.7\ kJ$$

Even though H_2 and O_2 collide at a rate of ~ 4 billion collisions/sec at room temperature and pressure, the collisions are ineffective (no chemical reaction takes place). In order for collisions to be reactive, they must occur with sufficient energy.

Chemical kinetics is the study of how a reaction occurs and how fast it occurs. A spontaneous reaction ($\Delta G < 0$) does not mean the reaction will be fast. A reaction can involve several elementary steps. How a reaction proceeds from reactants to products is called the reaction mechanism. Some of the steps in the mechanism may be fast and others may be slow. For a given reaction, more than one mechanism may be possible. Experiments must be done to determine the reaction mechanism.

Factors that Influence the Rates of Reaction

A rate is defined as change per unit time. A reaction rate is the change in concentration of a reactant or product per unit time. If the concentration is in units of molarity (mol/L) than the rate will be expressed in units of mol/L-sec. Factors which influence the rate of chemical reactions include the following:

1. The nature of the reactants.
2. The reactant concentration and surface area.
3. The temperature.
4. The presence or absence of a catalyst.

Nature of Reactants

Ions of opposite charge in solution tend to react quickly. Precipitation reactions as well as acid-base neutralization reactions are generally observed to be fast because of the high mobility of dissolved ions in solution and because the electrostatic attraction between the ions of opposite charge is strong. Covalently bound neutral molecules tend to react more slowly. The stronger the covalent bond the slower the reaction. Elemental nitrogen, for example, is unreactive and persists in the atmosphere because of the strong triple bond, $N≡N$. Chlorine, however, has only a single bond, Cl–Cl, and a much weaker bond dissociation energy. As a result, Cl_2 is observed to be much more reactive than N_2.

Reactant Concentration and Surface Area

Molecules must encounter one another in order to react. Increasing the solution concentration increases the number of reactant molecules per unit volume. The greater the number of molecules per unit volume the more likely they will collide with one another. As a result, increasing the concentration often increases the rate of reaction.

Similarly, increasing the surface area of a solid in a heterogeneous reaction, generally increases the rate of a reaction. For example, consider the reaction of zinc metal with aqueous hydrochloric acid to produce hydrogen gas.

$$Zn\ (s)\ +\ 2\ HCl\ (aq)\ \rightarrow\ ZnCl_2\ (aq)\ +\ H_2\ (g)$$

The rate of this type of a reaction tends to increase as the surface of contact increases. Thus, the smaller the pieces of zinc metal the faster the reaction. Also, the more concentrated the HCl solution, the faster the reaction.

Temperature

Temperature is a measure of the average kinetic energy of particles. Thus, increasing the temperature increases the average kinetic energy of reactant molecules. The greater the kinetic energy, the greater the average velocity and collision frequency between reactant molecules. Collisions are reactive only if the molecules collide with sufficient energy. Increasing the average kinetic energy of the reactants increases the fraction of molecules that collide with sufficient energy to react. Hence, an increase in temperature often increases the rate of reaction.

Catalysts

A catalyst is a substance that speeds up a chemical reaction but itself undergoes no permanent chemical change. A catalyst increases the rate of a reaction by providing an alternate path or mechanism that requires less energy for the reaction to occur. For example, enzymes catalyze biochemical reactions. Of the thousands of enzymes in living systems, most are highly specific and extremely efficient in assisting one particular step in a biochemical process.

Reaction Order and Rate Law

To determine the rate of a reaction, the rate of disappearance of reactants or the rate of appearance of products must be measured. Consider the following general reaction.

$$A\ \rightarrow\ B$$

For this reaction, the rate of product formation is expressed mathematically as the change in concentration with respect to time.

$$\text{rate of reaction} = \text{rate of product formation} = \frac{\text{change in concentration of B}}{\text{change in time}} = \frac{\Delta[B]}{\Delta t}$$

The reactant concentration decreases at the same rate as the product concentration increases.

$$\text{rate of reaction} = -\text{rate of disappearance of A} = -\frac{\Delta[A]}{\Delta t}$$

The rate of reaction is always positive. The concentration of A decreases as a function of time and thus the quantity $\Delta[A]/\Delta t$ is negative. The rate of disappearance of A is written as $-\Delta[A]/dt$ so that the rate of reaction will be positive.

In general, the rate of reaction is observed to be proportional to the concentration of the reactants.

$$\text{rate} \quad \alpha \quad [A]^n$$
$$\text{rate} = k\,[A]^n$$

In this equation, k is the rate constant and n is the order of reaction with respect to the reactant A. Both k and n are determined from experiment. n can be an integer or a fraction, either positive or negative.

Consider, for example, the reaction of nitrogen monoxide with hydrogen.

$$2\,NO + 2\,H_2 \quad \rightarrow \quad N_2 + 2\,H_2O \qquad \text{rate} = k\,[NO]^n\,[H_2]^m$$

In this equation, k, n and m must be determined from experiment. Given the following experimental data, the reaction order, rate law and the rate constant can be determined.

Run	[NO] (mol/L)	[H$_2$] (mol/L)	rate (mol/L-sec)
1	0.15	0.35	0.56
2	0.24	0.35	1.43
3	0.24	0.48	1.96

The concentration of H_2 is the same for runs 1 and 2 while the concentration of NO is increased. The corresponding rate expressions for runs 1 and 2 are as follows.

$$\text{rate}_1 = 0.56 = k\,(0.15)^n\,(0.35)^m \qquad \text{and} \qquad \text{rate}_2 = 1.43 = k\,(0.24)^n\,(0.35)^m$$

We can solve for n, by setting up a ratio, rate$_2$ to rate$_1$ as follows.

$$\frac{\text{rate}_2}{\text{rate}_1} = \frac{1.43}{0.56} = \frac{\cancel{k}\,(0.24)^n\,\cancel{(0.35)^m}}{\cancel{k}\,(0.15)^n\,\cancel{(0.35)^m}} = \left(\frac{0.24}{0.15}\right)^n$$
$$2.55 = (1.6)^n$$

Taking the logarithm of each side of the equation allows us to solve for n. Kinetics requires familiarity with powers and logarithms. Review both powers and logarithms if necessary.

$$\log (2.55) = n \log (1.6)$$

$$n = \frac{\log(2.55)}{\log(1.6)} = 2.0$$

The concentration of NO is the same for runs 2 and 3 while the concentration of H_2 is increased. Analogous to the procedure followed to solve for n, the ratio of $rate_3$ to $rate_2$, allows us to solve for m.

$$\frac{rate_3}{rate_2} = \frac{1.96}{1.43} = \frac{\cancel{k}\,\cancel{(0.24)^n}\,(0.48)^m}{\cancel{k}\,\cancel{(0.24)^n}\,(0.35)^m} = \left(\frac{0.48}{0.35}\right)^n$$

$$1.37 = (1.37)^m$$

$$m = 1$$

In this case, it is clear that m must be equal to 1 (there is no need to take the logarithm to determine m). Substituting n = 2 and m = 1 into the rate law expression yields the following.

$$rate = k\,[NO]^2[H_2]$$

The reaction "order" corresponds to the sum of the exponents in the rate law. In this example, the overall reaction is third order because the sum of the exponents is 2 + 1 = 3. The reaction order can also be specified with respect to each of the components. The rate law indicates that this reaction is second order with respect to NO, and first order with respect to H_2. Note that n and m do not correspond to the stoichiometric coefficients of the overall reaction. The mechanism must be determined to derive the rate law.

The rate constant k can be determined using the rate law and the data (the rate constant k should be independent of the data used, run 1, 2 or 3). Using the data for run 1, the rate constant k = 71 L^2/mol^2-sec. The other data give approximately the same value.

$$k = \frac{rate}{[NO]^2\,[H_2]} = \frac{0.56\;mol\,/\,L\cdot sec}{[0.15\;mol\,/\,L]^2\,[0.35\;mol\,/\,L]} = 71\frac{L^2}{mol^2\;sec}$$

The units of the rate constant, k, for this reaction are L^2/mol^2-sec but for a different reaction the units of k may be different.

Reaction Mechanism

When you initiate and observe a reaction, you know what reactants you started with, you may observe the products, but the path from reactants to products is generally not known. The path can involve several steps. The sequence of steps, or mechanism proposed, must be consistent with the observed overall balanced equation for the reaction and the experimental rate law. In a reaction mechanism there is often a slow step that is slower than all the other steps. The slow step in the reaction mechanism is called the rate determining step. The rate law for the overall reaction is derived from the rate law for the slow step. Consider for example, the decomposition of hydrogen peroxide, H_2O_2.

$$2 H_2O_2 \text{ (l)} \xrightarrow{\text{slow}} 2 H_2O \text{ (l)} + O_2 \text{ (g)}$$

This reaction is slow at room temperature but is catalyzed in several ways, including exposure to light, enzymes, KI, or $FeCl_3$. In the catalytic decomposition of hydrogen peroxide using potassium iodide,

$$2 H_2O_2 \text{ (l)} \xrightarrow{I^-} 2 H_2O \text{ (l)} + O_2 \text{ (g)}$$

the experimental rate law is:

$$\text{rate} = k [H_2O_2] [I^-]$$

The concentration of I^- is the same before and after the reaction. Thus, I^- must be consumed in one step and produced in another step. One of the proposed mechanisms is as follows.

Elementary step 1:	$H_2O_2 + I^- \rightarrow H_2O + IO^-$	slow
Elementary step 2:	$H_2O_2 + IO^- \rightarrow H_2O + O_2 + I^-$	fast
Overall reaction:	$2 H_2O_2 \rightarrow 2 H_2O + O_2$	

In the first step of this mechanism, the catalyst, I^-, reacts with H_2O_2 to produce the reaction intermediate IO^-. In the second step, the intermediate, IO^-, is consumed and the catalyst, I^-, is regenerated. Neither the catalyst, I^-, nor the intermediate, IO^-, appear in the overall balanced equation for the reaction. This is because an intermediate is produced and subsequently consumed, and a catalyst is consumed and regenerated in equal amounts.

Elementary step reactions are single step reactions and the rate law for an elementary step reaction is written directly from the reaction stoichiometry. Examples of elementary step reactions and corresponding rate laws are given in the table below.

Elementary Step	Rate Law
$A \rightarrow$ products	Rate = $k[A]$
$2A \rightarrow$ products	Rate = $k[A]^2$
$A + B \rightarrow$ products	Rate = $k[A][B]$
$2A + B \rightarrow$ products	Rate = $k[A]^2[B]$
$A + B + C \rightarrow$ products	Rate = $k[A][B][C]$

Thus, for the first step in the proposed mechanism for the decomposition of hydrogen peroxide, $H_2O_2 + I^- \rightarrow H_2O + IO^-$ the rate law is first order with respect to H_2O_2 and first order with respect to I^-.

$$\text{Rate} = k [H_2O_2] [I^-]$$

This rate law is the same as the experimental rate law for the overall reaction. Thus, if step 1 is much slower than step 2, then the overall rate of reaction is determined by the first step and the proposed mechanism is consistent with the experimental rate law. To prove the proposed mechanism is correct more experiments would have to be done. For example, a method to test for the production of the intermediate, IO^-, would be necessary. The modeling of reaction intermediates using density functional theory can be very insightful in elucidating reaction mechanisms. Density functional theory was developed by Nobel prize winner, Walter Kohn, at UCSB. Many chemists, including our research group, use this theory to calculate the energies of reaction intermediates and thereby determine if a proposed mechanism is reasonable. See for example, Carpenter, Van Koppen, Perry, Bush-nell, Bowers, Journal of American Chemical Society, 122 (2000) 392; Van Koppen, Perry, Bowers, International Journal of Mass Spectrometry, 185-7 (1999) 989.

The Reaction of Peroxydisulfate with Iodide

In this experiment the rate of reaction of peroxydisulfate, $S_2O_8^{2-}$, with iodide, I^-, will be measured.

$$S_2O_8^{2-} + 2 I^- \rightarrow I_2 + 2 SO_4^{2-}$$
$$\text{rate} = k [S_2O_8^{2-}]^x [I^-]^y$$

Because we do not know the mechanism for this reaction, the order of reaction with respect to each of the reactants must be determined. The exponents, x and y, are determined by measuring the reaction rate as a function of concentration of each of the reactants. Once the rate law is determined, the rate constant k is calculated.

How do we measure the rate of reaction? We start by preparing an aqueous solution of the salts, sodium thiosulfate $Na_2S_2O_3$ and potassium iodide KI. These salts dissociate to produce the ions, $S_2O_3^{2-}$, Na^+, I^- and K^+, in solution. The solution will be colorless. What happens if we add the salt $(NH_4)_2S_2O_8$ to this solution? This salt dissociates to produce $S_2O_8^{2-}$ and NH_4^+, and the $S_2O_8^{2-}$ will react with I^- in solution to produce I_2 according to the following reaction.

$$S_2O_8^{2-} + 2 I^- \xrightarrow{\text{slow}} I_2 + 2 SO_4^{2-}$$

To detect the presence of I_2 in solution, starch is added as an indicator. The solution turns a blue-black color due to a triiodide-starch complex formed (I_2 reacts with I^- to produce the triiodide,

I_3^-). The color change is very sudden and dramatic. Thus, the time required to produce the color change can be measured accurately.

We can repeat this experiment several times because an excess of $S_2O_8^{2-}$ is present in solution from the initial volume of $(NH_4)_2S_2O_8$ added to the solution. The experiment is repeated by adding 1 mL aliquots of $Na_2S_2O_3$ to the solution. When $Na_2S_2O_3$ is added, the solution turns colorless immediately because $S_2O_3^{2-}$ reacts very quickly with I_2 to produce I^- and $S_4O_6^{2-}$.

$$I_2 + 2 S_2O_3^{2-} \xrightarrow{\text{fast}} 2 I^- + S_4O_6^{2-}$$
$$\text{blue-black} \qquad\qquad \text{colorless}$$

The solution initially contains 1.0 mL of 0.4 M $Na_2S_2O_3$, that is, 4×10^{-4} moles of $S_2O_3^-$. The reaction stoichiometry indicates that 4×10^{-4} moles of $S_2O_3^-$ reacts to produce 4×10^{-4} moles of I^-. Because $S_2O_8^{2-}$ is present in solution and reacts with the I^- to produce I_2, a color change will be observed when 2×10^{-4} mol of I_2 is produced.

$$S_2O_8^{2-} + 2 I^- \xrightarrow{\text{slow}} I_2 + 2 SO_4^{2-}$$
$$\text{blue-black}$$

The time required to produce 2×10^{-4} mol of I_2 can be measured accurately. The reaction stoichiometry indicates that one mole of I_2 is produced for one mole of $S_2O_8^{2-}$ consumed. Thus, when 2×10^{-4} mol of I_2 is produced, 2×10^{-4} mol of $S_2O_8^{2-}$ has been *consumed*. By measuring the time required to consume 2×10^{-4} mol of $S_2O_8^{2-}$, in a given volume of solution, the rate can be calculated in units of mol/L-sec.

$$\text{rate of reaction} = \frac{\Delta [I_2]}{\Delta t} = -\frac{\Delta [S_2O_8^{2-}]}{\Delta t}$$

After the $Na_2S_2O_3$ is added, the solution becomes colorless. The reaction time is measured from the moment the solution turns colorless to the moment it turns a blue-black color. The reaction time corresponds to the time required to consume 2×10^{-4} moles of $S_2O_8^{2-}$.

$$I_2 + 2 S_2O_3^{2-} \xrightarrow{\text{fast}} 2 I^- + S_4O_6^{2-}$$
$$\text{blue-black} \qquad\qquad \text{colorless}$$

$$2 I^- + S_2O_8^{2-} \xrightarrow{\text{slow}} I_2 + 2 SO_4^{2-}$$
$$\text{colorless} \qquad\qquad\qquad \text{blue-black}$$
$$|\leftarrow \text{ measured time } \rightarrow|$$

The measurement is repeated several times for a given concentration of reactants and an average rate of reaction is determined. The concentration of $S_2O_8^{2-}$ and I^- will then be independently changed to measure the rate as a function of concentration. Once the rate law is obtained the rate constant can be calculated.

CHEMICALS AND EQUIPMENT

Digital timers are available for this experiment. Quantities indicated are sufficient for a pair of students. All the chemicals (except for the EDTA solution) will be available in labeled burettes in the hood. The EDTA solution will be in a bottle with an eyedropper.

> 0.2 M KI (200 mL)
> 0.4 M $Na_2S_2O_3$ (60 mL) FRESHLY PREPARED
> 1% starch solution, boiled
> 0.2 M KNO_3 (300 mL)
> 0.1 M Na_2H_2EDTA
> 0.2 M $(NH_4)_2S_2O_8$ (200 mL) FRESHLY PREPARED FROM SOLID

SAFETY
WEAR SAFETY GLASSES

EXPERIMENTAL PROCEDURE

For this experiment, you will work in pairs but you must analyze the data independently. Before you leave the lab, record all the data into your own lab notebook and show calculated rates as well as the rate law and rate constants to your instructor.

Quantitative Reaction Rate Measurements; Effects of Concentration

1. Clean and dry a 250-mL Erlenmeyer flask (cleanliness is crucial). Prepare Solution 1 in the 250-mL Erlenmeyer flask from solutions in labeled burettes in the hood. The EDTA solution is in a bottle with an eyedropper in the hood.

   > *Solution 1:*
   > 25.0 mL 0.2 M KI solution
   > 1.0 mL starch solution
   > 1.0 mL 0.4 M $Na_2S_2O_3$ solution
   > 48.0 mL 0.2 M KNO_3 solution
   > 1 drop EDTA solution

2. Clean and dry three small test tubes. From the burette in the hood measure a 1 mL aliquot of 0.4 M $Na_2S_2O_3$ into each of the three test tubes.

3. Clean and dry a 100-mL beaker (cleanliness is crucial). From a burette in the hood measure 25 mL of 0.2 M $(NH_4)_2S_2O_8$ solution into the 100-mL beaker.

   NOTE: Being efficient with steps 4 and 5 will increase the accuracy of this experiment.

4. To solution 1, add the 25 mL of 0.2 M $(NH_4)_2S_2O_8$. Start the digital timer when it is added, SWIRL THE SOLUTION VIGOROUSLY and stop the timer when the solution turns a blue-black color. Record the reaction time.

5. Add the first of the three 1 mL aliquots of 0.4 M $Na_2S_2O_3$ to the solution. <u>Wait until the solution turns colorless to start the timer</u>, SWIRL THE SOLUTION VIGOROUSLY <u>and stop the timer when the solution turns black-blue</u>. Record the reaction time. Repeat this step for the second and third 1 mL aliquots of 0.4 M $Na_2S_2O_3$. Remember that being efficient increases the accuracy of this experiment. Thus, after the solution turns a black-blue color, quickly add the next aliquot of $Na_2S_2O_3$ and start the timer when the solution turns colorless and stop the timer when it turns a blue-black.

6. Record the reaction time for each run. The color change is observed when 2×10^{-4} moles of I_2 is produced. From the reaction stoichiometry, this implies that 2×10^{-4} moles of $S_2O_8^{2-}$ is consumed.

$$S_2O_8^{2-} + 2 I^- \longrightarrow I_2 + 2 SO_4^{2-}$$
$$\text{colorless} \qquad\qquad \text{blue-black}$$

To calculate the rate of this reaction, the rate of $S_2O_8^{2-}$ consumption is calculated.

$$\text{Rate} = \frac{\text{moles } S_2O_8^{2-} \text{ consumed}}{(\text{Total Volume (L)})(\text{Reaction Time (sec)})} = -\frac{2 \times 10^{-4} \text{ mol } [S_2O_8^{2-}]}{(\text{Volume (L)})(\text{Time (sec)})}$$

Solution Added	Reaction Time (s)	Total Volume (L)	Rate (mol/L-sec)
25 mL $(NH_4)_2S_2O_8$		0.100	
1 mL $NA_2S_2O_3$		0.101	
1 mL $NA_2S_2O_3$		0.102	
1 mL $NA_2S_2O_3$		0.103	

7. Discard Solution 1 into the appropriately labeled waste container in the hood.

8. Clean and dry the 250-mL Erlenmeyer flask (cleanliness is crucial). Prepare solution 2 in the Erlenmeyer flask.

Solution 2:
25.0 mL 0.2 M KI solution
1.0 mL starch solution
1.0 mL 0.4 M $Na_2S_2O_3$ solution
23.0 mL 0.2 M KNO_3 solution
1 drop EDTA solution (0.1 M Na_2H_2EDTA)

9. From the burette in the hood measure 1 mL of 0.4 M $Na_2S_2O_3$ into each of the three small test tubes.

10. Clean and dry a 100-mL beaker (cleanliness is crucial). From a burette in the hood measure 50 mL of 0.2 M $(NH_4)_2S_2O_8$ solution into the 100-mL beaker. Note that the volume of $(NH_4)_2S_2O_8$ is 50 mL, making the total initial volume 100 mL.

   NOTE: To obtain good data, be efficient with steps 11 and 12.

11. To solution 2 add 50 mL of 0.2 M $(NH_4)_2S_2O_8$. Start the digital timer when it is added, SWIRL THE SOLUTION VIGOROUSLY and stop the timer when the solution turns a blue-black color. Record the reaction time.

12. Add the first of the three 1 mL aliquots of 0.4 M $Na_2S_2O_3$ to the solution. Wait until the solution turns colorless to start the timer, SWIRL THE SOLUTION VIGOROUSLY and stop the timer when the solution turns black-blue. Record the reaction time. Repeat this step for the second and third 1 mL aliquots of 0.4 M $Na_2S_2O_3$.

13. Calculate the reaction time and the rate of reaction.

Solution Added	Reaction Time (s)	Total Volume (L)	Rate (mol/L-sec)
50 mL $(NH_4)_2S_2O_8$			
1 mL $NA_2S_2O_3$			
1 mL $NA_2S_2O_3$			
1 mL $NA_2S_2O_3$			

14. Discard Solution 2 into the labeled waste beaker in the hood.

15. Clean and dry the 250-mL Erlenmeyer flask (cleanliness is crucial). Prepare solution 3 in the Erlenmeyer flask.

   Solution 3:
   50.0 mL 0.2 M KI solution
   1.0 mL starch solution
   1.0 mL 0.4 M $Na_2S_2O_3$ solution
   23.0 mL 0.2 M KNO_3 solution
   1 drop EDTA solution (0.1 M Na_2H_2EDTA)

16. From the burette in the hood measure 1 mL of 0.4 M $Na_2S_2O_3$ into each of the three small test tubes.

17. Clean and dry a 100-mL beaker (cleanliness is crucial). From a burette in the hood measure 25 mL of 0.2 M $(NH_4)_2S_2O_8$ solution into the 100-mL beaker. Note that the volume of $(NH_4)_2S_2O_8$ is 25 mL, making the total initial volume 100 mL.

18. To Solution 3 add the 25 mL of 0.2 M $(NH_4)_2S_2O_8$. Start the digital timer when it is added, SWIRL THE SOLUTION VIGOROUSLY and stop the timer when the solution turns a blue-black color. Record the reaction time.

19. Add the first of the three 1 mL aliquots of 0.4 M $Na_2S_2O_3$ to the solution. <u>Wait until the solution turns colorless to start the timer</u>, SWIRL THE SOLUTION VIGOROUSLY <u>and stop the timer when the solution turns black-blue</u>. Record the reaction time. Repeat this step for the second and third 1 mL aliquots of 0.4 M $Na_2S_2O_3$.

20. Calculate the reaction time and the rate of reaction.

Solution Added	Reaction Time (s)	Total Volume (L)	Rate (mol/L-sec)
25 mL $(NH_4)_2S_2O_8$			
1 mL $NA_2S_2O_3$			
1 mL $NA_2S_2O_3$			
1 mL $NA_2S_2O_3$			

21. Discard Solution 3 into the labeled waste beaker in the hood.

22. Clean and dry the 250-mL Erlenmeyer flask (cleanliness is crucial). Prepare solution 4 in the Erlenmeyer flask.

Solution 4:
12.5 mL 0.2 M KI solution
1.0 mL starch solution
1.0 mL 0.4 M $Na_2S_2O_3$ solution
35.5 mL 0.2 M KNO_3 solution
1 drop EDTA solution (0.1 M Na_2H_2EDTA)

23. From the burette in the hood measure 1 mL of 0.4 M $Na_2S_2O_3$ into each of the three small test tubes.

24. Clean and dry a 100-mL beaker (cleanliness is crucial). From a burette in the hood measure 50 mL of 0.2 M$(NH_4)_2S_2O_8$ solution into the 100-mL beaker. Note that the volume of $(NH_4)_2S_2O_8$ is 50 mL, making the total initial volume 100 mL.

25. To Solution 4 add the 50 mL of 0.2 M $(NH_4)_2S_2O_8$. Start the digital timer when it is added, SWIRL THE SOLUTION VIGOROUSLY and stop the timer when the solution turns a blue-black color. Record the reaction time.

26. Add the first of the three 1 mL aliquots of 0.4 M $Na_2S_2O_3$ to the solution. <u>Wait until the solution turns colorless to start the timer</u>, SWIRL THE SOLUTION VIGOROUSLY <u>and stop the timer when the solution turns black-blue</u>. Record the reaction time. Repeat this step for the second and third 1 mL aliquots of 0.4 M $Na_2S_2O_3$.

27. Calculate the reaction time and the rate of reaction.

Solution Added	Reaction Time (s)	Total Volume (L)	Rate (mol/L-sec)
50 mL $(NH_4)_2S_2O_8$			
1 mL $NA_2S_2O_3$			
1 mL $NA_2S_2O_3$			
1 mL $NA_2S_2O_3$			

28. For each of the solutions calculate the mean (average) rate of reaction and the average deviation from the mean. If some rates are much lower or higher than the mean, do not include them in calculating the mean.

29. For each of the solutions, calculate the initial concentration of I^- and $S_2O_8^{2-}$. Be sure to use the total initial volume (100 mL for each of the solutions).

Solution	$[I^-]_o$ (mol/L)	$[S_2O_8^{2-}]_o$ (mol/L)	Mean Rate (mol/L-sec)
1			
2			
3			
4			

30. From the data obtained determine the order, x and y, with respect to the reactants, $S_2O_8^{2-}$ and I^-. This yields the rate law for the reaction.

$$Rate = k[S_2O_8^{2-}]^x[I^-]$$

31. Calculate the rate constant for each of the solutions, the mean rate constant and the average deviation from the mean.

Solution	Rate Constant, k (L/mol-sec)
1	
2	
3	
4	

WASTE DISPOSAL

Dispose of all waste in the appropriately labeled waste bottle in the hood.

PRE-LAB QUESTIONS

1. Salts dissociate to form ions in aqueous solution.

   a) What ions are present in an aqueous solution of 0.2 M KI?
   b) Write the balanced equation for the dissociation of $(NH_4)_2S_2O_8$ in an aqueous solution.
   c) Write the balanced equation for KI reacting with $(NH_4)_2S_2O_8$ in an aqueous solution containing some starch. What color should the final solution be? What causes the color change?
   d) Write the balanced equation for the dissociation of $Na_2S_2O_3$ in an aqueous solution.
   e) When $Na_2S_2O_3$ is added to the solution containing KI and $(NH_4)_2S_2O_8$, what reactions will occur? Write the balanced equations for the reactions and indicate the color of the solution after each reaction.

2. In this experiment you will quantitatively measure a reaction rate of $S_2O_8^{2-}$ with I^- in solution to produce I_2 according to the following reaction:

$$S_2O_8^{2-} + 2\ I^- \xrightarrow{\text{slow}} I_2 + 2\ SO_4^{2-}$$

The color change is very sudden and dramatic when 2×10^{-4} mol of I_2 is produced. The time required to produce 2×10^{-4} mol of I_2 can be measured accurately.

$$\text{rate of reaction} = \frac{\Delta [I_2]}{\Delta t} = -\frac{\Delta [S_2O_8^{2-}]}{\Delta t}$$

a) Write the rate law for the reaction of $S_2O_8^{2-}$ with I^-.
b) How will you determine the order of reaction with respect to each of the reactants?
c) Calculate initial concentrations of $S_2O_8^{2-}$ and I^- in the solution **after 25 mL** of 0.2 M $(NH_4)_2S_2O_8$ have been added to solution 1.

Solution 1:
25.0 mL 0.2 M KI solution
1.0 mL starch solution
1.0 mL 0.4 M $Na_2S_2O_3$ solution
48.0 mL 0.2 M KNO_3 solution
1 drop EDTA solution

d) What reactions occur after the addition of 1 mL $Na_2S_2O_3$? Indicate the color changes after each reaction.
e) How many moles of $S_2O_8^{2-}$ are consumed between the time 1 mL $Na_2S_2O_3$ is added and when the solution turns blue?
f) The rate is measured four times. The first time after 25 mL of 0.2 M $(NH_4)_2S_2O_8$ has been added and three times after the addition of 1 mL aliquots of 0.4 M $Na_2S_2O_3$. Should the rates be the same or different? Explain your answer.
g) Calculate the initial concentration of $S_2O_8^{2-}$ and I^- in the solution after **50 mL** of 0.2 M $(NH_4)_2S_2O_8$ have been added to solution 2.

Solution 2:
25.0 mL 0.2 M KI solution
1.0 mL starch solution
1.0 mL 0.4 M $Na_2S_2O_3$ solution
23.0 mL 0.2 M KNO_3 solution
1 drop EDTA solution (0.1 M Na_2H_2EDTA)

3. Consider the following reaction: A + B → products
   The rate law for this reaction was found to be: rate = $k[A][B]^2$

   a) What is the reaction order with respect to A?
   b) What is the reaction order with respect to B?
   c) What is the overall order of the reaction?
   d) If the concentration of A is doubled while the concentration of B is kept constant, how will this affect the rate of reaction?
   e) If the concentration of B is doubled while the concentration of A is kept constant, how will this affect the rate of reaction?
   f) What do we call k in the rate law expression? What are the units of k for this reaction?

4. Suppose the following data is obtained for the reaction:

$$2\ NO\ (g)\ +\ 2\ H_2\ (g)\ \rightarrow\ N_2\ (g)\ +\ 2\ H_2O\ (g)$$

[NO]	[H_2]	Rate (mol L^{-1} s^{-1})
0.1 M	0.1 M	1.4×10^{-4}
0.2 M	0.1 M	5.6×10^{-4}
0.1 M	0.2 M	2.8×10^{-4}

a) Determine the rate law for this reaction.

b) Calculate the rate constant, k , and give the units.

DISCUSSION QUESTIONS

Write the balanced equation for the reaction of $S_2O_8^{2-}$ with I$^-$ and the rate law determined for this reaction. How precise are the rate measurements? What was the average deviation from the mean rate? Discuss possible errors in measuring the rate of reaction.

What were the initial concentrations of I$^-$ and $S_2O_8^{2-}$ in solutions 1 and 2? Which reactant concentration was changed and which was held constant? How did the change in concentration affect the rate? Compare the average rate obtained for solutions 1 and 2. Similarly, compare the initial concentrations of I$^-$ and $S_2O_8^{2-}$ in solutions 1 and 3 and in solutions 2 and 4. Compare the average rates for solutions 1 and 3 and solutions 2 and 4.

Were the rate constants the same for all the solutions? Why should the rate constant calculated for all four solutions be the same? What could be changed in the experiment to observe a change in the rate constant? Is this a good experiment to determine the rate constant for the reaction of $S_2O_8^{2-}$ with I$^-$? How can the experiment be modified to improve the accuracy and precision of the experiment?

QUESTIONS

1. a) Generally reactions of ions in solution tend to be fast. Explain why the reaction between the peroxydisulfate ion and iodide ion is slow.

$$S_2O_8^{2-}\ +\ 2\ I^-\ \rightarrow\ I_2\ +\ 2\ SO_4^{2-}$$

   b) What type of a reaction is this? Explain why.

2. If 2×10^{-4} mol of $S_2O_8^{2-}$ in 60 mL of solution is consumed in 185 seconds, what is the rate of consumption of $S_2O_8^{2-}$?

3. Suppose the following data is obtained for the reaction A → products:

[A] (mol L^{-1})	Rate (mol L^{-1}s^{-1})
0.50	2.0×10^{-5}
0.25	5.0×10^{-6}

a) Write the rate law for this reaction.
b) Calculate the rate constant k. Be sure to include the units!
c) Calculate the rate if the concentration of A is 0.6 M?

4. Given the following reaction mechanism,

$$H_2O_2 \rightarrow H_2O + O$$
$$O + CF_2Cl_2 \rightarrow ClO + CF_2Cl$$
$$ClO + O_3 \rightarrow Cl + 2 O_2$$
$$Cl + CF_2Cl \rightarrow CF_2Cl_2$$

a) Write the overall equation for the reaction?
b) Identify the reaction intermediate(s).
c) Identify the catalyst.
d) Write the rate law for each of the elementary steps.

■ **EXPERIMENT 11**

12

Chemical Kinetics:

Rate of Decomposition of Hydrogen Peroxide

PURPOSE AND LEARNING OBJECTIVES

To determine the effects of concentration and temperature on the rate of the catalyzed decomposition of hydrogen peroxide.

PRINCIPLES

The rate of a reaction is determined experimentally by measuring either the reactant or product concentration as a function of time. In this experiment you will measure the volume of oxygen gas produced as a function of time for the decomposition of hydrogen peroxide.

$$2 H_2O_2 \text{ (l)} \xrightarrow{\text{slow}} 2 H_2O \text{ (l)} + O_2 \text{ (g)}$$

Even though this reaction is calculated to be exothermic, $\Delta H° = -198.5$ kJ/mol, and spontaneous at 25°C, $\Delta G° = -211.0$ kJ/mol, we can not predict the rate of this reaction. The rate of decomposition of hydrogen peroxide is observed to be slow and therefore has a relatively long shelf-life. We have to explain why this reaction is slow.

Svante Arrhenius, a Swedish chemist, studied the effect of temperature on reaction rate constants. He found that for a bimolecular elementary reaction, in which bonds are broken and other bonds are formed, the observed rate constant was often less than the collision rate constant, that is, not every collision is reactive. Arrhenius proposed that a minimum energy requirement, called the activation energy, Ea, must be overcome to produce a chemical reaction.

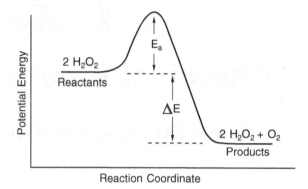

Arrhenius found that the rate constant increases exponentially with temperature according to the following equation.

Arrhenius equation: $k = A\, e^{-E_a/RT}$

In this equation A is a constant with the same units as the rate constant, k. The exponential factor, $f = e^{-E_a/RT}$, represents the fraction of collisions that occur with sufficient kinetic energy to react (the shaded area in the figure below). As the temperature increases from T_1 to T_2, the fraction of molecules with sufficient energy to react increases.

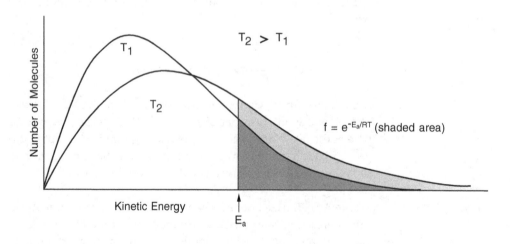

This figure shows only the effect of translational energy on the rate of a reaction; rotational and vibrational energy can also promote chemical reactions.

Taking the natural logarithm of the Arrhenius equation, yields the following equation.

$$\ln k = \ln A - \frac{E_a}{RT}$$

A plot of $\ln k$ versus $1/T$ results in a straight line with the slope equal to $-E_a/R$, and the intercept equal to $\ln A$. For many reactions the rate constant is observed to exhibit a temperature dependence consistent with this equation. In this experiment, the effect of temperature on the rate of reaction will be measured.

What other means do we have to increase the rate of a reaction? This is an important consideration for many biochemical reactions that are too slow at normal body temperatures. How can we increase the rate of these reactions without a significant increase in temperature? Catalysts increase the rate of reaction. Enzymes, for example, are proteins that catalyze biochemical reactions. Adding a catalyst speeds up a reaction by providing an alternate pathway with a lower activation energy, E_a. A catalyst does not affect the energy of the reactants relative to products (ΔE for the reaction remains the same).

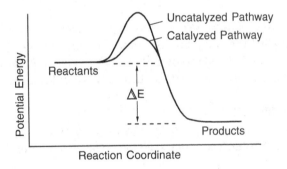

A catalyst may increase the rate at which equilibrium is attained but a catalyst has no effect on the equilibrium constant.

The decomposition of hydrogen peroxide is catalyzed by potassium iodide.

$$2\ H_2O_2\ (l) \xrightarrow{\ I^-\ } 2\ H_2O\ (l) + O_2\ (g)$$

In this experiment, the rate law for this reaction will be determined by measuring the rate of oxygen gas production as a function of both H_2O_2 and I^- concentration.

$$\text{rate} = k\,[H_2O_2]^x\,[I^-]^y$$

A catalyst is defined as a substance that speeds up a chemical reaction but itself undergoes no permanent chemical change. Thus, if the concentration of I^- is the same before and after the reaction then I^- must be consumed in one step and regenerated in another step. One of the proposed mechanisms for this reaction is as follows.

Elementary step 1:	$H_2O_2 + I^- \rightarrow H_2O + IO^-$
Elementary step 2:	$H_2O_2 + IO^- \rightarrow H_2O + O_2 + I^-$
Overall reaction:	$2\,H_2O_2 \rightarrow 2\,H_2O + O_2$

In the first step of this mechanism, the catalyst, I^-, reacts with H_2O_2 to produce the reaction intermediate IO^-. In the second step, the intermediate IO^- is consumed and the catalyst, I^-, is regenerated.

You can show that the concentration of I^- is the same before and after the reaction by titrating the solution with 0.1 M $AgNO_3$ using K_2CrO_4 as an indicator. The AgI (s) precipitate is formed according to the following reaction.

$$Ag^+ + I^- \rightarrow AgI\,(s)$$

Once all the iodide in the solution is consumed, Ag^+ complexes with CrO_4^{2-}, which is red in aqueous solution, signaling the end point. By comparing the moles of I- before and after the decomposition of H_2O_2, the % iodide recovered can be calculated. Because iodide is a catalyst and is not consumed in the reaction, 100% of the catalyst should be recovered.

CHEMICALS AND EQUIPMENT

Digital timers are available for this experiment. Quantities indicated are sufficient for a pair of students. The KI and H_2O_2 solutions will be available in labeled burettes in the hood.

0.10 M KI (80 ML)
3% H_2O_2 (40 mL)
0.1 M $AgNO_3$ (20 mL)
1 M K_2CrO_4 (indicator)

SAFETY
WEAR SAFETY GLASSES

Avoid contact with $AgNO_3$, it will stain skin brown. In case of contact with $AgNO_3$, rinse thoroughly. Always wash your hands before leaving the laboratory.

EXPERIMENTAL PROCEDURE

For this experiment, you will work in pairs but you must analyze the data <u>independently</u>. Before you leave the lab, record all the data into your own lab notebook and show calculated rates, the rate law and rate constants to your instructor.

Part 1. Reaction Rate Measurements; Effect of Concentration

1. The rate of decomposition of hydrogen peroxide, catalyzed by potassium iodide will be obtained.

$$2\ H_2O_2\ (l) \xrightarrow{\ I^-\ } 2\ H_2O\ (l) + O_2\ (g)$$

   The rate of oxygen gas production is measured as a function of both H_2O_2 and I^- concentration. Assemble the apparatus as shown in the figure below. A double burette clamp may be used to hold both the burette and the syringe body.

2. Fill a trough with water (about half-full) and let it equilibrate to room temperature. Cold tap water will generally be colder than room temperature, so add some hot water to attain room temperature (approximately 22-24°C). Record the temperature.

3. Add room temperature water to the burette. At the start of each run, the water level in the burette should be filled to the top and the syringe body should be nearly empty when the water levels are equal. During the experiment, the syringe body is moved down to equalize the water levels. The oxygen gas produced in the reaction displaces water from the burette into the syringe body.

4. Place 125 mL of water in a 125-mL Erlenmeyer flask. Stopper the flask as shown in Figure 1. Check for air leaks in the apparatus by lowering the syringe body. If there are no leaks, the water level in the burette will initially change some but then it must stop changing. If there are no air leaks discard the water and clean the Erlenmeyer flask.

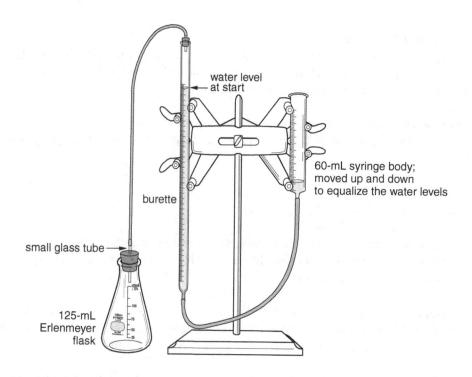

Figure 1. The 125-mL Erlenmeyer flask is placed in a water trough (not shown) to measure the rate of reaction as a function of temperature.

5.   In a clean 125-mL Erlenmeyer flask prepare solution 1.

   Solution 1:
   10 mL 0.1 M KI
   15 mL deionized water

   Stopper the flask and swirl the flask in the water trough for a few minutes to allow the solution to equilibrate to the temperature of the bath. If there is too much water in the trough and water spills out as you swirl the solution, remove some of the water in the trough.

6.   One student moves the syringe body to equalize the water levels and holds the flask, while the other student adds **5 mL 3% H_2O_2,** and quickly re-stoppers the flask.

7.   Equalize the levels while swirling the flask as vigorously as possible and read the initial volume. The other student records the initial burette reading and time. Record the volume and time at 2-mL intervals until 14 mL of oxygen gas has been produced. The water levels should be equalized throughout the run to make sure the volume of oxygen produced is measured at constant pressure. Use a digital timer. The solution must be swirled in the water bath to keep the temperature constant.

8. Read and record the temperature of the water in the trough. If the temperature has changed adjust it to the initial temperature by adding hot or cold water.

Solution 1: 10 mL 0.1 KI, 15 mL DI water, 5 mL 3% H_2O_2		
Temperature		
Burette Reading (mL)	**Volume of O_2 (mL)**	**Time (s)**
	0.0	0
Temperature		

9. Clean the Erlenmeyer flask and prepare solution 2 in the flask.

    Solution 2:
    10 mL 0.1 M KI
    10 mL deionized water

    Stopper the flask and swirl the flask in the water trough for a few minutes to allow the solution to equilibrate to the temperature of the bath.

10. One student moves the syringe body to equalize the water levels and holds the Erlenmeyer flask; the other student adds **10 mL 3% H_2O_2**, and quickly re-stoppers the flask.

11. Immediately equalize the levels, swirl the flask as vigorously as possible and read the initial volume. Record the volume and time at 2-mL intervals until 14 mL of oxygen gas has been produced. The water levels should be equalized throughout the run. <u>The solution must be swirled in the water bath to keep the temperature constant.</u>

■ EXPERIMENT 12

12. Read and record the temperature of the water in the trough. Is the temperature the same as it was at the start of this run? If not, adjust the temperature by adding hot or cold water.

Solution 2: 10 mL 0.1 KI, 10 mL DI water, 10 mL 3% H_2O_2		
Temperature		
Burette Reading (mL)	**Volume of O_2 (mL)**	**Time (s)**
	0.0	0
Temperature		

13. Clean the Erlenmeyer flask and prepare solution 3 in the flask.

   Solution 3:
   20 mL 0.1 M KI
   5 mL deionized water

   Stopper the flask and swirl the flask in the water trough for a few minutes to allow the solution to equilibrate to the temperature of the bath.

14. One student moves the syringe body to equalize the water levels and holds the Erlenmeyer flask; the other student adds **5 mL 3% H_2O_2,** and quickly re-stoppers the flask.

15. Immediately equalize the levels, swirl the flask as vigorously as possible and read the initial volume. Record the volume and time at 2-mL intervals until 14 mL of oxygen gas has been produced. The water levels should be equalized throughout the run. The solution must be swirled in the water bath to keep the temperature constant.

CHEMICAL KINETICS: RATE OF DECOMPOSITION OF HYDROGEN PEROXIDE ■

Solution 3: 20 mL 0.1 KI, 5 mL DI water, 5 mL 3% H_2O_2		
Temperature		
Burette Reading (mL)	**Volume of O_2 (mL)**	**Time (s)**
	0.0	0
Temperature		

Part 2. Reaction Rate Measurements; Effect of Temperature

1. Fill the trough with warm water (about half-full). The temperature of the water should be approximately 35 to 40°C. Read and record the temperature.

2. Clean the Erlenmeyer flask. Prepare solution 1 in the flask.

   Solution 1:
   10 mL 0.1 M KI
   15 mL deionized water

   Stopper the flask and swirl the flask in the water trough for a few minutes to allow the solution to equilibrate to the temperature of the bath.

3. One student moves the syringe body to equalize the water levels and holds the flask; the other student adds **5 mL 3% H_2O_2**, and quickly re-stoppers the flask.

4. Immediately equalize the levels, swirl the flask as vigorously as possible and read the initial volume. Record the volume and time at 2-mL intervals until 14 mL of oxygen gas has been produced. The water levels should be equalized throughout the run. The solution must be swirled in the water bath to keep the temperature constant.

5. Read and record the temperature of the water in the trough. The water should not have dropped more than a few degrees. **Let the reaction continue as indicated in the next step to determine the molar concentration of the catalyst I⁻ after the reaction has gone to completion.**

6. After 14 mL of oxygen has been collected, allow the reaction to go to completion. That is, until no more oxygen gas is produced. After the reaction goes to completion, read and record the final volume (be sure to equalize the water levels).

7. Read and record the temperature of the water in the trough. The temperature will have dropped more than a few degrees. **Save the solution to determine the molar concentration of the catalyst I⁻ in Part 3.**

8. Obtain the barometric pressure from your instructor.

Solution 1: 10 mL 0.1 KI, 15 mL DI water, 5 mL 3% H_2O_2		
Temperature		
Burette Reading (mL)	**Volume of O_2 (mL)**	**Time (s)**
	0.0	0
Temperature		
Total Volume O_2 (g) Collected (mL)		
Barometric Pressure (torr)		
Vapor Pressure of Water (torr) (at the temperature of the water in trough) See Appendix 2		

Part 3. Recovering the Catalyst

Even though the reaction has gone to completion the catalyst itself is not consumed in the reaction. To determine the concentration of I^- in the solution, the solution is titrated with 0.1 M $AgNO_3$. The yellow precipitate formed is AgI(s). K_2CrO_4 will be used as an indicator. Once all the iodide in the solution is consumed, Ag^+ complexes with CrO_4^{2-}, which is red in aqueous solution, signaling the end point.

1. Clean a 50.0 mL burette with soap and water. Do a final rinse with DI water. Make sure to run water through the tip of the burette. Water should run freely down the burette without adhering to the glass.

2. Carefully fill the burette with approximately 20 mL of 0.1 M $AgNO_3$. Avoid contact with $AgNO_3$, it will stain skin brown. In case of contact with $AgNO_3$, rinse thoroughly. The brown color will wear off in a few days.

3. Read and record the initial burette volume.

4. Add 1-2 drops of 1 M K_2CrO_4 of indicator to the solution containing the iodide.

5. Titrate the solution with 0.1 M $AgNO_3$ until the end point is reached. The yellow AgI(s) precipitate is very fine, suspended in a yellow chromate solution. At the end point the precipitates coagulates and the solution is red.

6. Read and record the final burette volume.

7. Calculate the moles of Ag^+ needed to reach the end point. From the reaction stoichiometry, determine the moles of I^- in the solution. $Ag^+ + I^- \rightarrow AgI$ (s)

   Compare the final moles of I^- to the initial moles of I^- to calculate the % I^- recovered. Was the I^- catalyst completely recovered? Calculate the % yield.

Titration of solution 1: 10 mL 0.1 KI, 15 mL DI water, 5 mL 3% H_2O_2 after the decomposition of H_2O_2 has gone to completion.	
Initial moles of I^- in solution (before decomposition of H_2O_2)	
Initial burette volume $AgNO_3$ (mL)	
Final burette volume $AgNO_3$ (mL)	
Total volume of $AgNO_3$ (mL)	
Moles of Ag^+	
Final moles of I^- in solution	
% I^- recovered	

WASTE DISPOSAL

Dispose of all waste in the appropriately labeled waste bottle in the hood.

CALCULATIONS

Part 1.

1. Use Excel to graph the data for each of the three solutions; plot Volume of O_2 (g) on the y-axis versus Time (s) on the x-axis. Clearly label the axis, indicate which solution the graph corresponds to and the temperature at which the experiment was done.

2. Do a linear least square fit of the data or draw the best straight line through the points.

3. Calculate the slope of each line. What does the slope correspond to? What are the units of the slope?

Solution	V_{H2O_2} (mL)	V_{KI} (mL)	Rate (mL of O_2/s)
1	5	10	
2	10	10	
3	5	20	

4. From the data obtained determine the order, x and y, with respect to the reactants, H_2O_2 and I^-. This yields the rate law for the reaction.

$$\text{Rate} = k\,[H_2O_2]^x\,[I^-]^y$$

Part 2.

1. Use Excel on the computer to graph the data; plot Volume of O_2 (g) on the y-axis versus Time (s) on the x-axis. Clearly label the axis, indicate which solution the graph corresponds to and the temperature at which the experiment was done.

2. Do a least linear square fit of the data or draw the best straight line through the points.

3. Calculate the slope of the line.

4. Compare the rate obtained for solution 1 in Parts 1 and 2.

Solution 1: 10 mL 0.1 KI, 15 mL DI water, 5 mL 3% H_2O_2	
Temperature	Rate (mL/s)

5. What was the temperature increase? Calculate the factor that the rate increased.

6. Calculate the partial pressure of O_2 (g) inside the burette.

$$\text{Barometric Pressure} = P_{total} = P_{O_2} + P_{H_2O}$$

7. Calculate the total moles of O_2 collected using the ideal gas law. Show your calculations.

8. Calculate the molar concentration of the 3% hydrogen peroxide.

PRE-LAB QUESTIONS

1. In Part 1 of this experiment, you will determine the rate law for the catalyzed decomposition of hydrogen peroxide.

$$2\,H_2O_2\,(l) \xrightarrow{\;I^-\;} 2\,H_2O\,(l) + O_2\,(g)$$

   a) How will the rate of this reaction be measured?
   b) Write the mechanism proposed for the catalyzed decomposition of hydrogen peroxide.
   c) Identify the intermediate in this mechanism. The catalyst and intermediate are not in the overall reaction. How can you distinguish between a catalyst and an intermediate?
   d) Write the rate law for the overall catalyzed decomposition of hydrogen peroxide.

2. In Part 2 of this experiment you will observe the effect of temperature on the rate of decomposition of hydrogen peroxide.

   a) Draw a schematic reaction coordinate diagram for the decomposition of hydrogen peroxide. Indicate the position of the reactants, products, the activation energy, E_a, and the change in energy, ΔE.
   b) Do you expect that an increase in temperature will increase the rate of this reaction? Explain how.
   c) Does the temperature effect the activation energy, E_a? Explain why or why not.
   d) Does a catalyst effect the activation energy, E_a? Explain how.

3. In Part 3 of this experiment, you will show that the catalyst is not consumed in the reaction. You started with 10 mL 0.1 M KI in 15 mL of DI water and 5 mL of 3% H_2O_2. After the decomposition of H_2O_2 is complete, you should end up with the same number of moles of I^- that you started with. The solution is titrated with 0.1 M $AgNO_3$ to determine the moles of I^- present.

   a) Write the reaction, which occurs as you titrate this solution.
   b) If the catalyst, I^-, is not consumed in the reaction and is completely recovered, what volume of the 0.1 M $AgNO_3$ is required to reach the end point?
   c) What indicator is used and how will you detect the end-point?

4. Suppose the following data is obtained at 25˚C for the following reaction.

A + B + C → products

[A] (mol L⁻¹)	[B] (mol L⁻¹)	[C] (mol L⁻¹)	Rate (mol L⁻¹s⁻¹)
0.1	0.2	0.3	0.063
0.3	0.4	0.2	0.084
0.6	0.4	0.2	0.168
0.3	0.4	0.1	0.021
0.6	0.2	0.2	0.168

a) Write the rate law for this reaction.
b) Calculate the rate constant k. Be sure to include the units!
c) Calculate the rate if the concentration of A, B and C are 0.4 M, 0.3 M and 0.1 M, respectively.

DISCUSSION QUESTIONS

Write the reaction and the determined rate law for the decomposition of hydrogen peroxide, catalyzed by iodide. How precise are the rate measurements? For the three solutions, where the concentrations of the reactants were changed while the temperature was held constant, were the rate constants the same? Should the rate constant be the same for these solutions? What was the average deviation from the mean rate measured for these solutions? Discuss possible errors in measuring the rate of reaction.

What were the initial concentrations of I⁻ and H_2O_2 in solutions 1 and 2? Which reactant concentration was changed and which was held constant? How did the change in concentration affect the rate? What were the initial concentrations of I⁻ and H_2O_2 in solutions 1 and 3? Which reactant concentration was changed and which was held constant? How did the change in concentration affect the rate?

What was the effect of temperature on the rate? Does the rate increase or decrease with temperature. Explain why. How can the experiment be modified to improve the accuracy and precision of the experiment?

Were you able to show that iodide is a catalyst and is not consumed in the reaction? How much of the iodide was recovered?

CHEMICAL KINETICS: RATE OF DECOMPOSITION OF HYDROGEN PEROXIDE ■

QUESTIONS

1. If a solution is 3% H_2O_2 by mass calculate its molarity. Assume the density is 1 g/mL. How does this molarity compare with the molarity of H_2O_2 determined in this experiment?

2. A balloon is filled with a ratio of 2:1 of H_2 and O_2 gas. If left undisturbed no reaction takes place. A small flame or spark will cause a loud explosion, burning H_2 to produce H_2O.

   a) Write the balanced equation for this reaction.
   b) Draw a reaction coordinate diagram showing the energy of the reactants, the products and the transition state. Clearly label the axis.
   c) Is the reaction exothermic or endothermic?
   d) Why do we need a spark or flame to get this reaction to go?

3. The exponential factor, $f = e^{-E_a/RT}$, in the Arrhenius equation, represents the fraction of collisions with sufficient kinetic energy to react. If the activation energy, E_a, for a reaction is 40 kJ/mol, calculate the fraction of collisions with sufficient energy to react at

   a) 25°C
   b) 65°C

■ EXPERIMENT 12

13

Reaction Reversibility and Le Chatelier's Principle

PURPOSE AND LEARNING OBJECTIVES

To observe reaction reversibility. To study a number of chemical reactions at equilibrium. To observe and understand the shift in equilibrium in response to changes in temperature or changes in concentration of reactants or products.

PRINCIPLES

Many reactions go to completion and the theoretical product yield can be calculated for a given quantity of reactants. In calculating the theoretical yield, it is assumed that the limiting reagent is used up in the reaction. In reality, many reactions do not go to completion. Consider, for example, the thermal decomposition of calcium carbonate (limestone) to produce calcium oxide (lime) and carbon dioxide.

$$CaCO_3 \text{ (s)} \quad \rightarrow \quad CaO \text{ (s)} + CO_2 \text{ (g)}$$

If the reaction takes place in an open container, as in a lime kiln, all the CO_2 (g) escapes and the reaction goes to completion. However, if CaO (s) is placed in a closed container with sufficient CO_2 (g) pressure, the reverse reaction is observed.

$$CaO \text{ (s)} + CO_2 \text{ (g)} \quad \rightarrow \quad CaCO_3 \text{ (s)}$$

This reaction is therefore reversible. In a closed container, at a given temperature and pressure, this reaction will approach a state of equilibrium.

$$CaCO_3 \text{ (s)} \quad \rightleftharpoons \quad CaO \text{ (s)} + CO_2 \text{ (g)}$$

At equilibrium the CO_2 (g) pressure is constant. This does not indicate, however, that the reaction has stopped. At equilibrium the rate of the forward reaction equals the rate of the reverse reaction resulting in a constant CO_2 (g) pressure. This state of equilibrium can be approached from either the reactant side or the product side. The rate at which equilibrium is attained can be fast or slow. The reactions in this experiment are all fast so you can observe the effect of changes in concentration or temperature and the effect these changes have on the position of equilibrium.

In the thermal decomposition of limestone, if some CO_2 (g) escapes from the container, the sudden change in pressure disturbs the equilibrium causing the system to react in a way to counteract the change. In this case, the equilibrium shifts right to produce more CO_2 (g) until equilibrium is restored and the pressure of CO_2 (g) remains constant. This is shown schematically in the following figure. At the start of the reaction, at time equals zero seconds, only $CaCO_3$ (s) is in the container and there are no products, the CO_2 pressure is zero torr ($P_{CO_2} = 0$ torr). As the $CaCO_3$ (s) starts to decompose, CaO (s) and CO_2 (g) are produced. When sufficient quantities of products have been formed, the reverse reaction occurs. At equilibrium both the forward and reverse reactions occur at equal rates and the pressure of CO_2 is constant (to the right of the dashed line). The equilibrium is referred to as a **dynamic equilibrium**. Even though the system appears to be static, at the molecular level the reactions are occurring but at equal and opposite rates.

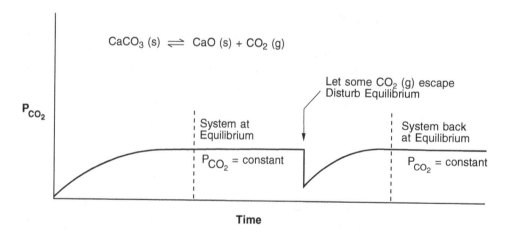

In general, chemical reactions either release heat (exothermic reactions) or consume heat (endothermic reactions). The thermal decomposition of limestone consumes heat in the reaction. Thus, heat can be treated as a reactant.

$$\text{heat} + CaCO_3 \text{ (s)} \quad \rightleftharpoons \quad CaO \text{ (s)} + CO_2 \text{ (g)}$$

When the temperature is increased, the system must respond to counteract this change. Because heat is consumed when $CaCO_3$ (s) decomposes, the equilibrium will shift to the right, increasing the pressure of CO_2 (g) until equilibrium is reestablished and the pressure of CO_2 (g) remains constant as a function of time.

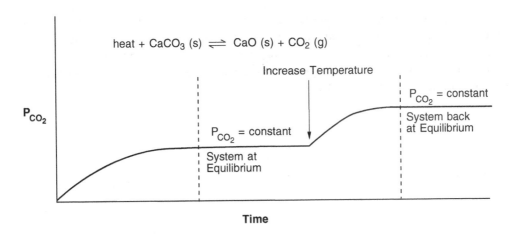

These observations are summarized in **Le Chatelier's Principle**, which states the following. When a system in equilibrium is subjected to a change that affects the equilibrium, the system will react so as to counteract (or reduce) the change.

In this experiment you will qualitatively observe the behavior of systems at equilibrium and the effects of changes in concentration or temperature on the equilibrium. A more quantitative approach, Experiments 6 and 8, will allow you to determine the magnitude of equilibrium constants. In lab today you will present a brief discussion of the results obtained on one of the equilibrium systems studied.

SAFETY
WEAR SAFETY GLASSES

Concentrated 12 M HCl must remain in the hood. If any strong acids or bases come in contact with your skin, rinse immediately with lots of water. Always wash your hands before leaving the laboratory.

■ EXPERIMENT 13

ORAL PRESENTATION

Before leaving the lab each student will explain one of the following systems to the instructor.

Part 1. Chromate/Dichromate Ion Equilibrium

Part 2. Indicators: Weak Acid-Base Equilibria

Part 4. The Common Ion Effect in a Complex Ion Equilibrium

Part 6. The Effect of an Acid-Base Equilibrium on a Solubility Equilibrium

Each student explains one of the above systems and shows the chemical reactions to demonstrate the shift in equilibrium. Students can do their presentation anytime during the lab period. If everyone waits until the end of the lab students will end up waiting to get a turn. Guidelines for the oral presentation are as follows. Students explain the system to their lab partner before presenting it to the instructor.

Oral Report Evaluation Form

Date: _____

Title: _____

Speaker: _____

SCORE

Presentation style

____ Was the talk given in a clear voice; did the speaker speak to the entire group or to the instructor (and not to the chalkboard)?

____ Voice was raised and lowered for variety and emphasis.

____ Board work appeared organized and legible.

Content of presentation

____ Was the presentation well organized?

____ Relevant reaction(s) were clearly and correctly written.

____ Discussion of the experimental procedure, results, conclusions or problem solving techniques was clearly presented (Note that the topics of discussion will vary depending on the title).

Pace

____ Was the oral paced in such a way to stay within the time limits for the talk, 3-7 minutes?

Audience's interest

____ Did the talk keep the audience interested? This can be done through dynamic speaking, or by asking questions to check student understanding, etc.

Questions and Answers

____ Were questions from the group or the instructor answered correctly and effectively?

Reminder: The purpose of this exercise is to help you develop your presentation skills. Comments are meant to help you towards that goal.

Best aspect(s) of the talk:

One area that needs improving:

■ EXPERIMENT 13

PROCEDURE

For this experiment, you will work independently or with a partner. You're encouraged to discuss results with your partner or neighbor. In **Part 4** please share the aqueous $FeSCN^{2+}$ solution with a neighboring group to minimize wasting chemicals.

Part 1. Chromate/Dichromate Ion Equilibrium

In the presence of the hydrogen ion, H^+, chromate ions, CrO_4^{2-}, react to produce dichromate ions, $Cr_2O_7^{2-}$, according to the following reaction.

$$CrO_4^{2-} \text{ (aq)} + 2\,H^+ \text{ (aq)} \rightleftharpoons Cr_2O_7^{2-} \text{ (aq)} + H_2O \text{ (l)}$$
$$\text{yellow} \qquad\qquad\qquad\qquad \text{orange}$$

1. In a clean small test tube place 1 to 2 mL of 1 M K_2CrO_4. Add several drops of 3 M H_2SO_4. Shake the test tube to mix the solution. Record your observations.

2. Add several drops of 6 M NaOH, until you observe a change (mixing after each drop). Observe and record changes.

3. Add several drops of 3 M H_2SO_4 until you observe a change.

4. Add several drops of 6 M NaOH, until you observe a change.

5. Explain the results; include equations for reactions. Why do you observe each of the changes? How does the addition of H_2SO_4 effect the chromate/dichromate equilibrium? How does the NaOH effect the equilibrium? Why do we use 3 M H_2SO_4 and 6 M NaOH?

Part 2. Indicators: Weak Acid-Base Equilibria

Two indicators commonly used in acid-base titrations are methyl orange and phenolphthalein. Methyl orange is yellow in basic solutions and red in acidic solutions whereas phenolphthalein is red-pink in basic solutions and colorless in acidic solutions. In acid-base titrations, the color change signals the end-point in a titration, the point at which the base has been exactly neutralized by the acid. The indicators themselves are weak acid-base equilibria as shown in the following reaction.

$$HIn \rightleftharpoons H^+ + In^-$$
$$\text{methyl orange:} \quad \text{red} \qquad\qquad \text{yellow}$$

HIn represents the protonated acid form of the indicator and In^- represents the deprotonated base form of the indicator.

■ EXPERIMENT 13

HIn (red)   In⁻ (yellow-orange)

1. Place 2-3 mL of DI water in a clean small test tube. Add a drop of 1% methyl orange. Then add 2 drops of 6 M HCl. Observe and record the color change. Add 4 drops of 6 M NaOH. Observe and record the color change.

2. Repeat this procedure for phenolphthalein. Place 2-3 mL of DI water in a small test tube. Add a drop of 0.1% phenolphthalein. Then add 2 drops of 6 M HCl. Observe and record the color change. Add 4 drops of 6 M NaOH. Observe and record the color change.

3. Explain the results, including equations for reactions. Why do you observe each of the color changes? How does the addition of HCl effect the HIn/In⁻ equilibrium? How does the NaOH effect the equilibrium?

HCl is a strong acid and NaOH is a strong base, both dissociate completely in aqueous solution.

$$HCl \ (aq) \quad \rightarrow \quad H^+ \ (aq) + Cl^- \ (aq)$$

$$NaOH \ (aq) \quad \rightarrow \quad Na^+ \ (aq) + OH^- \ (aq)$$

The single arrow (→) indicates the reaction goes to completion and a double reversible arrow (⇌) indicates an equilibrium where both the forward and reverse reaction occurs. Now consider the indicator equilibrium in addition to a weak acid equilibrium.

$$HIn \ (aq) \quad \rightleftharpoons \quad H^+ \ (aq) + In^- \ (aq) \tag{1}$$

methyl orange: red   yellow

Acetic acid (vinegar), CH_3COOH, is a weak acid, it dissociates only 1% in aqueous solution, according to the following equilibrium.

$$CH_3COOH \ (aq) \quad \rightleftharpoons \quad H^+ \ (aq) + CH_3COO^- \ (aq) \tag{2}$$

Both CH_3COOH and CH_3COO^- are present in solution but 99% of the CH_3COOH remains undissociated.

4. Clean two small test tubes. Place 1-2 mL of 0.1 M CH_3COOH in each test tube. Add a drop of methyl orange to each sample.

5. To one of the test tubes, add 1 M sodium acetate, $NaCH_3COO$, a few drops at a time. Mix the solution and compare the color of this solution to the solution in the other test tube. Record your observations.

   The observed shift in equilibrium is due to the **common ion effect**, defined as follows. Sodium acetate is a salt that dissociates completely in aqueous solution according to the following reaction.

$$NaCH_3COO \ (aq) \quad \rightarrow \quad Na^+ \ (aq) + CH_3COO^- \ (aq)$$

   The acetate ion, CH_3COO^-, formed in this reaction was already in solution because it is also produced in the dissociation of CH_3COOH. Thus, by adding $NaCH_3COO$, the concentration of CH_3COO^- increases. The acetate ion, CH_3COO^-, is a "common ion" in solution. Observe, record and explain the shift that occurs in both equilibrium (1) and (2) by adding $NaCH_3COO$.

6. Add a few drops of 1 M NH_4OH, a weak base, to each of the solutions. Observe, record and explain your results, include equations showing reactions.

Part 3. Temperature Dependence in a Complex Ion Equilibrium

Metal ions such as Co^{2+} will form complex ions, where ligands surround the metal ion. A **ligand** is either a molecule or ion that donates electron density to the metal ion to form a bond. Examples of ligands include H_2O, NH_3, Cl^-, and OH^-. $CoCl_2(H_2O)_2$ is a complex metal ion with two Cl^- and two H_2O ligands surrounding the Co^{2+} in a tetrahedral geometry. $Co(H_2O)_6^{2+}$ is also a complex ion with six water molecules surrounding the central metal ion, Co^{2+}, in an octahedral geometry.

In aqueous solution, we can observe the conversion between the tetrahedral complex ion, $CoCl_2(H_2O)_2$, which is blue, and the hydrated octahedral complex ion, $Co(H_2O)_6^{2+}$, which is pink, according to the following equilibrium.

$$CoCl_2(H_2O)_2 + 4 \ H_2O \quad \rightleftharpoons \quad Co(H_2O)_6^{2+} + 2 \ Cl^-$$
$$\text{blue} \qquad\qquad\qquad \text{pink}$$

By dissolving $CoCl_2 \bullet (H_2O)_6$ in methanol a blue solution is obtained. When water is added to this solution, water ligands displace the chloride ligands and the solution turns pink. Because of a substantial difference in energy between the products and reactants, the equilibrium is temperature dependent, that is, we can observe the color change from pink to blue and from blue to pink with a change in temperature.

1. Place 4 mL of 0.15 M $CoCl_2 \cdot (H_2O)_6$ (dissolved in methanol) into a small test tube. Using a dropper, add just enough water to turn this blue solution pink. Too much water will ruin the experiment.

2. Pour 2 mL of the pink solution into another test tube.

3. To one of the test tubes add concentrated 12 M HCl, drop wise (in the hood), until you observe a color change. The 12 M HCl must remain in the hood. Record your observations and explain your results in terms of Le Chatelier's principle.

4. Heat the other test tube in a beaker of hot water. You can heat the beaker of water using a Bunsen burner. Observe and record the color change. If you do not observe a color change you may have added too much water and you need to repeat step 1 of this part of the experiment. If you do observe a color change, explain your results in terms of Le Chatelier's principle. Does the reaction produce or consume heat? Write the equation for the equilibrium reaction including the heat (is heat on the reactant or product side)?

5. If heating the solution caused the equilibrium to shift in one direction, cooling the solution will shift the equilibrium in the reverse reaction. Cool the solution in an ice water bath. Observe and record the color change. Explain your results; include equations showing reactions.

Part 4. The Common Ion Effect in a Complex Ion Equilibrium

In aqueous solution, we can observe the equilibrium between metal ion, Fe^{3+}, and the deep red $Fe(SCN)^{2+}$ complex ion, according to the following reaction.

$$Fe^{3+} + SCN^- \rightleftharpoons Fe(SCN)^{2+}$$
$$\text{deep red}$$

1. In a 125-mL Erlenmeyer flask, place 3 mL of 0.1 M $Fe(NO_3)_3$, a yellow-orange solution. Add 3 mL 0.1 M KSCN and 60 mL deionized water. Swirl the solution. Share this solution with a neighboring group to minimize chemical waste.

2. Clean four medium test tubes. In each of the four test tubes, place 5 mL of the $Fe(SCN)^{2+}$ solution, from step 1.

Test tube 1: This is your control for color comparison.
Test tube 2: Add 1 mL of 0.1 M KSCN, observe and record color changes.
Test tube 3: Add 1 mL (~20 drops) 0.1 M $Fe(NO_3)_3$, observe and record color changes.
Test tube 4: Add 5-6 drops 6 M NaOH, observe and record changes.
(Note: $Fe(OH)_3(s)$ is essentially insoluble.)

3. Compare the colors of test tubes 2, 3, and 4 to the control (test tube 1). Explain the observed results in terms of Le Chatelier's Principle, include equations showing the reactions.

Part 5. Concentration and Temperature Effects in a Dissolution-Precipitation Equilibrium (Solubility Equilibrium)

In solubility equilibria, the equilibrium exists between the solute and its saturated solution (some solid must be present for equilibrium to exist). The dissolution-precipitation equilibrium of sodium chloride will be studied.

$$NaCl\ (s) \rightleftharpoons Na^+\ (aq) + Cl^-\ (aq)$$

1. Place 4 mL of saturated sodium chloride solution, 5.4 M NaCl, into a small test tube. Add 2 mL of concentrated 12 M HCl. Mix the solution. Record your observations and explain the results using Le Chatelier's principle.

2. Heat the solution by placing the test tube in a beaker of hot water, heated with a Bunsen burner. Record your observations. Does the reaction produce or consume heat? Is heat on the reactant or product side? Write the reaction for the dissolution-precipitation equilibrium of sodium chloride, including the heat.

Part 6. The Effect of an Acid-Base Equilibrium on a Solubility Equilibrium

If you wanted to precipitate out the Ca^{2+} in a given solution, adding the oxalate ion would produce calcium oxalate precipitate according to the following equilibrium.

$$Ca^{2+}\ (aq) + C_2O_4^{2-}\ (aq) \rightleftharpoons CaC_2O_4\ (s) \tag{1}$$

To precipitate out all the Ca^{2+} in solution, you need to drive the equilibrium as far to the right as possible. We can increase the concentration of $C_2O_4^{2-}$ (aq) by adding the sodium oxalate salt, $Na_2C_2O_4$ or oxalic acid, $H_2C_2O_4$, a weak acid.

sodium oxalate   Oxalic acid

The sodium oxalate salt dissociates completely in aqueous solution according to the following reaction.

$$Na_2C_2O_4\ (aq) \rightarrow 2\ Na^+\ (aq) + C_2O_4^{2-}\ (aq)$$

Oxalic acid is a weak acid and dissociates only slightly. Oxalic acid is called a diprotic acid because it loses two hydrogen ions according to the following two equilibria.

$$H_2C_2O_4 \text{ (aq)} \quad \rightleftharpoons \quad H^+ \text{ (aq)} + HC_2O_4^- \text{ (aq)} \tag{2}$$

$$HC_2O_4^- \text{ (aq)} \quad \rightleftharpoons \quad H^+ \text{ (aq)} + C_2O_4^{2-} \text{ (aq)} \tag{3}$$

Will the addition of sodium oxalate or oxalic acid drive equilibrium (1) further to the right? To answer this question do the following experiment.

1. Using a medium test tube, add 4 mL of 0.1 M $CaCl_2$ and 4 mL of deionized water.

2. Divide the solution equally into three small test tubes.
    Test tube 1: Add 6 drops of 0.25 M $H_2C_2O_4$.
    Test tube 2: Add 6 drops of 0.25 M $Na_2C_2O_4$.

    Observe and record the results. Compare the results for the two solutions. Explain any differences observed and write equations for the corresponding reactions. Use the solution in test tube 1 for further experiments in the next step.

3. Add the following to the solution in test tube 1, made in step 2.
    Test tube 1: Add 6 M HCl drop-wise until solution is clear (10 to 20 drops). Explain the results observed.

    Add 6 M NH_4OH drop-wise until a slight excess has been added. Record and explain the observed results, noting the following reaction.

    $$NH_4OH \text{ (aq)} \quad \rightleftharpoons \quad NH_4^+ \text{ (aq)} + OH^- \text{ (aq)}$$

    What does the OH^- react with in the solution?

4. Is the precipitate formed in step 3, $Ca(OH)_2$ (s) or CaC_2O_4 (s)?

    Test tube 3: To rule out formation of $Ca(OH)_2$(s) precipitate add a few drops of 6 M NH_4OH to the $CaCl_2$ solution in test tube 3. Record and discuss your observations. Does this rule out the formation of $Ca(OH)_2$ (s) in step 3?

WASTE DISPOSAL
Dispose of all waste in the appropriately labeled waste bottle in the hood.

PRE-LAB QUESTIONS

1. Define the terms reversible reaction and dynamic equilibrium.

2. State Le Chatelier's principle.

3. Consider the following equilibrium.

$$\text{heat} + CaCO_3 \text{ (s)} \rightleftharpoons CaO \text{ (s)} + CO_2 \text{ (g)}$$

   a) If the pressure of CO_2 (g) is increased, in which direction will the equilibrium shift?
   b) If the temperature is decreased, in which direction will the equilibrium shift?
   c) If the temperature is increased, in which direction will the equilibrium shift?

4. Under what conditions can we make the thermal decomposition of calcium carbonate go to completion?

$$CaCO_3 \text{ (s)} \rightleftharpoons CaO \text{ (s)} + CO_2 \text{ (g)}$$

5. Explain why the concentrations of a mixture at equilibrium are constant as a function of time.

6. In Part 1 of this lab you will study the chromate/dichromate ion equilibrium:

$$2\,CrO_4^{2-} \text{ (aq)} + 2\,H^+ \text{ (aq)} \rightleftharpoons Cr_2O_7^{2-} \text{ (aq)} + H_2O \text{ (l)}$$
   yellow   orange

   a) What color will a solution be, if it contains only K_2CrO_4?
   Complete the reaction: K_2CrO_4 (aq) → ?

   b) What color will the solution be if we add H_2SO_4 to the K_2CrO_4 solution?

   $$H_2SO_4 \text{ (aq)} \rightarrow H^+ \text{ (aq)} + HSO_4^- \text{ (aq)}$$

   $$HSO_4^- \text{ (aq)} \rightleftharpoons H^+ \text{ (aq)} + SO_4^{2-} \text{ (aq)}$$

   How does increasing the concentration of H^+ affect the chromate/dichromate equilibrium? What color will the solution be?

   c) What if we add NaOH to the solution? How does it affect the equilibrium? What does OH^- react with in the solution? What color will the solution be?

DISCUSSION QUESTIONS

In this lab the discussion is completed at the end of each part. Equations showing the reactions must be included in each section and the experimental observations clearly explained in terms of Le Chatelier's principle. Be sure to answer all the questions in each part of the procedure.

QUESTIONS

Try to answer the following questions without referring back to your data to make sure you understand Le Chatelier's principle.

1. Consider the following equilibrium.

$$CrO_4^{2-} \text{ (aq)} + 2 \text{ H}^+ \text{ (aq)} \rightleftharpoons Cr_2O_7^{2-} \text{ (aq)} + H_2O \text{ (l)}$$

    yellow   orange

    If a strong acid, such as HCl, is added to the solution, in which direction will the equilibrium shift and what color will the resulting solution be.

2. Consider the following two equilibria occurring simultaneously in solution.

    $$HIn \text{ (aq)} \rightleftharpoons H^+ \text{ (aq)} + In^- \text{ (aq)} \tag{1}$$

    methyl orange: red   yellow

    $$CH_3COOH \text{ (aq)} \rightleftharpoons H^+ \text{ (aq)} + CH_3COO^- \text{ (aq)} \tag{2}$$

    If the salt, sodium acetate, is added to the solution, in which direction will equilibrium (2) shift? Explain why. How will the shift in equilibrium (2) affect equilibrium (1)? Explain why. What color will the resulting solution be?

3. Consider the following three equilibria occurring simultaneously in solution.

    $$Ca^{2+} \text{ (aq)} + C_2O_4^{2-} \text{ (aq)} \rightleftharpoons CaC_2O_4 \text{ (s)} \tag{1}$$

    $$H_2C_2O_4 \text{ (aq)} \rightleftharpoons H^+ \text{ (aq)} + HC_2O_4^- \text{ (aq)} \tag{2}$$

    $$HC_2O_4^- \text{ (aq)} \rightleftharpoons H^+ \text{ (aq)} + C_2O_4^{2-} \text{ (aq)} \tag{3}$$

    If NaOH is added to the solution, will the amount of CaC_2O_4 (s) precipitate increase or decrease? Explain why by discussing the direction of the shift in each equilibrium reaction.

4. CaC_2O_4 (s) is the salt of the weak acid, $H_2C_2O_4$, whereas $CaSO_4$ (s) is the salt of the strong acid, H_2SO_4. Why does the concentration of H^+ have a greater effect on the precipitation of the salt of a weak acid than on the salt of a strong acid? Hint: What is the difference between the extent of dissociation in weak acid (equilibria (2) and (3) in problem 3) and the extent of dissociation of a strong acid (equilibria as follows)?

$$Ca^{2+} (aq) + SO_4^{2-} (aq) \quad \rightleftharpoons \quad CaSO_4 (s) \qquad (1)$$

$$H_2SO_4 (aq) \quad \rightarrow \quad H^+ (aq) + HSO_4^- (aq) \qquad (2)$$

$$HSO_4^- (aq) \quad \rightleftharpoons \quad H^+ (aq) + SO_4^{2-} (aq) \qquad (3)$$

■ **EXPERIMENT 13**

14

Determination of an Equilibrium Constant

Using a Spectrophotometer

PURPOSE AND LEARNING OBJECTIVES

To study the chemical reaction of Fe^{3+} and SCN^- to produce $Fe(SCN)^{2+}$ in aqueous solution. To measure concentrations of ions in solution using a spectrophotometer. To determine the equilibrium constant of this reaction at a given temperature.

NOTE: Turn on the spectrophotometer at the beginning of the lab period. It takes at least an hour to warm up and stabilize. Set the wavelength at 450 nm.

PRINCIPLES

Two important characteristics of a given reaction are the position of equilibrium (the extent of reaction) and the rate at which equilibrium is established. The relative concentrations of reactants and products at equilibrium indicate the position of equilibrium. The equilibrium position depends on the relative stabilities of the reactants and products. It is characterized by the equilibrium constant, K. Consider, for example, the reaction of nitrogen and hydrogen to produce ammonia.

$$N_2\,(g) + 3H_2\,(g) \;\rightleftharpoons\; 2\,NH_3\,(g)$$

This reaction is reversible and in a closed container, independent of the choice of initial pressures, once equilibrium is established the ratio of product to reactant concentrations, raised to their respective stoichiometric coefficients, is constant. This is the equilibrium constant, K_p (the subscript "p" indicates partial pressures are used in the equilibrium constant expression).

$$\frac{\left(P_{NH_3}\right)^2}{\left(P_{N_2}\right)\left(P_{H_2}\right)^3} = constant = K_p$$

For the general reaction, where A and B react to produce C and D, the equilibrium constant (or "mass action") expression is given as follows.

$$aA + bB \rightleftharpoons cC + dD \qquad K = \frac{[C]^c[D]^d}{[A]^a[B]^b} \quad or \quad K_p = \frac{\left(P_C\right)^c\left(P_D\right)^d}{\left(P_A\right)^a\left(P_B\right)^b}$$

In these expressions, a, b, c and d are the stoichiometric coefficients. The square brackets around each component indicate units of concentration.

Quantities in the Equilibrium Constant (or "Mass Action") Expression

1. Gases normally enter as partial pressures in atmospheres. Gas equilibrium problems can also be set up in terms of concentrations in moles/L.

2. Dissolved species in solution enter as concentrations, in moles/L (molarity, M).

3. The concentration of <u>pure solids</u> and <u>pure liquids</u> do not appear in the equilibrium expression. Neither does the concentration of the solvent taking part in a chemical reaction in dilute solution ($\leq$ 1 M) as shown in the following examples.

$$H_2O\ (l) \rightleftharpoons H_2O\ (g) \qquad\qquad K_p = P_{H_2O}$$

$$Sb^{3+}\ (aq) + Cl^-\ (aq) + H_2O\ (l) \rightleftharpoons 2\ H^+\ (aq) + SbOCl\ (s) \qquad K = \frac{[H^+]^2}{[Sb^{3+}][Cl^-]}$$

In the first equilibrium, $H_2O(l)$ is not included in the equilibrium constant expression because the amount of $H_2O(l)$ present does not affect the partial pressure of water at equilibrium. At a given temperature, the partial pressure of water is constant and thus the equilibrium constant K does not depend on the partial pressure of water. As long as some $H_2O(l)$ is present, equilibrium will be established. In the second equilibrium the reaction takes place in aqueous solution. Water, $H_2O(l)$, the solvent, is not included in the equilibrium constant expression because in dilute solutions, the concentration of water is constant, it does not affect the position of equilibrium. The SbOCl(s) is not included because as long as some solid is present, equilibrium will be established. The amount of solid present does not affect the equilibrium position.

4. <u>Equilibrium constants do not have units.</u> In rigorous work this is accomplished by dividing the pressures of all gases by a standard reference pressure of 1 atm, and dividing the concentrations of all solutes by a standard reference concentration of 1 mole/L. This gives relative pressures and concentrations which have no units, but have the same numerical values.

The Value of the Equilibrium Constanst

If the value of K is large (K >> 1), mostly products are present at equilibrium and the position of equilibrium lies on the right side of the equation. If the value of K is small (K << 1), mostly reactants are present at equilibrium and the position of equilibrium lies on the left side of the equation.

In this experiment, the value of the equilibrium constant, K, will be measured for the reaction of $Fe(H_2O)_6^{3+}$ and SCN^- to produce $Fe(H_2O)_5(SCN)^{2+}$ in aqueous solution.

$$Fe(H_2O)_6^{3+} (aq) + SCN^- (aq) \rightleftharpoons Fe(H_2O)_5(SCN)^{2+} (aq) + H_2O (l)$$

Dilute solutions will be used throughout the experiment and thus, the concentration of water is constant and the waters of hydration may be omitted, simplifying the reaction as follows.

$$Fe^{3+} (aq) + SCN^- (aq) \rightleftharpoons Fe(SCN)^{2+} (aq) \qquad K = \frac{[FeSCN^{2+}]}{[Fe^{3+}][SCN^-]}$$

As long as the temperature remains constant, the value of K will remain constant. Once equilibrium is established, the value of K will be independent of the choice of initial reactant concentration. In order to evaluate K, the equilibrium concentration of each product and reactant must be known. If reactant solutions of known concentrations are prepared, as the reaction proceeds and equilibrium is established, how can the reactant and product concentrations be calculated? The reaction does not go to completion so the moles of products formed and the moles of reactants left can not be calculated from the reaction stoichiometry. A method is needed to measure the concentration of the products and reactants at equilibrium.

Spectrophotometer

In this experiment, a spectrophotometer is used to measure the equilibrium concentration of the product, $Fe(SCN)^{2+}$. The color of the $Fe(SCN)^{2+}$ solution is red, indicating it transmits the wavelengths which your eyes perceive as red, and absorbs the rest of white light. The visible spectrum of light, shown in Figure 1, gives the approximate relationship of wavelength of visible light absorbed to the color observed.

■ **EXPERIMENT 14**

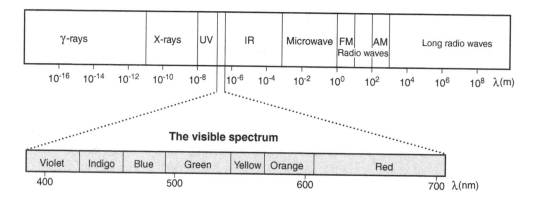

Figure 1. The electromagnetic spectrum. The visible spectrum is only a small portion of the electromagnetic spectrum.

Absorbed Color and Wavelength (nm)		Observed Color
Violet	400	Yellow
Blue	450	Orange
Green	500	Red
Yellow	580	Violet
Orange	600	Blue
Red	650	Green

Figure 2. The color wheel shows the complementary colors opposite each other. Generally, the color observed is the complementary color of the color absorbed. In addition, if all wavelengths of visible light are absorbed except for one color, the color transmitted corresponds to the color observed.

The spectrophotometer will be used to measure the amount of light absorbed at a given wavelength. The absorbance of light by the sample is measured relative to the light absorbed by a reference sample. The transmittance of light, T, is defined as the ratio of the transmitted light, It to the intensity of the incident light, I_o.

$$T = (I_t/I_o)$$ (1)

The intensity of the incident light, I_o, is proportional to the number of photons per second passing through the reference sample. The transmitted light, I_t, is proportional to the number of photons per second passing through the sample of interest. For a given substance, the amount of light absorbed depends on the concentration of absorbing molecules in the sample, the path length, the wavelength of light and the solvent. The number of photons available for absorption decays exponentially as the light passes through the sample.

$$(I_t / I_o) = 10^{-\epsilon bc}$$ (2)

In this equation, b is the thickness of the absorbing sample in centimeters, c is the concentration of the sample in moles/L, and ϵ is the molar absorptivity coefficient in units of L mol^{-1}cm^{-1}. The absorbance of light, A, is directly proportional to the concentration of the absorbing sample, $A \propto c$.

$$A = \epsilon bc \tag{3}$$

Combining equations (2) and (3) yields equation (4), the Beer-Lambert law.

$$A = \epsilon bc = \log (I_o/I_t) \tag{4}$$

Calibration Line
In this experiment a light brown solution containing iron(III) nitrate, $Fe(NO_3)_3$, is combined with a colorless solution containing potassium thiocyanate, KSCN, to produce a red solution due to the formation of the $Fe(SCN)^{2+}$ complex ion.

$$Fe^{3+} (aq) + SCN^- (aq) \rightleftharpoons Fe(SCN)^{2+} (aq) \qquad K = \frac{[FeSCN^{2+}]}{[Fe^{3+}][SCN^-]}$$

The $Fe(SCN)^{2+}$ strongly absorbs light at the wavelength 450 nm in the visible portion of the spectrum. The equilibrium concentration of $Fe(SCN)^{2+}$ for a given reaction mixture, can be determined by measuring the absorbance, A, and calculating the concentration, c using the relationship, $c = A/\epsilon b$. What is the value of ϵb? Because of the linear relationship between absorbance and concentration ($A = \epsilon bc$) the absorbance, A, is plotted as a function of $Fe(SCN)^{2+}$ concentration; the slope of the line yields the value of ϵb. This **calibration line** allows us to determine equilibrium concentrations of $Fe(SCN)^{2+}$ by measuring the absorption.

How can solutions of known equilibrium concentration of $Fe(SCN)^{2+}$ be produced? In a mixture of $Fe(NO_3)_3$ and KSCN, if the concentration of SCN^- is much less than the concentration of Fe^{3+}, the equilibrium will shift far to the right (the reaction will go essentially to completion). To a good approximation SCN^- is completely consumed in the reaction and the equilibrium concentration of $Fe(SCN)^{2+}$ is thus equal to the initial concentration of SCN^-.

To evaluate the equilibrium constant, K, a solution in which all three species are present at equilibrium is required. If approximately equal concentrations of the reactants Fe^{3+} and SCN^- are used, an equilibrium mixture of all three species, Fe^{3+}, SCN^- and $Fe(SCN)^{2+}$, will be produced. To determine the composition of the equilibrium mixture, the absorbance of the resulting solution is measured. **The equilibrium concentration of $Fe(SCN)^{2+}$ is determined from the calibration line.** The equilibrium concentrations of Fe^{3+} and SCN^- and the equilibrium constant, K, can then be calculated.

EQUIPMENT AND PREPARATION

Special test-tubes for the Spectronic 20 Spectophotometer will be provided. Solutions A-1 through A-7 for the calibration curve need to be freshly prepared, just before the experiment is conducted. The instructor will prepare these solutions in the labeled squeeze bottles provided and have them available in the hood.

SAFETY

WEAR SAFETY GLASSES

Nitric acid, HNO_3, is a strong acid. Even though very dilute nitric acid solutions are used, spills must be cleaned up immediately. In case of contact with your skin, rinse thoroughly with water.

PROCEDURE

Part 1. Calibration Curve Using Standard Solutions

1. Clean and rinse seven test tubes specified for the Spectrophotometer. Use DI water for a final rinse. Label the test tubes near the very top, A-1 through A-7. The test tubes must be free of scratches. Fill each of the test tubes two thirds full with the corresponding solutions.

2. Set the wavelength of the spectrophotometer at 450 nm. Calibrate it according to the directions outlined in Appendix 3, using solution A-1 as your reference sample. Use tissues, referred to as Kimwipes, to clean the outside of the test tubes. Finger prints will interfere with the light. Thus, handle test tubes only near the top to ensure accurate absorbance readings.

3. Measure and record the absorbance of solutions A-1, A-2, A-3 and A-4.

4. Check the calibration, using solution A-1 as your reference sample, to make sure no drift has occurred. If significant drift is observed, recalibrate the spectrophotometer and repeat the absorbance measurements.

5. Measure and record the absorbance of solutions A-5, A-6 and A-7.

6. Check the calibration, using solution A-1 as your reference sample, to make sure no drift has occurred. If significant drift is observed, recalibrate the spectrophotometer and repeat the absorbance measurements.

7. The standard solutions of known $Fe(SCN)^{2+}$ concentration have been prepared from the given mixture of reactants. When two solutions are mixed the total volume of the solution must be used when calculating the concentration of each of the species. For example, in

solution A-2, a mixture of 25.0 mL 0.200 M $Fe(NO_3)_3$, 1.00 mL 0.00200 M KSCN, and 74.0 mL 0.1 M HNO_3, yields the following concentrations (see equations below).

$$[Fe^{3+}] = \frac{\text{moles } Fe^{3+}}{\text{Total Volume}} = 0.200 \text{ M } Fe(NO_3)_3 \left(\frac{25.0 \text{ mL}}{25.0 \text{ mL} + 1.0 \text{ mL} + 74.0 \text{ mL}} \right) = 5.0 \times 10^{-2} \text{ M}$$

$$[SCN^-] = \frac{\text{moles } SCN^-}{\text{Total Volume}} = 0.00200 \text{ M KSCN} \left(\frac{1.00 \text{ mL}}{25.0 \text{ mL} + 1.00 \text{ mL} + 74.0 \text{ mL}} \right) = 2.0 \times 10^{-5} \text{ M}$$

Because $[SCN^-] \ll [Fe^{3+}]$, it will be completely consumed in the reaction and the final concentration of $[Fe(SCN)^{2+}]$ will be equal to the initial concentration of $[SCN^-]$. Thus, $[Fe(SCN)^{2+}]$ = 2.0 x 10^{-5} M for solution 2. Calculate the $[Fe(SCN)^{2+}]$ concentrations for the remaining standard solutions.

SOLUTIONS FOR CALIBRATION CURVE					
Solution	0.200 M $Fe(NO_3)_3$	0.00200 M KSCN	0.1 M HNO_3	$[Fe(SCN)^{2+}]$	Absorption
A-1	25.0 mL	0.00 mL	75.0 mL	0	
A-2	25.0 mL	1.00 mL	74.0 mL	2 ×10^{-5} M	
A-3	25.0 mL	2.00 mL	73.0 mL		
A-4	25.0 mL	4.00 mL	71.0 mL		
A-5	25.0 mL	6.00 mL	69.0 mL		
A-6	25.0 mL	8.00 mL	67.0 mL		
A-7	25.0 mL	10.00 mL	65.0 mL		

8. Using Excel on the computer, plot Absorbance (y-axis) versus Concentration (x-axis). Label the axis, including units. Do a least linear square fit through the points and indicate the equation of the line and the correlation coefficient on your graph. If the points do not fall on a line, that is if the correlation is less than 0.99, repeat the experiment. Save the reference sample, solution A-1, for part 2 of this experiment.

Part 2. Solutions to Determine the Equilibrium Constant, K

1. Clean and rinse five test tubes specified for the spectrophotometer. Use DI water for the final rinse. Label the test tubes near the very top, B-1 through B-5.

2. There are three burettes in the hood. One is filled with 0.00200 M $Fe(NO_3)_3$, another is filled with 0.00200 M KCN and a third is filled with 0.1 M HNO_3. Make solutions B-1 through B-5 as indicated in the following table.

NOTE: Be sure to use the 0.00200 M $Fe(NO_3)_3$, this is a much lower concentration then the $Fe(NO_3)_3$ used in Part 1. In Part 2, why do you need to use similar concentrations of $Fe(NO_3)_3$ and KSCN? If you used a much greater concentration of $Fe(NO_3)_3$ relative to KSCN would the measured concentration of $Fe(SCN)^{2+}$ at equilibrium be different for solutions B-1 through B-5?

SOLUTIONS FOR THE DETERMINATION OF THE EQUILIBRIUM CONSTANT					
Solution	0.00200 M $Fe(NO_3)_3$	0.00200 M KSCN	0.1 M HNO_3	Absorption Measured	$[Fe(SCN)^{2+}]$ From Calibration Curve
B-1	5.0 mL	1.00 mL	5.00 mL		
B-2	5.0 mL	2.00 mL	4.00 mL		
B-3	5.0 mL	3.00 mL	3.00 mL		
B-4	5.0 mL	4.00 mL	2.00 mL		
B-5	5.0 mL	5.00 mL	1.00 mL		

3. Calibrate the Spectrophotometer according to the directions outlined in Appendix 3, using solution A-1 as your reference sample. Use Kimwipes, to clean the outside of the test tubes. Make sure the wavelength is set at 450 nm. Tap the test tube to remove air bubbles.

4. Measure and record the absorbance of solutions B-1 through B-5.

5. Check the calibration, using solution A-1 as your reference sample, to make sure no drift has occurred. If significant drift is observed, recalibrate the spectrophotometer and repeat the absorbance measurements.

6. **From the absorbance measured, determine the equilibrium concentration of $Fe(SCN)^{2+}$ <u>using the calibration curve</u> (or calculate the value using the equation of the line).**

7. Determine the equilibrium concentrations of Fe^{3+}, SCN^- and $FeSCN^{2+}$ for solution B-1. Remember to use the total volume when calculating the initial concentrations. For example, for solution B-1, the initial concentration for Fe^{3+} is calculated as follows.

$$[Fe^{3+}]_{initial} = 0.00200 \text{ M } Fe^{3+} \left(\frac{5.00 \text{ mL}}{5.00 \text{ mL} + 1.00 \text{ mL} + 5.00 \text{ mL}} \right) = 0.00091 \text{ M}$$

NOTE: Initial concentration means the concentration of a given species in solution after the solutions are mixed but before any reaction takes place. In this case it is the initial number of moles of Fe^{3+} in the total volume of solution.

DETERMINATION OF AN EQUILIBRIUM CONSTANT USING A SPECTROPHOTOMETER ■

	[Fe^{3+}]	**[SCN$^-$]**	**[Fe(SCN)$^{2+}$]**
Initial Concentration (M)			
Change in Concentration (M)			
Equilibrium Concentration (M)			

8. Calculate the equilibrium constant, K, for solutions B-1 through B-5.

$$K = \frac{[FeSCN^{2+}]}{[Fe^{3+}][SCN^-]}$$

9. The equilibrium constant is independent of the initial reactant concentrations. How do your values of the equilibrium constant compare for the five solutions?

10. Calculate the average value for K and the average deviation from the mean. If one of the values is completely inconsistent with the other values, do not include it in the average calculation and discuss the possible errors to account for this low or high value.

WASTE DISPOSAL

Dispose of all waste in the appropriately labeled waste bottle in the hood.

PRE-LAB QUESTIONS

1. Consider the following equilibrium equation and equilibrium constant expression.

$$aA + bB \rightleftharpoons cC + dD \qquad\qquad K = \frac{[C]^c [D]^d}{[A]^a [B]^b}$$

   a) If K is large (K>>1), does equilibrium lie on the reactant or product side? What is the relative concentration of reactants and products at equilibrium?

   b) If K is small (K<<1), does equilibrium lie on the reactant or product side? What is the relative concentration of reactants and products at equilibrium?

2. In this experiment, the value of the equilibrium constant, K, will be measured for the following reaction.

$$Fe^{3+} (aq) + SCN^- (aq) \rightleftharpoons Fe(SCN)^{2+} (aq)$$

Write the equilibrium constant expression for this reaction.

3. The instructor will illustrate how concentration measurements are made using a Spec-20. See Appendix 3. Solution A-1 contains only $Fe(NO_3)_3$ and HNO_3. Because no KSCN is present, no $Fe(SCN)^{2+}$ is produced. This solution is used as the reference sample. Why don't we use water as the reference sample?

4. Spectroscopy is an analytical method for measuring concentration of a substance in solution. For a given substance the <u>amount of light absorbed depends on</u> the <u>concentration</u> of the absorbing molecules in the sample, the <u>path length</u>, the <u>wavelength of light</u> and the <u>solvent</u>. According to Beer's Law, the absorbance of light, A, is directly proportional to the concentration of the absorbing sample, $A \propto c$.

$$A = \epsilon bc = \log (I_o/I_t)$$

In this equation, define the variables: b, c, ϵ, I_o, and I_t. What are the units of b, c, and ϵ?

5. In Part 1 of this experiment, how are solutions of known concentration of $Fe(SCN)^{2+}$ made?

6. In Part 1 of this experiment, what is the purpose of the calibration line? In the equation $c = A/\epsilon b$, how is the value of ϵb determined?

7. In Part 2 of this experiment, why are approximately equal concentrations of the reactants, Fe^{3+} and SCN^-, used? What is measured to determine equilibrium concentrations of $Fe(SCN)^{2+}$? How do you determine equilibrium concentrations of $Fe(SCN)^{2+}$?

8. If the absorption reads off scale, what is the problem?

9. The following table is used to evaluate the equilibrium constant for the formation of the $Fe(SCN)^{2+}$ complex ion.

$$Fe^{3+} (aq) + SCN^- (aq) \rightleftharpoons Fe(SCN)^{2+} (aq) \qquad K = \frac{[FeSCN^{2+}]}{[Fe^{3+}][SCN^-]}$$

	[Fe³⁺]	**[SCN⁻]**	**[Fe(SCN)²⁺]**
Initial Concentration (M)	1×10^{-3}	1×10^{-4}	0
Concentration (M)	$-x$	$-x$	$+x$
Equilibrium Concentration (M)	$1 \times 10^{-3} - x$	$1 \times 10^{-4} - x$	x

$$K = \frac{[FeSCN^{2+}]}{[Fe^{3+}][SCN^-]} = \frac{[x]}{[1 \times 10^{-3} - x][1 \times 10^{-4} - x]}$$

What does x represent in the equilibrium constant expression? How is x obtained from the experimental data?

10. What volume of 0.200 M $Fe(NO_3)_3$ is needed to make 50 mL of 0.00200 M $Fe(NO_3)_3$.

11. What are the concentrations of Fe^{3+} and NO_3^- in a 0.200 M $Fe(NO_3)_3$ solution?

12. If 5.00 mL 0.00200 M $Fe(NO_3)_3$ is mixed with 5.00 mL 0.00200 M KSCN, calculate the initial concentration of Fe^{3+} and SCN^- in the solution.

DISCUSSION QUESTIONS

Briefly summarize your results and the methods used in this experiment to obtain the results. Discuss the average value of K and the average deviation from the mean. Considering the value of K, what can be said about the equilibrium position of this reaction? Which is greater at equilibrium, the concentration of products or reactants? Discuss the possible sources of error in this experiment.

QUESTIONS

1. For a given substance, the amount of light absorbed depends on a number of factors. State four factors that affect the absorbance.

2. If the absorbance of one of your samples is off scale, what is the most likely problem? What should be done to reduce the absorbance? Why should it be reduced?

3. A solution is made by mixing 5.00 mL 0.00300 M $Fe(NO_3)_3$ with 4.00 mL 0.00300 M KSCN and 3.00 mL 1.0 M HNO_3. After equilibrium is established, the concentration of $Fe(SCN)^{2+}$ was determined to be 2.72×10^{-4} M. Calculate the equilibrium constant for this reaction.

$$Fe^{3+} (aq) + SCN^- (aq) \rightleftharpoons Fe(SCN)^{2+} (aq)$$

4. Write the equilibrium constant expression, K, in terms of reactant and product concentrations, for each of the following reactions (assume all solutions are dilute).

    a) $N_2 (g) + 3 H_2 (g) \rightleftharpoons 2 NH_3 (g)$
    b) $2 NH_3 (g) \rightleftharpoons N_2 (g) + 3 H_2 (g)$
    c) $2 CrO_4^{2-} (aq) + 2 H^+ (aq) \rightleftharpoons Cr_2O_7^{2-} (aq) + H_2O (l)$
    d) $CH_3COOH (aq) \rightleftharpoons H^+ (aq) + CH_3COO^- (aq)$
    e) $Fe^{3+} (aq) + 3 OH^- (aq) \rightleftharpoons Fe(OH)_3 (s)$

5. Consider the following equilibrium. A (g) + 2 B (g) $\rightleftharpoons$ 3 C (g)

    At a certain temperature, 2.00 moles of A and 2.00 moles of B are placed in a 3.0-liter container. After equilibrium is established, the concentration of A is 0.5 mol/L. What is the value of the equilibrium constant, K?

Experiment 15

15

Antacid Analysis

And the Determination of the Percent Acetic Acid in Vinegar

PURPOSE AND LEARNING OBJECTIVES

To use acid-base titration as a method to determine the percent acetic acid in vinegar and to determine the neutralization capacity of antacid tablets. To learn the technique of standardizing a solution.

PRINCIPLES

According to Bronsted-Lowry definition of acids and bases, an acid is a proton (H^+) donor and a base is a proton acceptor. However, there is more than one way to define acids and bases. According to Arrhenius, a base is defined as a substance that, when dissolved in water, increases the concentration of the hydroxide ion, OH^-, over that in pure water. An acid is defined as a substance that, when dissolved in water, increases the concentration of the hydrogen ion, H^+, over that in pure water. The reaction of an acid with a base produces a salt and water, a process known as neutralization. For example, the reaction of hydrochloric acid with sodium hydroxide produces sodium chloride and water.

$$HCl\ (aq) + NaOH\ (aq) \quad \rightarrow \quad NaCl\ (aq) + H_2O\ (l)$$

This reaction can also be written as the total ionic equation to show which species are present in solution and the net ionic equation which clearly shows the neutralization reaction.

Total Ionic Equation: H^+ (aq) $+ \cancel{Cl^-}$ (aq) $+ \cancel{Na^+}$ (aq) $+ OH^-$ (aq) $\rightarrow \cancel{Na^+}$ (aq) $+ \cancel{Cl^-}$ (aq) $+ H_2O$ (l)

Net Ionic Equation: H^+ (aq) $+ OH^-$ (aq) $\rightarrow H_2O$ (l)

pH Scale

In aqueous solutions, the concentration of the hydrogen ion, $[H^+]$, can range from very large values, 10.0 M, to very small values, 1.0×10^{-15} M. To compress this large range in values, a logarithmic scale is used. This is called the pH scale. The pH of a solution is defined as the negative logarithm of the hydrogen ion concentration.

$$pH = -\log [H^+] \quad \text{or} \quad [H^+] = 10^{-pH}$$

Water autoionizes to a small but measurable extent to produce H^+ and OH^- according to the following equation.

$$H_2O \text{ (l)} \rightleftharpoons H^+ \text{ (aq)} + OH^- \text{ (aq)} \qquad K_w = [H^+][OH^-] = 1 \times 10^{-14} \text{ at } 25°C$$

$$[H^+] = [OH^-] = 1.0 \times 10^{-7} \text{ M}$$

When $[H^+] = [OH^-]$, the solution is said to be neutral (neither acidic or basic). That is, $pH = -\log[H^+] = -\log(1.0 \times 10^{-7}) = 7.00$. Thus, the pH of a neutral solution is 7.00. When the pH of a solution is less than 7 it is acidic, and if it is greater than 7 it is basic.

pH	<	7		$[H^+]$	>	$[OH^-]$ acidic solution
pH	=	7		$[H^+]$	=	$[OH^-]$ neutral solution
pH	>	7		$[H^+]$	<	$[OH^-]$ basic solution

Strong Acid-Strong Base Titration

A titration is used to determine the concentration of either an acid or a base. If the concentration of either an acid or base is known, the concentration of the other can then be determined. The solution of known concentration is placed in a burette and added to a solution of unknown concentration until the equivalence point is reached. In this experiment a strong acid, HCl, is titrated with a strong base, NaOH. HCl is a monoprotic acid, it donates a single proton. The stoichiometric ratio of HCl reacting with NaOH is one to one.

$$H^+ \text{ (aq)} + OH^- \text{ (aq)} \rightarrow H_2O \text{ (l)}$$

Thus, at the equivalence point the number of moles of hydroxide ions is equal to the number of moles of hydrogen ions.

At the equivalence point: moles of H^+ = moles of OH^-

The equivalence point is shown by a change in some physical property, such as a change in color. In colorless reactions an indicator is used to signal the equivalence point. An indicator is a substance that changes color dramatically with one drop of additional titrant. Phenolphthalein is an indicator which is colorless in acidic solution and violet in basic solution at pH > 8.2. Thymol blue is an indicator that has two end points. It is pink in acidic solution with pH < 2, turns yellow in acidic solution when pH ≈ 3.0, and is blue in basic solution, pH > 9.0.

Weak Acid-Strong Base Titration

Unlike strong acids, weak acids dissociate less than 1% in aqueous solution. In titrating a weak acid, HA, with a strong base such as NaOH, the acid HA reacts with OH^- according to the following reaction.

$$HA \text{ (aq) } + \text{ OH}^- \text{ (aq) } \rightarrow A^- \text{ (aq) } + H_2O \text{ (l)}$$

At the equivalence point in the titration the moles of acid equals the moles of hydroxide ions.

At the equivalence point: moles of HA = moles of OH^-

Thus, by titrating a sample of vinegar with NaOH of known concentration, the concentration of acetic acid in the vinegar can be determined.

Titration of Antacids

In this experiment the neutralization capacity of stomach antacids, such as Tums and Rolaids, will be determined. The active ingredients in antacids include $Mg(OH)_2$, $CaCO_3$, or a combination of both. These are bases and dissociate to increase OH^- in solution.

$$Mg(OH)_2 \text{ (s) } \rightleftharpoons Mg_2^+ \text{ (aq) } + 2 \text{ OH}^- \text{ (aq)} \qquad K_{sp} = [Mg^{2+}][OH^-]^2$$

In contrast to the $Mg(OH)_2$, which produces OH^- directly upon dissociation, the $CaCO_3$ dissociates in water to produce the carbonate ion, CO_3^{2-}, which reacts with water to produce OH^-.

$$CaCO_3 \text{ (s) } \rightleftharpoons Ca^{2+} \text{ (aq) } + CO_3^{2-} \text{ (aq)} \qquad K_{sp} = [Ca^{2+}][CO_3^{2-}]$$

$$CO_3^{2-} \text{ (aq) } + H_2O \text{ (l) } \rightleftharpoons HCO_3^- \text{ (aq) } + OH^- \text{ (aq)} \qquad K_b = \frac{[HCO_3^-][OH^-]}{[CO_3^{2-}]}$$

$$HCO_3^- \text{ (aq) } + H_2O \text{ (l) } \rightleftharpoons H_2CO_3 \text{ (aq) } + OH^- \text{ (aq)} \qquad K_b = \frac{[H_2CO_3][OH^-]}{[HCO_3^-]}$$

Thus, an aqueous solution of the antacid could be titrated directly with an acid. However, both $Mg(OH)_2$ and $CaCO_3$ are relatively insoluble in water, the solubility product constants, K_{sp}, are small, 1.2×10^{-11} and 8.7×10^{-9}, respectively. To get around this problem, a procedure called back-titration is used. In back-titration, the antacid is dissolved in excess acid, in this experiment HCl is used. Stomach acid is 0.14 M HCl. The base in the antacid reacts with the HCl. Because an excess of HCl is added, some HCl remains in solution. The solution is titrated with a base to determine the concentration of excess HCl. By subtracting the excess HCl from the original volume of HCl added, the amount of HCl consumed by the antacid is determined. This back-titration method is an accurate way to determine the neutralization capacity of the antacid.

The titration curve for the back-titration of an antacid containing $CaCO_3$ is shown in the figure 1. A standardized 3 M NaOH solution is used as the titrant and thymol blue as the indicator. The thymol blue indicator was chosen because the first end point occurs at pH ≈ 3, where the color changes from red to yellow. Due to the sharp increase in pH, the second end point, signaled by a change in color from yellow to blue, occurs immediately after the first end point. The first end point is not as sharp, changing slowly from red at pH ≈ 1.0 to peach at pH ≈ 1.5 to yellow at pH ≈ 3.0. However, even if the first end point is missed, the second end point is within 0.2 to 0.5 mL of the first end point, as shown in figure 1.

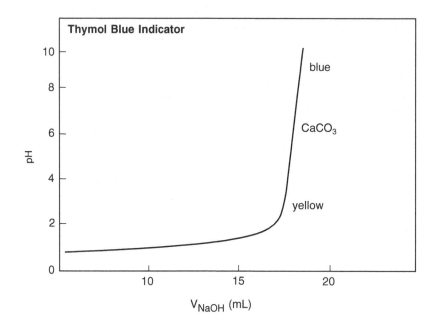

Figure 1. After 50 mL of 0.3 M HCl was added to dissolve the antacid tablet containing $CaCO_3$, the excess acid is titrated with standardized 0.3 M NaOH. The thymol blue indicator is red/pink in acidic solution. The solution is titrated to the yellow endpoint. One to two additional drops of 0.3 M NaOH turns the solution blue.

Standardization of NaOH Solution

In this experiment the solution of NaOH will be standardized to determine its exact concentration. In the standardization process, a sample of potassium hydrogen phthalate (abbreviated as KHP) is accurately weighed and dissolved in water. KHP is a monoprotic acid, donating a single proton in its reaction with the NaOH.

KHP ($C_8H_5O_4K$)

The KHP solution is titrated with the NaOH. In this reaction, 1 mole of NaOH reacts with 1 mole of KHP. Thus, at the equivalence point, the moles of NaOH equals the moles of KHP.

At the equivalence point: Moles OH^- = Moles KHP

NOTE: The only acidic hydrogen in KHP is bonded to the oxygen. The proton is lost more easily when it is bound to an electronegative atom, such as the oxygen bound to an electron withdrawing atom or group of atoms such as COO^-.

R represents either a hydrocarbon or hydrogen atom. The product anion formed in this reaction is stable in aqueous solution.

Example Calculation

A 50 ml solution of 0.2 M HCl is titrated with 0.1 M NaOH. What volume of 0.1 M NaOH is required to neutralize 50 mL of 0.2 M HCl?

What reaction takes place when we titrate this solution with NaOH?

Molecular Equation: $HCl\ (aq) + NaOH\ (aq)\ \rightarrow\ NaCl\ (aq) + H_2O\ (l)$

Net Ionic Equation: $H^+\ (aq) + OH^-\ (aq)\ \rightarrow\ H_2O\ (l)$

If we calculate the moles of H^+ initially in 50 mL of 0.2 M HCl, we can determine the moles of OH^- needed to neutralize the moles of H^+.

The concentration of HCl is 0.2 M. Square brackets are generally used to indicate concentration:

$$[HCl] = 0.2 \text{ M} = 0.2 \frac{\text{moles}}{\text{L}}$$

To determine the moles of HCl in solution, simply multiply the concentration by the volume.

$$\text{moles of HCl} = [HCl] \, V_{HCl} = \left(0.2 \frac{\text{moles}}{\text{L}}\right) 0.050 \text{ L} = 0.01 \text{ moles HCl}$$

HCl dissociates in water according to the following equation:

$$HCl \, (aq) \quad \rightarrow \quad H^+ \, (aq) + Cl^- \, (aq)$$

Thus, 1 mole of HCl produces 1 mole of H^+.

$$0.01 \text{ moles HCl} \left(\frac{1 \text{ mol } H^+}{1 \text{ mol HCl}}\right) = 0.01 \text{ mol } H^+$$

The number of moles of OH^- needed to neutralize 0.01 mol of H^+ is calculated using the neutralization reaction.

$$H^+ \, (aq) + OH^- \, (aq) \quad \rightarrow \quad H_2O \, (l)$$

Because 1 mole of H^+ reacts with 1 mole of OH^-, it takes 0.01 moles of OH^- to neutralize 0.01 moles of H^+.

$$0.01 \text{ moles } H^+ \left(\frac{1 \text{ mol } OH^-}{1 \text{ mol } H^+}\right) = 0.01 \text{ mol } OH^-$$

Finally we need to determine the volume of NaOH used. According to the following reaction, 1 mole of NaOH produces 1 mol of OH^-.

$$NaOH \, (aq) \quad \rightarrow \quad Na^+ \, (aq) + OH^- \, (aq)$$

$$V_{NaOH} = \frac{0.01 \text{ mol NaOH}}{0.1 \text{ mol}/\text{L}} = 0.1 \text{ L} \qquad 0.1 \text{ L} \left(\frac{1000 \text{ mL}}{\text{L}}\right) = 100 \text{ mL}$$

Thus, if 0.01 mol of OH⁻ is needed to neutralize 0.01 mol of H⁺, 0.01 moles of NaOH was used. The volume of NaOH is calculated by dividing the moles of NaOH by its concentration.

It takes 100 ml of 0.1 M NaOH to neutralize 50 ml of 0.2 M HCl.

SAFETY
WEAR SAFETY GLASSES!!!

Take caution when working with potassium hydrogen phthalate (KHP). It is an irritant! NaOH is a strong base and HCl is a strong acid and can burn your skin and clothing if contact is made. In case of contact, flush with water immediately.

PROCEDURE
This experiment will be performed in pairs. It is important to stay consistent when taking measurements. One partner reads the burette until the titration is complete; the other partner reads the burette for the next titration.

Part 1. Standardization of NaOH Solution
1. Weigh and record three samples of potassium hydrogen phthalate (KHP) between 1.2 and 1.8 g to the nearest 0.001 g. Put the samples in three separate, labeled Erlenmeyer flasks, indicate the mass of KHP on each flask. Add 50.0 mL of DI water to each flask.

2. Warm the KHP solutions with a low flame Bunsen burner until the KHP is completely dissolved. **Do not boil the KHP solutions.** Let solutions cool to room temperature.

3. In a 500-mL Erlenmeyer flask, prepare 500.0 mL of 0.3 M NaOH solution starting from 6 M NaOH. The amount of 6 M NaOH needed was calculated in your pre-lab. The volume of the NaOH solution does not have to be known accurately because this solution will be titrated to determine the exact concentration. Stopper the flask.

   NOTE: The NaOH solution must be stoppered when not in use because the NaOH slowly reacts with CO_2 (g) in the air to produce carbonic acid, H_2CO_3.

   $$CO_2 \text{ (g)} + H_2O \text{ (l)} \quad \rightarrow \quad H_2CO_3 \text{ (aq)}$$

   The carbonic acid dissociates to increase the H⁺ concentration in solution.

   $$H_2CO_3 \text{ (aq)} \quad \rightleftharpoons \quad HCO_3^- \text{ (aq)} + H^+ \text{ (aq)}$$

   $$HCO_3^- \text{ (aq)} \quad \rightleftharpoons \quad CO_3^{2-} \text{ (aq)} + H^+ \text{ (aq)}$$

H⁺ (aq) reacts with OH⁻ (aq) in solution, decreasing the concentration of OH⁻, which would affect the end point in the titration.

$$H^+ \text{ (aq)} + OH^- \text{ (aq)} \quad \rightarrow \quad H_2O \text{ (l)}$$

4. Clean a 50.0 mL burette with soap and water. Do a final rinse of the burette with DI water. Make sure to run water through the tip of the burette. If the burette is clean water runs uniformly down the burette without adhering to the glass.

5. Rinse the burette with two 5 mL portions of the 0.3 M NaOH solution. Drain some of the NaOH through the tip.

6. Fill the burette with the NaOH solution to the zero mark or below the zero mark. If the burette is filled above the zero mark drain some of the solution into an empty 600-mL beaker (this beaker will be your waste beaker for the lab). To make sure there are no air bubbles in the tip, briefly open the stopcock to drain some of the solution through the tip and into your waste beaker.

7. Allow the solution to sit for a minute so all of the liquid settles in the burette. Read and record the initial volume of the NaOH in the burette.

8. Select one of the flasks containing KHP. Record the mass of KHP in your notebook.

9. Add two drops of 0.1% phenolphthalein to each of the KHP solutions and swirl.

10. Slowly titrate the KHP solution with sodium hydroxide solution while gently swirling the flask. As the NaOH solution is added a pink color will appear in the KHP solution. When the KHP solution is swirled the color disappears. As the end point is approached the pink disappears more slowly at which point the base should be added drop wise until the solution remains pink when swirled. A single drop can be sufficient to reach the end point. Remove any hanging drops from the burette tip by rinsing the tip with DI water into the flask, using a squirt bottle.

11. Once the end point is reached, record the final volume of the NaOH solution in the burette.

12. Repeat steps 6-11 for the other two KHP samples. At least two of the NaOH concentrations determined have to be the same, within 1.0 %.

ANTACID ANALYSIS AND THE DETERMINATION OF THE PERCENT ACETIC ACID IN VINEGAR ■

13. Calculate the molarity of each of the NaOH solutions.

	Trial 1	**Trial 2**	**Trial 3**
Mass of KHP			
Moles of KHP			
Initial Burette Volume NaOH (mL)			
Final Burette Volume NaOH (mL)			
Total Volume of NaOH (mL)			
Moles of NaOH			
Molarity of NaOH (mol/L)			

14. Calculate the average molarity of NaOH and the average deviation.

Average Molarity:	
Average Deviation:	

Part 2. Titration of Vinegar

1. Fill the burette with the standardized 0.3 M NaOH. Read and record the initial volume.

2. Using a graduated cylinder, measure 20 mL of vinegar and place it in a 250 mL Erlenmeyer flask. Add two drops of 0.1% phenolphthalein.

3. Titrate the vinegar with the 0.3 M NaOH until the end point (faint pink color) is reached.

4. Repeat the above procedure until you get two determinations of the percent acetic acid in vinegar that are the same within 5 to 10 %.

	Trial 1	Trial 2	Trial 3
Volume of Vinegar (mL)			
Initial Burette Volume NaOH (mL)			
Final Burette Volume NaOH (mL)			
Total Volume of NaOH (mL)			
Moles of NaOH			
Moles of CH_3COOH in Vinegar (mol/L)			
Molarity of NaOH (mol/L)			
% acetic acid in Vinegar = $\left(\dfrac{[CH_3COOH] \text{ in vinegar}}{17.4 \text{ M Glacial } CH_3COOH} \right) 100$			

Part 3. Titration of Antacid Tablets

1. Weigh and record the mass of one tablet of antacid to the nearest 0.001g. Record the brand of antacid used. Transfer the tablet to an Erlenmeyer flask; add 50 mL of 0.3 M HCl. Gently heat the solution on a hot plate, or over a low Bunsen burner flame, until the tablet is dissolved. Some solid residue may remain. This is most likely due to starch binders added to the antacid tablets.

2. Cool the antacid solution to room temperature by putting the bottom of the Erlenmeyer flask under running tap water. Add 10 drops of 0.1% thymol blue indicator. Thymol blue is red when the solution is very acidic (pH < 2). If your solution is not red add 10.0 mL more of the 0.3 M HCl in order to consume all the base in the antacid and to have excess acid present in solution. **Record the total volume of HCl added.**

ANTACID ANALYSIS AND THE DETERMINATION OF THE PERCENT ACETIC ACID IN VINEGAR ■

3. Titrate the acidic antacid solution with 0.3 M NaOH to the yellow end point (pH = 3). Watch the color change carefully. The solution will turn pink, then a faded pink and peach. At this point add the basic solution drop-wise until the yellow end point is reached. After the first end point, one or two drops will turn the solution blue, which is the second end point. Record both end points.

4. Repeat the titration for another brand of antacid.

Data	Antacid 1	Antacid 2
Brand of antacid tablet		
Mass of antacid tablet (g)		
Total volume 0.3 M HCl added (mL)		
Millimoles of HCl		
Initial volume in burette (mL)		
Final Volume in the burette (mL)		
Total Volume of NaOH titrated (mL)		
Millimoles of NaOH		
Millimoles HCl reacted with base in antacid		
Identify the active ingredient in the antacid from the manufacturer's label.		
Write the balanced equation for the base in the antacid reacting with HCl.		
Millimoles of $CaCO_3$ in antacid		
Calculate the mass of the active ingredient in the antacid tablet.		
Calculate the % composition of active ingredient in the antacid		

■ EXPERIMENT 15

PRE-LAB QUESTIONS

1. Write the neutralization reaction for a strong acid-strong base titration, where HCl (aq) reacts with NaOH (aq).

2. Write the net ionic equation for the neutralization reaction in question 1.

3. Define the equivalence point in a strong acid-strong base titration.

4. In Part 1 of this experiment, what is the purpose of standardizing the solution of 0.3 M NaOH? If you take a reagent bottle of 0.3 M NaOH from the storeroom, does this mean it is 0.300 M? Is there a possibility that it is 0.27 M?

5. Explain why only one hydrogen is acidic in KHP.

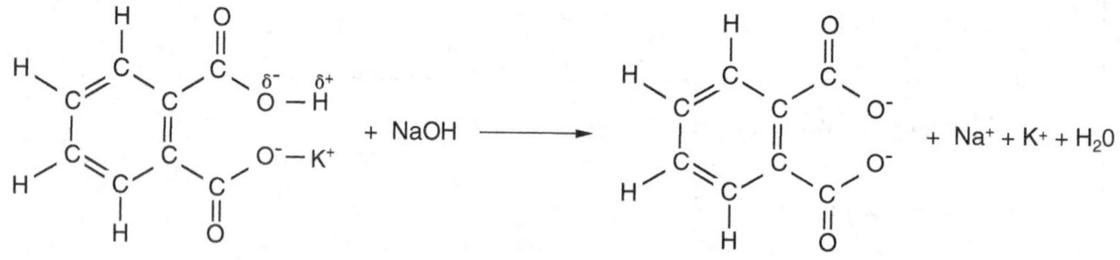

KHP ($C_8H_5O_4K$)

6. KHP is titrated with NaOH until the equivalence point is reached. Why is it true that, the number of moles of OH⁻ equals the number of moles of KHP, at the equivalence point?

7. You will standardize a 0.3 M NaOH solution. Why must the solution be stoppered?

8. In Part 2 of this experiment, you will determine the percent acetic acid in vinegar. Acetic acid, CH_3COOH, is a weak acid. Write the net ionic equation for the following reaction:

$$CH_3COOH \text{ (aq)} + NaOH \text{ (aq)} \quad \rightarrow \quad NaCH_3COO \text{ (aq)} + H_2O \text{ (l)}$$

9. Write the neutralization reaction for a weak acid-strong base titration. Use HA to represent the weak acid and NaOH to represent the strong base.

10. Define the equivalence point in a weak acid-strong base titration.

ANTACID ANALYSIS AND THE DETERMINATION OF THE PERCENT ACETIC ACID IN VINEGAR ■

11. In Part 3, you will analyze antacids for the active ingredients, $Mg(OH)_2$ and $CaCO_3$.

     a) Write the equilibrium constant expression for the following reaction:

$$Mg(OH)_2 \text{ (s)} \quad \rightleftharpoons \quad Mg^{2+} \text{ (aq)} + 2 \, OH^- \text{ (aq)}$$

     b) If any species are not included in the equilibrium constant expression, explain why they are not included.

12. Write the equilibrium constant expression for each of the following reactions:

$$CaCO_3 \text{ (s)} \quad \rightleftharpoons \quad Ca^{2+} \text{ (aq)} + CO_3^{2-} \text{ (aq)}$$

$$CO_3^{2-} \text{ (aq)} + H_2O \text{ (l)} \quad \rightleftharpoons \quad HCO_3^- \text{ (aq)} + OH^- \text{ (aq)}$$

$$HCO_3^- \text{ (aq)} + H_2O \text{ (l)} \quad \rightleftharpoons \quad H_2CO_3 \text{ (aq)} + OH^- \text{ (aq)}$$

13. Both $Mg(OH)_2$ and $CaCO_3$ are relatively insoluble in water, the solubility product constants, K_{sp}, are small, 1.2×10^{-11} and 8.7×10^{-9}, respectively. Does a small value of K mean that there are more products or more reactants at equilibrium? In other words, is the equilibrium position on the left or on the right?

14. a) To determine the amount of $Mg(OH)_2$ and $CaCO_3$ in antacids, why can't we do a direct titration with HCl?

     b) Expla in how back-titration is used to determine the amount of $Mg(OH)_2$ and $CaCO_3$ in antacids.

15. Calculate the volume of 6 M NaOH required to prepare 500 mL of 0.3 M NaOH.

DISCUSSION QUESTIONS

Discuss your results. In standardizing the NaOH solution, were the NaOH concentrations determined within 1.0%? In standardizing the NaOH solution, what was the average NaOH concentration and the deviation? Vinegar is approximately 3% acetic acid by mass. Compare this value with your results. How did the percent composition of active ingredient compare in the two brands of antacids? Were the results obtained accurate? Are you confident in your analysis of percent acetic acid in vinegar and the percent composition of the active ingredients in antacid tablets? Discuss the main sources of error in the experiment.

QUESTIONS

1. If a solution of NaOH is standardized using a sample of KHP which is contaminated with KCl, how would the molarity of NaOH calculated be affected? Would the molarity of NaOH be too high or too low? Explain your answer.

2. a) What volume of 0.4 M HCl is required to neutralize 100.0 mL of 0.3 M LiOH?

   b) What volume of 0.4 M HCl is required to neutralize 100.0 mL of 0.3 M $Mg(OH)_2$?

3. A Rolaids antacid tablet weighed 1.50 g and contained 0.532 g of the active ingredient, $NaAl(OH)_2CO_3$. Assume that the active ingredient reacts with HCl according to the following reaction:

$$NaAl(OH)_2CO_3 + 4\ HCl \quad \rightarrow \quad NaCl + AlCl_3 + 3\ H_2O\ +\ CO_2$$

How many moles of HCl would one Rolaid tablet neutralize?

4. Determine the number of moles of HCl that can be neutralized by an over the counter antacid tablet that contains 400 mg $Al(OH)_3$.

5. How many acidic hydrogens are there in acetic acid, CH_3COOH? Explain your answer.

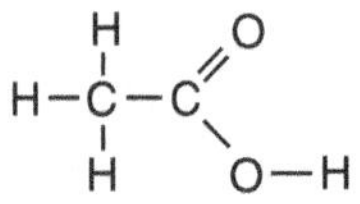

Experiment 16

16

Acid-Base Equilibria:

Determination of Acid Ionization Constants

PURPOSE AND LEARNING OBJECTIVES

To obtain quantitative values of acid ionization constants by measuring the pH. To prepare buffer solutions and observe their resistance to change in pH.

PRINCIPLES

According to Bronsted-Lowry definition of acids and bases, an acid is a proton (H^+) donor and a base is a proton acceptor. The stronger the acid, the greater its ability to donate protons. Consider, for example, the reaction of HCl with water.

$$HCl\ (aq) + H_2O\ (l) \rightleftharpoons H_3O^+\ (aq) + Cl^-\ (aq)$$

or

$$HCl\ (aq) \rightleftharpoons H^+\ (aq) + Cl^-\ (aq)$$

HCl is observed to dissociate completely in water. The K_a value is large, $K_a = \sim 10^7$, indicating the equilibrium position lies far to the right. HCl is therefore considered to be a strong acid. All acids with $K_a > 1$ are considered strong acids.

In this experiment the reaction of acetic acid, CH_3COOH, with water will be studied. Unlike HCl, CH_3COOH is a weak acid and dissociates only slightly in water.

$$CH_3COOH\ (aq) \rightleftharpoons H^+\ (aq) + CH_3COO^-\ (aq)$$

For CH_3COOH, the value of K_a is fairly small, $K_a = 1.76 \times 10^{-5}$, indicating the equilibrium lies far to the left. In a 1.0 M CH_3COOH solution, 99% of the acetic acid molecules remain undissociated.

Buffer Solutions and the Determination of K_a

Acid-base reactions belong to a very important class of reactions. For example, in living systems the control of pH by acid-base equilibria is crucial for survival. Our average blood pH is 7.4. A 0.2 unit shift in pH results in serious changes in blood chemistry causing severe illness. A 0.4 unit shift in pH is generally fatal. An understanding of acid-base equilibria is necessary to understand how blood pH is controlled. Buffer solutions are remarkably resistant to pH changes. All living systems contain buffer solutions. Buffer solutions generally consist of a weak acid and its conjugate base or a weak base and its conjugate acid. According to the Bronsted-Lowry theory, acid-base reactions produce a conjugate acid-base pair. Consider, for example, the reaction of an acid, HA, with water.

$$HA\ (aq) + H_2O\ (l) \rightleftharpoons H_3O^+\ (aq) + A^-\ (aq) \qquad K_a = \frac{[H_3O^+][A^-]}{[HA]}$$

acid　　　　base　　　　conjugate acid　　conjugate base

In this reaction, the HA gives up a proton to produce A^-, its conjugate base, and H_2O acts as a base by accepting a proton to produce H_3O^+, its conjugate acid. A weak acid produces a strong conjugate base and a strong acid produces a weak conjugate base. A buffered solution must contain appreciable amounts of both a weak acid and its conjugate base to resist a change in pH when a small amount of a strong acid or base is added to the solution. When a small amount of strong acid is added to a buffered solution, it reacts completely with the base, A^-.

$$H^+\ (aq) + A^-\ (aq) \rightarrow HA\ (aq)$$

When a small amount of strong base is added to a buffered solution, it reacts completely with the weak acid, HA.

$$OH^-\ (aq) + HA\ (aq) \rightarrow A^-\ (aq) + H_2O\ (l)$$

As long as the ratio of [HA] to [A^-] remains fairly constant, the pH will remain fairly constant.

The equilibrium constant for the dissociation of a weak acid in aqueous solution is written as follows.

$$HA\ (aq)\quad \rightleftharpoons \quad H^+\ (aq) + A^-\ (aq) \qquad\qquad K_a = \frac{[H^+][A^-]}{[HA]}$$

By rearranging the equilibrium constant expression, K_a, and taking the negative logarithm of both sides, the relationship between the pH of the solution and the pK_a is obtained; where $pK_a = -\log K_a$ by definition.

$$[H^+] = K_a\ [HA]/[A^-]$$

$$-\log [H^+] = -\log K_a - \log ([HA]/[A^-])$$

$$pH = pK_a + \log ([A^-]/[HA])$$

In the titration of a weak acid, HA, with a strong base, such as NaOH, the OH^- reacts with HA to produce H_2O and A^-.

$$HA + OH^- \quad \rightarrow \quad H_2O + A^-$$

The equivalence point is reached when HA has been completely consumed by OH^-. At this point, the number of moles of HA equals the number of moles of OH^-.

At the equivalence point: moles of HA = moles of OH^-

At half the equivalence point, half of HA has been consumed and $[HA] = [A^-]$. In this case, the ratio $[A^-]/[HA] = 1$, the $\log(1) = 0$ and $pH = pK_a$. In the region where $[HA] \approx [A^-]$, the solution is a buffer solution.

$$pH = pK_a \quad \text{when } [HA] = [A^-]$$

$$pH = pK_a \quad \text{at half the equivalence point}$$

In this first part of this experiment, the pH of the solution is measured at regular intervals during the titration and is plotted as a function of the volume of NaOH added, shown in Figure 1 below.

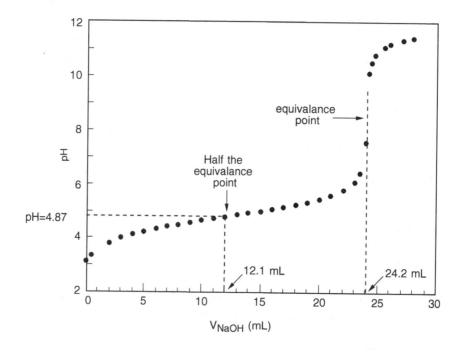

Figure 1. Titration of a weak acid, HA, with a strong base, NaOH.

The equivalence point occurs in the region where the steep increase in pH is observed. The corresponding volume of NaOH at this point is obtained from the graph. From the data shown, the equivalence point occurs after 24.2 mL of NaOH has been added. Thus, the volume of NaOH at half the equivalence point is 24.2/2 = 12.1 mL, which corresponds to a pH of 4.87.

Because pH = pK_a at half the equivalence point, the pK_a for this acid is 4.87. By definition $pK_a = -\log K_a$ and therefore $K_a = 10^{-pK_a}$.

$$pK_a = 4.87 \qquad\qquad K_a = 10^{-pK_a} = 10^{-4.87} = 1.35 \times 10^{-5}$$

According to Appendix 4 in this lab manual, a K_a value of 1.35×10^{-5} corresponds to propionic acid.

Note that, for a weak acid titrated with a strong base, the pH is greater than seven at the equivalence point. This is due to the fact that the conjugate base, A^-, of a weak acid, HA, has significant affinity for protons and will react with water to produce a basic solution according to the following hydrolysis reaction.

$$A^- \text{ (aq)} + H_2O \text{ (l)} \quad \rightarrow \quad HA \text{ (aq)} + OH^- \text{ (aq)}$$

This reaction occurs because the equilibrium position for weak acids is far to the right, on the side of the undissociated acid, HA.

In the second part of this experiment, by measuring the pH of an acetic acid solution of known concentration, you will calculate the equilibrium constant, K_a, using the equilibrium constant expression. Consider, for example, a 1.0 M CH_3COOH solution.

	CH_3COOH (aq) $\rightleftharpoons$ H$^+$ (aq) + CH_3COO^- (aq)		
Initial Concentration (M)	1.0	0	0
Change in Concentration	$- x$	$+ x$	$+ x$
Concentration at Equilibrium	$1.0 - x$	x	x

$$K_a = \frac{[H^+][CH_3COO^-]}{[CH_3COOH]} = \frac{x^2}{1 - x} \text{ where } x = [H^+] = 10^{-pH}$$

You will determine K_a by measuring the pH of a number of solutions including a CH_3COOH solution of known concentration as well as mixtures of CH_3COOH and $NaCH_3COO$ of known concentrations. Your experimental value will be compared to the actual K_a value of acetic acid which is 1.76×10^{-5}.

In the third part of this experiment, the capacity of a buffer solution to absorb small quantities of strong acid and strong base is explored. The capacity of the buffer solution to resist change in pH will be compared to that of water.

The pH Meter and its Operation
The simplest method to measure the pH is by using a pH meter. A pH meter consists of two electrodes, one of which is a glass electrode sensitive to [H$^+$] and the other is a reference electrode. Inside the glass electrode, a silver wire coated with silver chloride is in contact with an HCl solution of known concentration, typically 1.0 M. When the pH meter electrodes are immersed in a solution containing H$^+$, a potential develops across the thin glass membrane due to the concentration differential between the solution and the 1.0 M HCl. The resulting voltage is

indicated on the pH meter. Even though the pH meter used in this experiment appears to have a single electrode, the probe contains both the reference and sensing electrode.

The pH meter is calibrated by immersing the electrodes at least $1/_2$" into standard buffer solutions of known pH. Gently swirl the pH meter in the solution to make sure good contact is made. There are two types of pH meters. Either press the CAL button or adjust the pH reading to the buffer pH using the narrow tip of a spatula as a screw-driver in the appropriate adjustment slot on top of the pH meter. Calibrate pH = 7 first, then pH = 4.

The electrodes are delicate and careful handling of the pH meters is essential for its continued operation. Please turn off the pH meter when it is not in use to save batteries. If the batteries or electrodes need to be replaced please notify the instructor.

SAFETY
WEAR SAFETY GLASSES

NaOH is a strong base but fairly dilute solutions are used (0.1 M and 1.0 M NaOH). In case of spills or contact with your skin, rinse with water.

PROCEDURE
This experiment will be performed in pairs. It is important to stay consistent when taking measurements. One partner reads the burette throughout the entire titration for consistency. In the second trial, the other partner reads the burette throughout the entire titration.

Part 1. Determination of the Dissociation Constant, K_a, of Acetic Acid by Measuring the Titration Curve using a pH Meter

1. Read the instructions for the calibration and use of a pH meter (see previous page). Standardize the pH meter using standard solutions pH = 7 then pH = 4. Rinse the electrode with DI water each time the pH of a different solution is measured. Carefully wipe off excess water on the outside of the electrode using a Kimwipe. Save standard solutions. If your pH meter does not work properly ask your instructor or the stock room for a new one.

2. Clean a 50.0 mL burette with soap and water. Do a final rinse of the burette with DI water. Make sure to run water through the tip of the burette. The water should run freely down the burette without adhering to the glass.

3. Rinse the burette with two 5 mL portions of the 0.1 M NaOH solution. Again drain some of solution out of the tip.

4. Fill the burette with 0.1 M NaOH. If the initial volume in the burette is at the zero mark, it will be easier to add 1.0 mL portions of NaOH. Make a table in your lab notebook to record the pH as a function of volume of NaOH added.

ACID-BASE EQUILIBRIA: DETERMINATION OF ACID IONIZATION CONSTANTS ■

5. A burette containing 0.10 M acetic acid is located in the hood. Note the initial and final volumes on the burette to accurately measure 25.0 mL of 0.10 M acetic acid into a 150-mL beaker. Measure and record the pH of the solution.

6. Add 1.0 mL portions of NaOH solution to the 0.10 M acetic acid, swirl the solution, record the pH and volume in the burette. When the pH begins to increase at a faster rate (after approximately 22 mL of 0.1 M NaOH has been added), add 0.1 to 0.2 mL portions of the NaOH solution, swirl and record the pH value and volume. If a drop is left hanging at the tip of the burette, raise the beaker until the solution just touches the drop and pulls it into solution.

7. Continue the titration until you reach a pH value of 11.5.

8. Use Excel on the computer to graph pH values, along the y-axis, versus the volume of NaOH added, along the x-axis. Note the volume where a steep rise in pH occurs for the second trial.

9. Second Trial: Repeat the titration, partners should switch roles so each person does a titration.

Data	Trial 1	Trial 2
Volume of NaOH at the equivalence point		
Volume of NaOH at <u>half</u> the equivalence point		
pH at <u>half</u> the equivalence point		
pK_a at <u>half</u> the equivalence point		
Dissociation Constant, K_a		

Part 2. The Dissociation Constant of Acetic Acid

$$CH_3COOH \ (aq) \ \rightleftharpoons \ H^+ \ (aq) + CH_3COO^- \ (aq) \qquad K_a = \frac{[H^+][CH_3COO^-]}{[CH_3COOH]}$$

1. Recalibrate the pH meters using the standard solutions of pH = 7 and 4.

2. Rinse the electrodes in DI water. Blot excess water off the outside of the electrodes with a Kimwipe. Be careful not to damage the electrodes.

3. Place 10 mL 1.0 M acetic acid (HA) into a 50 mL beaker. Measure and record the pH.

4. Calculate the dissociation constant of acetic acid.

Solution: 10.0 mL 1.0 M HA	
Observed pH	
Hydrogen ion concentration, $[H^+]$, from pH	
Acetate ion concentration, $[A^-]$, at equilibrium	
Acetic acid concentration, $[HA]$, at equilibrium	
Dissociation Constant, K_a	

5. Add 25.0 mL of 1.0 M sodium acetate (NaA) to the 10.0 mL of 1.0 M acetic acid, and mix well. Measure the pH of this solution. Calculate the H^+, A^-, HA concentrations in the solution and the dissociation constant. Save the solution for the next step.

Solution: 25.0 mL 1.0 M NaA + 10.0 mL 1.0 M HA	
Observed pH	
Hydrogen ion concentration, $[H^+]$, from pH	
Total Volume	
Acetate ion concentration, $[A^-]$, at equilibrium	
Acetic acid concentration, $[HA]$, at equilibrium	
Dissociation Constant, K_a	

6. In a 100 mL beaker, thoroughly mix 5.0 mL of 1.0 M sodium acetate with 30.0 mL of 1.0 M acetic acid. Measure and record the pH. Calculate the H^+, A^-, HA concentrations in the

ACID-BASE EQUILIBRIA: DETERMINATION OF ACID IONIZATION CONSTANTS ■

solution and the dissociation constant.

Solution: 5.0 mL 1.0 M NaA + 30.0 mL 1.0 M HA	
Observed pH	
$[H^+]$ at equilibrium (from pH)	
Total Volume	
$[A^-]$ at equilibrium	
[HA] at equilibrium	
K_a	

7. For the above solutions calculate the pH using the accepted value of the acetic acid dissociation constant, $K_a = 1.76 \times 10^{-5}$, and compare it to the measured pH in steps 5 and 6.

Solutions	Measured pH	Calculated pH	% Error
25.0 mL 1.0 M NaA + 10.0 mL 1.0 M HA			
5.0 mL 1.0 M NaA + 30.0 mL 1.0 M HA			

■ **EXPERIMENT 16**

Part 3. Buffering Capacity: Addition of Strong Acid and Strong Base to Buffered and Unbuffered Solutions

1. Use a 50 mL beaker for each of the following solutions. Measure and record the pH.

Unbuffered Solution	Measured pH	Calculated pH
30 mL DI water		
30 mL DI water + 2 mL 1.0 M HCl		
30 mL DI water + 2 mL 1.0 M NaOH		

2. Use a 150 mL beaker to make the NaA/HA buffer solution. Measure and record the pH. Measure 30 mL of this buffer solution and place it in 50 mL beakers for the next two solutions. Measure and record the pH.

Buffer Solution	Measured pH	Calculated pH
30 mL 1.0 M NaA + 30.0 mL 1.0 M HA		
30 mL buffer + 2 mL 1.0 M HCl		
30 mL buffer + 2 mL 1.0 M NaOH		

3. What is the increase in pH after the strong acid was added to the buffer solution, relative to the pH of the buffer solution? What is the increase in pH when the strong acid was added to DI water, relative to the pH of pure DI water? Does this show that buffer solutions resist a change in pH when a small amount of a strong acid or base is added to the solution?

PRE-LAB QUESTIONS

1. In Part 1 of this experiment, acetic acid is titrated with NaOH.
    a) Write the net ionic equation for acetic acid reacting with NaOH.
    b) Define the equivalence point. How will you detect the equivalence point in this part of the experiment?
    c) In titrating acetic acid with NaOH, why is pH > 7 at the equivalence point? Show the reaction which causes a pH > 7 at the equivalence point.
    d) How will you determine the pK_a for acetic acid?

ACID-BASE EQUILIBRIA: DETERMINATION OF ACID IONIZATION CONSTANTS ■

2. Determine the pH for each of the following solutions and indicate if the solution is neutral, acidic, or basic.
   a) $[H^+]$ = 5.8×10^{-5} M
   b) $[OH^-]$ = 2.3×10^{-9} M
   c) $[OH^-]$ = 1.9×10^{-7} M

3. If the K_a of an acid is 2.3×10^{-5} what is the corresponding pK_a?

4. In Part 2 of this experiment, the dissociation constant of acetic acid will be determined by measuring the pH of a given solution.
   a) Calculate the pH of a 1.0 M CH_3COOH solution.
   b) The measured pH = 5.18 for a solution containing 25.0 mL 1.0 M $NaCH_3COO$ and 10.0 mL 1.0 M CH_3COOH. Calculate the corresponding value of K_a for acetic acid.

5. What is a buffer? Why are buffer solutions important in living organisms?

6. Identify the buffer region in the titration curve obtained in Part 1 of this experiment (in the figure shown on Pg. 78).

DISCUSSION QUESTIONS

Discuss your results. What are the greatest sources of error in this experiment? Compare your experimental value of K_a for acetic acid with the accepted value, K_a = 1.76×10^{-5}. Include net ionic equations for the reactions discussed. For part 2, compare K_a values obtained with the accepted value, K_a = 1.76×10^{-5}. Should the K_a values obtained for the sodium acetate/acetic acid solutions be the same or different? Explain why or why not. Compare the difference in pH when a strong acid or a strong base was added to water and to the acetic acid/sodium acetate buffer solution. Is the acetic acid/sodium acetate buffer solution resistant to change in pH when small amounts of strong acid or strong base are added?

QUESTIONS

1. A typical aspirin tablet contains 324 mg of aspirin ($C_9O_4H_8$), a monoprotic acid with K_a = 2.8×10^{-4}. A monoprotic acid donates a single proton. If you dissolve two aspirin tablets in a 300 mL glass of water, what is the pH of the solution?

2. For a 0.13 M solution of formic acid, HCOOH, the pH = 2.40. Calculate K_a for formic acid.

$$HCOOH \rightleftharpoons HCOO^- (aq) + H^+ (aq)$$

■ EXPERIMENT 16

3. Consider the following reaction at equilibrium.

$$CH_3COOH \rightleftharpoons CH_3COO^- (aq) + H^+ (aq)$$

If $NaCH_3COO$ is added to the solution will the following quantities increase, decrease or remain the same? Explain your answers.

a) $[H^+]$
b) $[OH^-]$
c) $[CH_3COOH]$
d) pH
e) pK_a

5. If a solution is made by mixing 20.0 mL 0.4 M $NaCH_3COO$ with 30 mL 0.4 M CH_3COOH, calculate the pH? For acetic acid, $K_a = 1.76 \times 10^{-5}$.

Experiment **17**

17

Recycling Aluminum

PURPOSE AND LEARNING OBJECTIVES

To synthesize an inorganic salt, $KAl(SO_4)_2 \cdot 12H_2O$, from aluminum foil. To perform qualitative tests for the presence of K^+, Al^{3+}, SO_4^{2-}, and H_2O in $KAl(SO_4)_2 \cdot 12H_2O$. To observe the growth of crystals using a variety of crystal growth techniques.

PRINCIPLES

Most metals are found on the earth in the form of minerals and ores. Aluminum is the third most abundant element in the earth's crust and the most common ore of aluminum is a hydrated aluminum oxide, $Al_2O_3 \cdot 2H_2O$, whose common name is bauxite. Even though there is a large amount of aluminum on the earth the process of extracting aluminum from bauxite is expensive. The Hall-Heroult process to produce aluminum in an electrolytic cell, from Al_2O_3 dissolved in molten cryolyte (Na_3AlF_6), requires an enormous amount of energy. It is therefore important to recycle aluminum.

Aluminum metal is commonly used in construction and aluminum compounds are used in many applications, including the production of paper, dyes, anti-perspirants, etc. What are the advantages of using aluminum over other metals in the construction of bicycles, airplanes or soda cans? First, the strength to weight ratio of aluminum is very high. Second, aluminum is highly resistant to corrosion when exposed to air and water. The fact that aluminum is resistant to corrosion is interesting because the positive cell potential for the oxidation of aluminum by water indicates that aluminum should dissolve in water.

$$2 \text{ Al (s)} + 6 \text{ H}_2\text{O (l)} \rightarrow 2 \text{ Al}^{3+} \text{ (aq)} + 3 \text{ H}_2 \text{ (g)} + 6 \text{ OH}^- \text{ (aq)} \quad E^0 = 0.88 \text{ V}$$

So how can soft drinks be stored in aluminum cans? The reason aluminum does not dissolve in water is because aluminum oxidizes in air to produce a thin, tough, transparent aluminum oxide coating, Al_2O_3 (s).

$$4 \text{ Al (s)} + 3 \text{ O}_2 \text{ (g)} \rightarrow 2 \text{ Al}_2\text{O}_3 \text{ (s)} \quad\quad\quad\quad E^0 = 2.7 \text{ V}$$

The aluminum oxide is relatively inert and protects the aluminum from further oxidation. However, because Al_2O_3 is amphoteric, it will react with either acids or bases. An aluminum can is therefore susceptible to corrosion if its contents are acidic or basic and must be coated on the inside walls with some kind of resin or plastic.

In this experiment you will see how aluminum can be recycled. You will synthesize an aluminum compound, $KAl(SO_4)_2 \cdot 12H_2O$, from aluminum foil. $KAl(SO_4)_2 \cdot 12H_2O$ or aluminum potassium sulfate docecahydrate is commonly called alum. It is a hydrated salt and dissolves in water to produce Al^{3+}, K^+ and SO_4^{2-}. After you synthesize the alum you will check its composition by analyzing for Al^{3+}, K^+ and SO_4^{2-} and H_2O.

The first step in the synthesis of alum is the treatment of the aluminum foil with the base, KOH. The aluminum metal and aluminum oxide will form potassium aluminate, $KAlO_2$ according to the following reactions.

$$Al_2O_3 \text{ (s)} + 2 \text{ KOH (aq)} \rightarrow 2 \text{ KAlO}_2 \text{ (aq)} + \text{H}_2\text{O (l)}$$

$$2 \text{ Al (s)} + 2 \text{ KOH (aq)} + 2 \text{ H}_2\text{O (aq)} \rightarrow 2 \text{ KAlO}_2 \text{ (aq)} + 3 \text{ H}_2 \text{ (g)}$$

The potassium aluminate reacts with sulfuric acid to form solid aluminum hydroxide, $Al(OH)_3$(s).

$$2 \text{ KAlO}_2\text{(aq)} + \text{H}_2\text{SO}_4 \text{ (aq)} + 2 \text{ H}_2\text{O (aq)} \rightarrow 2 \text{ Al(OH)}_3\text{(s)} + \text{K}_2\text{SO}_4 \text{ (aq)}$$

By heating the solution and adding excess sulfuric acid the hydroxide is neutralized causing aluminum hydroxide to dissolve, producing aluminum ions and sulfate ions in solution.

molecular equation: $2 \text{ Al(OH)}_3 \text{ (s)} + 3 \text{ H}_2\text{SO}_4 \text{ (aq)} \rightarrow \text{Al}_2(\text{SO}_4)_3 \text{ (aq)} + 6 \text{ H}_2\text{O (l)}$

total ionic equation: $\text{Al(OH)}_3 \text{ (s)} + 3 \text{ H}^+ \text{ (aq)} + \text{SO}_4^{2-} \rightarrow \text{Al}^{3+} \text{ (aq)} + \text{SO}_4^{2-} + 3 \text{ H}_2\text{O (l)}$

net ionic equation: $\text{Al(OH)}_3 \text{ (s)} + 3 \text{ H}^+ \text{ (aq)} \rightarrow \text{Al}^{3+} \text{ (aq)} + 3 \text{ H}_2\text{O (l)}$

The solution contains Al^{3+}, SO_4^{2-}, and K^+. Evaporation saturates the solution and if the solution is cooled, alum crystals will form.

$$K^+(aq) + Al^{3+}(aq) + 2\,SO_4^{2-} + 12\,H_2O(l) \rightarrow KAl(SO_4)_2 \bullet 12\,H_2O\,(s)$$

In general, the solubility of an ionic compound decreases as the temperature decreases. The alum crystals that are isolated will be white and powder-like.

However, alum can form large gem-like crystals. This can be done through a process called recrystallization. If the powdery solid is dissolved in warm water, and cooled slowly in air these gem-like crystals can be formed. Crystals of alum can also be formed by carefully layering the warm solution of alum with ethanol. The ions are not soluble in ethanol and precipitate out of the water solution as the ethanol diffuses into the alum solution. If this interaction happens slow enough the ions will precipitate, pack, and form larger crystals. A slower and more effi-cient form of recrystallization can occur by vapor diffusion. When the alum solution is set in an atmosphere of ethanol, or ethanol vapor, the interaction occurs more slowly. In order to obtain large crystals you must have patience. Nature forms the most beautiful crystals when given time. That is why diamonds and jewels tend to be very expensive. You will be able to try three methods of recrystallization and let your crystals grow over several weeks. You can try other methods as well.

SAFETY
WEAR GOGGLES.

Hydrogen gas is produced in the first part of the lab. Because hydrogen is extremely flammable, this part of the procedure will be carried out in the hood.

CHEMICALS
Aluminum foil
few drops of 0.1 M $BaCl_2$
25 mL of 4 M KOH
few drops of 0.1 M KOH
20 mL of 9 M H_2SO_4
5 mL of 6 M HNO_3
12 mL of 50% ethanol (by volume)
30 mL of 95% ethanol

EXPERIMENTAL PROCEDURE

This is a lab that will be performed in one week. However, you will follow the growth of crystals over several weeks. You will work in pairs but the questions and lab report are done <u>individually</u>.

Part 1. Synthesis of Alum from Aluminum Foil

1. Weigh 0.5 grams of aluminum foil (9 cm × 9 cm) and record the mass to the nearest 0.001 g. Cut the piece of aluminum foil into smaller pieces to increase the surface area of aluminum. An increase in surface area generally increases the rate of a reaction. Reweigh the aluminum and place it in a labeled, 250-mL Erlenmeyer flask.

2. In the hood, slowly add 25 mL of 4 M KOH to the flask. Swirl the flask as you add the base. Caution should be taken at this step because it is a vigorous reaction that evolves hydrogen gas. Record your observations.

$$2\ Al\ (s) + 2\ OH^-\ (aq) + 6\ H_2O\ (l)\ \rightarrow\ 2\ Al(OH)_4^-\ (aq) + 3\ H_2\ (g)$$

3. Once the reaction has slowed down considerably, gently heat the flask on a hot plate in the hood until all of the aluminum has reacted. **Do not boil the mixture to dryness.**

4. Set up a filtration apparatus using a 60-mm Büchner funnel and a piece of 55-mm filter paper. Filter the warm mixture. The filtrate should be clear.

5. Transfer the filtrate to a clean, dry 250-mL Erlenmeyer flask. Very slowly, add 20 mL of 9 M H_2SO_4 by running the acid down the side of the flask. Swirl the flask periodically as the acid is added. An aluminum hydroxide precipitate may form at this point.

6. Carefully, heat the flask to reduce the volume of the solution to approximately 25 mL. Use a boiling stick to ensure the solution will not boil over. In excess acid, the precipitate will dissolve as you heat the solution. Make sure it all dissolves.

$$Al(OH)_3(s) + 3\ H^+(aq)\ \rightarrow\ Al^{3+}\ (aq) + 3\ H_2O(l)$$

7. Remove the solution from the heat. Allow the flask to cool until it is just warm to the touch. Place the flask in an ice bath for 20 minutes. Alum crystals should form. Record your observations. If crystals do not form, try to scrape the inside of the flask with a glass rod. If crystals still do not form, heat the flask again to reduce the volume of the solution. Be careful that you do not heat the reaction to dryness.

$$K^+(aq) + Al^{3+}(aq) + 2\ SO_4^{2-}(aq) + 12\ H_2O(l)\ \rightarrow\ KAl(SO_4)_2 \bullet 12\ H_2O\ (s)$$

8. Using a 60-mm Büchner funnel and a piece of 55-mm filter paper, vacuum-filter the crystals. Wash the crystals in the funnel with four 3 mL portions of 50% ethanol in water. Continue suction for a few minutes to dry the crystals.

9. Weigh the crystals and record the mass in your notebook. Put the alum crystals in a 125-mL Erlenmeyer flask.

10. Calculate the theoretical and percent yield. To determine the limiting reagent and the percent yield of alum, the overall equation for the alum synthesis is used.

$$2\,Al\,(s) + 2\,KOH + 22\,H_2O + 4\,H_2SO_4 \;\rightarrow\; 2\,KAl(SO_4)_2 \bullet 12H_2O\,(s) + 3\,H_2\,(g)$$

Part 2. Qualitative Analysis of the Composition of Alum; Al^{3+}, SO_4^{2-}, K^+ and H_2O

1. Clean two small test tubes. Add one spatula of alum to each of the test tubes and dissolve the crystals in a few milliliters of DI water.

2. To the first test tube, add a few drops of 0.1 M $BaCl_2$. Record your observations. Write the net ionic equation for the reaction observed.

3. To the second test tube, add dropwise 0.1 M KOH. It is very important that you add the KOH solution drop by drop. Once a change occurs, record your observations and write the net ionic equation for this reaction. Then add several more drops of KOH to the solution. Record your observations. Explain the changes. Write the net ionic equation for the reaction observed.

4. To test for the presence of water (the hydrates in the alum crystal, $KAl(SO_4)_2 \bullet 12H_2O$, add a spatula of alum to a clean, *dry* test tube. Gently, heat the test tube over a flame. Look for condensation on the sides of the tube.

Flame Test

1. Set up a Bunsen burner. Clean a piece of nichrome wire in 6 M HNO_3 solution. Rinse the wire with DI water.

2. Clean two small test tubes.

3. Add one spatula of alum to one of the test tubes and a spatula of potassium chloride to the second test tube. Dissolve the crystals in each of the test tubes in a few milliliters of DI water.

4. Dip the nichrome wire into the KCl solution. Place the wire in the flame of the Bunsen burner. Record your observation. What is giving rise to the change in color?

5. Clean the nichrome wire in the 6 M HNO_3 solution and rinse it with DI water. Dip the wire in the alum solution and place it in the flame. Record your observations. How does the color of the alum in the flame compare with that of potassium chloride?

Part 3. Growing Alum Crystals from a Seed Crystal
Week 1

1. Weigh 3 grams of alum and record the mass to the nearest 0.001 g. Put the alum in a 50-mL Erlenmeyer flask.

2. Add 20 mL of DI water to the crystals. Swirl the flask.

3. Heat the solution on a hot plate to 50-60°C. Stir the solution until it is clear. If all of the crystals have not dissolved, filter the warm mixture.

4. Tie a piece of thread around a wooden stick. The length of the thread should be long enough so that the end of the thread is 0.5-1 cm below the surface of the liquid when the stick is placed across the opening of the flask. Put a small amount of grease on the portion of the string that will be above the solution. Place the string in the solution, tape the wooden stick to the flask, and cover the flask with parafilm.

5. Store this set up in your drawer until next week. Be careful when opening and closing the locker. Go onto Part 4.

Week 2

1. There should be a small crystal formed in the solution. This is a seed crystal. Use the best seed crystal to grow a larger crystal.

2. Weigh 5 grams of alum and record the mass to the nearest 0.001 g. Put the alum in a 50-mL Erlenmeyer flask and add 35 ml of DI water.

3. Heat the solution on a hot plate to 50-60°C until all of the alum is dissolved. If the solution is not clear, filter the warm mixture.

4. Suspend the seed crystal so it is entirely submersed in the alum solution. Tape the wooden stick in place and cover the flask with parafilm. Place the flask in your drawer until next week.

5. Continue this process every week until the crystal is as large as you like. Describe it in your notebook.

6. Put the crystal in a labeled vial and turn it in to your TA.

Part 4. Growing Crystals by Layering
Week 1

1. Weigh 1 gram of alum and dissolve it in a large test tube with 10 mL of DI water. Mix the solution. If any solid does not dissolve filter the mixture.

2. Place a small test tube in a 250-mL beaker so the test tube is leaning against the side of the beaker.

3. Fill the test tube, $^1/_3$ full, with the alum solution. Save the rest of the alum solution for Part 5.

4. Using a Pasteur pipette, carefully add 95% ethanol to the test tube. You want to form two layers in the test tube with the alum solution on the bottom and ethanol on the top. For the best results, slowly run the ethanol down the side of the test tube. Add enough ethanol so the total volume of liquid in the test tube is $^2/_3$ full. Stopper the test tube.

5. Carefully, place the beaker and test tube in your drawer until next week. Go onto part 5.

Week 2
1. Describe the crystals that are formed in your notebook. You may leave them for a another week if you wish for them to grow larger. You may need to add more ethanol to the large test tube.

2. When your crystal growth is complete, collect the crystals and turn them in to the TA.

Part 5. Crystal Growth by Vapor Diffusion
Week 1
1. Fill a clean, dry, small test tube $^2/_3$ full with the remaining alum solution from Part 4.

2. Place the small test tube in a large test tube by tilting the large test tube and gently sliding the small test tube to the bottom.

3. Using a Pasteur pipette, carefully fill the large test tube with ethanol to the same height as the alum solution in the small test tube. Do not get any of the ethanol in the small test tube.

4. Stopper the large test tube and place it in your drawer until next week.

WASTE DISPOSAL
Dispose of all waste in the appropriately labeled waste bottle in the hood.

PRE-LAB QUESTIONS
1. The fact that aluminum is resistant to corrosion is interesting because the positive cell potential for the oxidation of aluminum by water indicates that aluminum should dissolve in water.

$$2 \, Al \, (s) + 6 \, H_2O \, (l) \;\; \rightarrow \;\; 2 \, Al^{3+} \, (aq) + 3 \, H_2 \, (g) + 6 \, OH^- \, (aq) \quad E^0 = 0.88 \, V$$

Explain why soft drinks and other liquids can be stored in aluminum cans. Is there a problem with storing acidic or basic solutions in aluminum cans? Explain why or why not.

2. Aluminum potassium sulfate docecahydrate is commonly called alum. Write the molecular formula for alum and calculate its molar mass.

3. In Part 1 of this experiment you will synthesize alum from aluminum foil. In step 2 of the synthesis, 4 M KOH is added to aluminum foil.

   a) Write the balanced equation for this reaction.

   b) What safety precautions must be taken in this step? Why must the KOH be added to the aluminum foil in the hood?

4. Aqueous aluminum hydroxide, $Al(OH)_4^-(aq)$, is produced in step 2. How is $Al(OH)_4^-(aq)$ converted to solid aluminum hydroxide? What is the molecular formula for solid aluminum hydroxide?

5. If 0.5 g of Al(s) reacts with 25 mL of 4 M KOH, 20 mL of 9 M H_2SO_4, and excess water, calculate the theoretical yield for the production of alum using the following equation.

$$2\,Al\,(s) + 2\,KOH + 22\,H_2O + 4\,H_2SO_4 \rightarrow 2\,KAl(SO_4)_2 \bullet 12H_2O\,(s) + 3\,H_2\,(g)$$

6. In Part 2 of this experiment you will qualitatively analyze the composition of alum, $KAl(SO_4)_2 \bullet 12H_2O$ (s), by analyzing for Al^{3+}, SO_4^{2-}, K^+ and H_2O.

   a) When 0.1 M $BaCl_2$ is added to an aqueous solution of alum, what reaction produces a precipitate? Write the net ionic equation for the reaction. Use the solubility table in Appendix 1 to help you determine what precipitate is formed.

   b) By adding 0.1 M KOH to an aqueous solution of alum, what ion are you analyzing for? Why must you add the KOH drop by drop? What reaction occurs when excess KOH is added?

   c) How will you analyze for the presence of H_2O in alum?

   d) What ions in alum are you analyzing for in the flame test, Al^{3+}, SO_4^{2-}, or K^+? Why is a flame test done using an aqueous KCl solution as well as an aqueous alum solution?

DISCUSSION QUESTIONS

Summarize the reactions involved in the synthesis of alum. Include the overall equation for the synthesis. What was your percent yield? Describe the crystals that were formed at the end of the synthesis.

Write the net ionic reactions for the analysis of the aluminum and sulfate ions. What changes were observed for each? Discuss your observations from the flame test. Discuss your observations from when the alum crystals were heated. What method could you use to quantitatively determine the amount of water in alum crystals?

QUESTIONS

1. Calculate the percentage of potassium, aluminum, oxygen, and sulfur in alum, $KAl(SO_4) \cdot 12H_2O$.

2. Given the following unbalanced molecular equation:

$$KAl(SO_4) \cdot 12H_2O(aq) + BaCl_2(s) \rightarrow KCl(aq) + AlCl_3(aq) + BaSO_4(s)$$

   a) Balance the reaction and calculate the amount of barium chloride needed to react with a 25 mL of a 0.10 M alum solution.
   b) What is the percent yield of barium sulfate if 1.02 grams is isolated.

3. A 10.0 gram sample of alum is heated to drive off all of the water from the solid. Determine the mass of the dehydrated alum.

4. Which of the three methods of recrystallization do you think will grow the largest crystals. Do you think the crystal growth by vapor diffusion or by layering will be better? Explain why.

■ EXPERIMENT 17

Experiment 18

18

Oxidation of Vitamin C

PURPOSE AND LEARNING OBJECTIVES

To introduce antioxidant properties of ascorbic acid (Vitamin C). To show Vitamin C is oxidized by iodine. To determine if cooking foods containing Vitamin C, degrades Vitamin C. To determine the Vitamin C content in Vitamin tablets.

PRINCIPLES

Ultra violet radiation and other high-energy radiation can damage DNA in skin cells and in other cells undergoing rapid division, including bone marrow and reproductive organs. Cancer cells are very sensitive to radiation because they also divide rapidly. A large dose of radiation will destroy cancer cells more quickly then normal cells in surrounding tissue because the normal cells divide more slowly.

Radiation can remove electrons from molecules producing free radicals. A radical is defined as an atom or molecule with an unpaired electron. Free radicals are often unstable causing undesirable reactions in biological systems. These reactions can be prevented if reactive radicals are destroyed. Vitamin C can react with a reactive radical, R•, to produce an unreactive radical.

In this reaction Vitamin C is oxidized; it lost an electron. The ease with which Vitamin C is oxidized makes it an excellent antioxidant. An antioxidant is a compound that inhibits oxidation; it protects other compounds from being oxidized because an antioxidant itself is readily oxidized. Vitamin C is added to food as a preservative (an antioxidant).

Vitamin C also plays a number of important physiological roles. It is essential in the synthesis of collagen, a structural protein in tendons and cartilage. A deficiency of Vitamin C causes the disease known as scurvy; bleeding gums; slow healing wounds; anemia and muscle pain. Human beings do not possess the metabolic pathway to synthesize Vitamin C in the body. We must therefore consume Vitamin C from food sources in fairly high amounts, a minimum of 65 mg per day is recommended. Many fruits and vegetables including green and red peppers, spinach, and citrus juices are good sources of Vitamin C. However, Vitamin C is highly soluble in water and flushes out of the body relatively quickly. It is therefore important to consume Vitamin C daily.

Vitamin C in foods is sensitive to temperature and storage. Vitamin C is oxidized by O_2 in air and O_2 dissolved in water. The oxidation of Vitamin C increases with temperature. Cooking foods will therefore degrade Vitamin C. It does retain some of the physiological functions but once Vitamin C is oxidized it will not be effective as an antioxidant. Refrigeration slows down the oxidation of Vitamin C, but 2-3 weeks of storage of orange juice can oxidize as much as 50% of the Vitamin C.

In the first part of this experiment, a sample of ascorbic acid is oxidized by iodine.

Ascorbic acid is titrated with 0.10 M KIO_3. The solution contains HCl and KI. The iodate ion reacts with iodide, I^-, and H^+ to produce iodine and water.

$$IO_3^- + 5\,I^- + 6\,H^+ \rightarrow 3\,I_2 + 3\,H_2O$$

When all the ascorbic acid has reacted, the concentration of I_2 increases. The excess I_2 reacts with I^- to produce I_3^-, signaling a blue end-point. Triiodide, I_3^-, complexes with starch to produce the dark navy blue color.

$$I_2 + I^- \rightarrow I_3^-$$

In the second part of this experiment an aqueous solution of ascorbic acid is boiled for 10 minutes. The solution is cooled to room temperature and the amount of ascorbic acid in solution is determined. This will show the effect of an increase in temperature on ascorbic acid. The content of Vitamin C in commercial tablets will be determined in the final part of this experiment.

SAFETY
WEAR SAFETY GLASSES

Aqueous hydrochloric acid, HCl (aq), is a strong acid and will burn your skin and clothing if contact is made. If you spill chemicals on your skin, flush with water immediately.

PROCEDURE
Part 1. The oxidation of ascorbic acid
1. Weigh two 0.4-g samples of ascorbic acid to the nearest 0.001 g. Be sure to use weighing paper and tare the balance. Record the mass.

2. Copy the table below into your lab notebook and record the mass of each ascorbic acid sample.

3. Place each sample into its own clearly labeled 250-mL Erlenmeyer flask (indicate the mass of the ascorbic acid sample on the label). Add 50 mL of DI water to each flask. Swirl the flasks until the ascorbic acid has completely dissolved.

4. Set up a clean, 50-mL burette using a burette clamp and a ring stand. Pour approximately 50 mL of 0.10 M KIO_3 into a clean beaker. Rinse the burette with 5 mL of 0.10 M KIO_3. Be sure to run some of the KIO_3 out of the bottom and the top of the burette into a waste beaker to ensure the burette is sufficiently rinsed.

5. Pour the remainder of the 0.10 M KIO_3 into the burette. Titrate a few milliliters into a waste beaker making sure that there are no air bubbles in the tip of the burette. Use a piece of white paper to accurately read the starting point of the KIO_3 solution in the burette, read the bottom of the meniscus at eye level. Record the initial volume.

6. Add 1.0 g KI to one of the 250-mL Erlenmeyer flasks. Swirl the flask to dissolve the KI. Add 5 mL of 1 M HCl and 2 to 3 mL of 1.0 % starch solution. Titrate the flask by slowly adding KIO_3 until the solution turns blue. Be sure to swirl the flask as you titrate. Near the endpoint the solution turns blue but remains blue only momentarily. Once the solution turns blue permanently, read and record the final volume of the burette.

7. Repeat step 6 with the second Erlenmeyer flask. Make sure the volumes of KIO_3 used are recorded with the respective mass of each ascorbic acid sample.

8. Determine the mass of ascorbic acid for each of the trials. Do a third trial if there is significant discrepancy between the first two trials.

Data	Trial 1	Trial 2	Trial 3 (if needed)
Mass of $C_6H_8O_6$			
Initial volume in the burette			
Final volume in the burette			
Volume of KIO_3 used			
Moles of KIO_3			
Moles of $C_6H_8O_6$			
Mass of $C_6H_8O_6$			

Part 2. Effect of Temperature on Ascorbic Acid

1. Weigh a 0.4-g sample of ascorbic acid to the nearest 0.001 g. Be sure to use weighing paper and tare the balance. Record the mass.

2. Place the ascorbic acid sample in a clean 250-mL Erlenmeyer flask (indicate the mass of the ascorbic acid sample on the label). Add 100 mL of DI water to the flask. Set up a ring stand and Bunsen burner. Boil the solution for 10 minutes. If the volume of the solution reduces to less than 50 mL, add some DI water to make the volume approximately 50 mL. While the solution boils, weigh another 0.4-g sample of ascorbic acid and place it in a second clean 250-mL Erlenmeyer flask (indicate the mass of the ascorbic acid sample on the label). Add 100 mL of DI water and boil the solution for 10 minutes.

3. Allow solutions to cool down to room temperature. Running cold water over the outside of the Erlenmeyer flask will cool the solution more quickly. Hold the flask at an angle under a slow stream of cool water, making certain no water goes into the flask.

4. Fill the burette with 0.10 M KIO_3. Titrate a couple milliliters into a waste beaker to make sure that there are no air bubbles in the tip of the burette. There should be 30-40 mL in the burette at the start of the titration. Record the initial volume.

5. Add 1.0 g KI to one of the 250-mL Erlenmeyer flasks. Swirl to dissolve the KI. Add 5 mL of 1 M HCl and 2 to 3 mL of 1.0 % starch solution. Titrate the flask by slowly adding KIO_3 until the solution turns blue. Be sure to swirl the flask as you titrate. At the endpoint, read and record the final volume of the burette.

6. Repeat step 5 with the second Erlenmeyer flask. Make sure the volumes of KIO_3 used are recorded with the respective mass of each ascorbic acid sample.

7. Determine the mass of ascorbic acid for each of the trials. Did the ascorbic acid degrade by boiling the solution? Will cooking foods that contain Vitamin C make Vitamin C less affective as an antioxidant?

Part 3. Analysis of Vitamin C Tablets.

1. Weigh two 500-mg Vitamin C tablets to the nearest 0.001 g. Be sure to use weighing paper and tare the balance. Record the mass.

2. Place each sample into its own clearly labeled 250-mL Erlenmeyer flask (indicate the mass of the Vitamin C tablets on the label). Add 50 mL of DI water to each flask. Swirl the flask and use a stirring rod to crush the Vitamin C tablet until it has completely dissolved. As observed in Parts 1 and 2 of this experiment, ascorbic acid is soluble in water. Vitamin C tablets should therefore readily dissolve in water. If after a couple minutes, a small quantity of solid remains, it is probably a binder that is added to keep the tablet intact.

3. Fill the burette with 0.10 M KIO_3. Titrate a couple milliliters into a waste beaker to make sure that there are no air bubbles in the tip of the burette. Record the initial volume.

4. Add 1.0 g KI to one of the 250-mL Erlenmeyer flasks. Swirl the flask to dissolve the KI. Add 5 mL of 1 M HCl and 2 to 3 mL of 1.0 % starch solution. Titrate with KIO_3 until the solution turns blue. Be sure to swirl the flask as you titrate. Once the solution turns blue, read and record the final burette volume.

5. Repeat step 4 with the second Erlenmeyer flask. Make sure the volumes of KIO_3 used are recorded with the respective mass of each Vitamin C tablet.

6. Determine the % mass of Vitamin C in the Vitamin C tablet for each of the trials.

WASTE DISPOSAL

When titrations are complete dispose of the solutions in the appropriately labeled waste bottle in the hood. If the waste bottle is full (to the bottom of the neck) notify the TA or the stockroom personnel to provide another waste container.

PRE-LAB QUESTIONS

1. Assign the oxidation states of all the atoms in each of the following compounds and anions.

   a) K_2SO_4
   b) IO_3^-
   c) $Cr_2O_7^{2-}$
   d) $Ca(NO_3)_2$

2. In an oxidation-reduction reaction electrons are transferred from one substance to another. The substance that loses electrons is oxidized and the substance that gains electrons is reduced. Consider the reaction of Vitamin C and iodine, I_2.

In this reaction Vitamin C is oxidized by losing two electrons as shown in the following half reaction.

The oxidation of one substance is accompanied by the reduction of another substance. In this reaction, iodine is reduced; it gains two electrons. To conserve charge in the reaction the number of electrons gained is equal to the number of electrons lost.

$$I_2 + 2e^- \rightarrow 2 I^- \quad \text{reduction}$$

a) Show that the overall reaction is the sum of the oxidation and the reduction half-reactions.

b) What is the oxidation state of each iodine atom in I_2?

c) When I_2 reacts to produce 2 I^-, how many electrons does each iodine atom gain?

3. A 0.400-g sample of ascorbic acid is titrated with 0.10 M KIO_3. The solution contains 5 mL of 1 M HCl and 1 g of KI (s). The iodate ion reacts with iodide, I^-, and H^+ to produce iodine and water.

$$IO_3^- + 5\ I^- + 6\ H^+ \rightarrow 3\ I_2 + 3\ H_2O$$

The ascorbic acid reacts immediately with the I_2.

Vitamin C

When all the ascorbic acid has reacted, an increase in the concentration of I_2 and the reaction of I_2 with I^- to produce I_3^- signals the blue end-point. Triiodide, I_3^-, complexes with starch to produce the dark navy blue color.

$$I_2 + I^- \rightarrow I_3^-$$

What volume of 0.10 M KIO_3 is required to reach the end-point?

4. In Part 2 of this experiment the solution containing a known amount of ascorbic acid is boiled for 10 minutes. The solution is cooled to room temperature and the amount of ascorbic acid in solution is determined. How is an increase in temperature expected to affect the ascorbic acid?

DISCUSSION QUESTIONS

What questions were addressed in this experiment? What was the method used to answer these questions? Include balanced equations for each reaction discussed. Did boiling the oxalic acid solution have an affect on the oxalic acid? Discuss possible sources of error in this experiment. Compare the trials and discuss which you feel is the more accurate value and why. Is the content of Vitamin C in the tablet consistent with the amount indicated on the label of the container? Are you confident in your ability to determine the content of Vitamin C in tablets using this method?

■ EXPERIMENT 18

REVIEW QUESTIONS

1. In each of the following reactions, assign oxidation states to each of the atoms to identify the substance that is oxidized (loses electrons) and the substance that is reduced (gains electrons).

   a) $Cr_2O_3 + 2\,Al \;\rightarrow\; Al_2O_3 + 2\,Cr$

   b) $3\,H_2 + Fe_2O_3 \;\rightarrow\; 2\,Fe + 3\,H_2O$

   c) $6\,Ag + 3\,HS^- + 2\,CrO_4^{2-} + 5\,H_2O \;\rightarrow\; 3\,Ag_2S + 2\,Cr(OH)_3 + 7\,OH^-$

2. For each of the reactions in question 1, indicate the total number of electrons transferred.

Experiment 19

19

Oxidation-Reduction Electrochemistry

PURPOSE AND LEARNING OBJECTIVES

To measure relative reduction potentials of metals. To understand the relationship between reduction potentials and reaction spontaneity. To determine the Faraday constant and Avogadro's number by electrolysis.

PRINCIPLES
Galvanic (Voltaic) Cells

Electrochemistry deals with processes that convert chemical energy to electrical energy and vice versa. For example, in batteries and fuel cells chemical reactions produce electrical current. On the other hand, the process of electroplating metals and the electrolysis of water to produce hydrogen and oxygen, are examples of processes which require electrical energy to produce a chemical change. These types of reactions are classified as oxidation-reduction reactions (redox reactions), in which electrons are transferred from one substance to another. Consider, for example the reaction of copper reacting with silver ions in aqueous solution.

$$Cu\ (s)\ +\ 2\ Ag^+\ (aq)\ \rightarrow\ Cu^{2+}\ (aq)\ +\ 2\ Ag\ (s)$$

In this reaction copper metal dissolves to produce copper ions in solution according to the following half-reaction.

$$Cu \ (s) \quad \rightarrow \quad Cu^{2+} \ (aq) \ + \ 2 \ e^- \qquad\qquad \text{oxidation}$$

Copper is oxidized by losing two electrons. In redox reactions, the oxidation of one substance is accompanied by reduction of another substance. In this case, the silver ions are reduced by gaining electrons to produce the silver metal.

$$Ag^+ \ (aq) \ + \ e^- \quad \rightarrow \quad Ag \ (s) \qquad\qquad \text{reduction}$$

In order to conserve charge in the reaction, the electrons lost and gained must be balanced. To balance the number of electrons, the silver half-reaction is multiplied by a factor of two. Adding the half-reactions gives the overall balanced equation.

$$
\begin{array}{l}
Cu \ (s) \ \rightarrow \ Cu^{2+} \ (aq) \ + \ 2 \ e^- \\
\underline{2 \ Ag^+ \ (aq) \ + \ 2 \ e^- \ \rightarrow \ 2 \ Ag \ (s)} \\
Cu \ (s) + 2 \ Ag^+ \ (aq) \ \rightarrow \ Cu^{2+} \ (aq) + 2 \ Ag \ (s)
\end{array}
$$

If the reaction occurs in a single container, the electrons are transferred and no electrical work is obtained. However, if the half reactions take place in separate containers, the electrical current produced can be used to obtain electrical work. The electron current is measured using an ammeter. The oxidation half-reaction occurs at the anode and the reduction half-reaction occurs at the cathode. Electrons flow from the anode to the cathode. What causes the electrons to flow? Analogous to a ball rolling down a hill due to a difference in gravitational potential, the cell potential, ϵ, drives the electron flow in an electrochemical cell. The units of cell potential are volts (the work in joules per unit charge in coulombs).

$$1 \ \text{Volt} = \frac{1 \ \text{joule}}{\text{coulomb}}$$

Recall from thermodynamics, a negative change in enthalpy, $\Delta H < 0$, indicates the reaction is favorable in the direction written. A reaction is spontaneous if the change in free energy is negative, $\Delta G < 0$. ΔG is directly proportional to the change in cell potential, E_{cell}^{0}

$$\Delta G \ = \ -n \, F E_{cell} \qquad\qquad \Delta G° \ = \ -n \, F E_{cell}^{0}$$

In this equation, n is the number of moles of electrons transferred and F is Faraday's constant (the charge on 1 mole of electrons).

charge on a single electron: $e = 1.602 \times 10^{-19} \ C$

charge on 1 mole of electrons: $F = (N_A)(e) = (6.022 \times 10^{23} \ mol^{-1})(1.602 \times 10^{-19} \ C)$
$F = 96{,}485 \ C/mol$

The equation, $\Delta G = -n F E_{cell}$ shows that ΔG and E_{cell} have opposite signs. That is, for a spontaneous reaction $\Delta G < 0$ and $E_{cell} > 0$. Thus, $E_{cell} > 0$ implies spontaneous electron flow.

$$Cu\ (s)\ +\ 2\ Ag^+\ (aq)\ \rightarrow\ Cu^{2+}\ (aq)\ +\ 2\ Ag\ (s) \qquad E_{cell}^0\ =\ 0.46\ V$$

$$\Delta G^\circ\ =\ -n F E_{cell}^0\ =\ -(2\ mol\ electrons)(96,485\ C/mol)\ (0.46\ J/C)$$

$$\Delta G^\circ\ =\ -88.77\ kJ$$

NOTE: If the reaction is multiplied by a factor of two the cell potential remains the same, only the change in free energy is multiplied by two. This is simply because of the way E_{cell} is defined.

$$Cu\ (s)\ +\ 2\ Ag^+\ (aq)\ \rightarrow\ Cu^{2+}\ (aq)\ +\ 2\ Ag\ (s) \qquad E_{cell}^0\ =\ 0.46\ V$$

$$\Delta G^\circ\ =\ -n F E_{cell}^0\ =\ -(4\ mol\ electrons)(96,485\ C/mol)\ (0.46\ J/C)\ =\ -177.5\ kJ$$

$$or\quad \Delta G^\circ\ =\ (-88.77\ kJ)\ 2\ =\ -177.5\ kJ$$

Half-Cell Potentials

In constructing an electrochemical cell, when electrons flow spontaneously, $E_{cell}^0 > 0$, the cell is referred to as a Galvanic or Voltaic cell. The voltage produced by the cell can be measured directly. If all possible Galvanic cells were constructed, the voltages could be measured and tabulated as a source of reference. However, this would create a very long list. Instead, if the cell potentials for the half reactions are tabulated, the half-reactions can be combined in all the possible ways to determine the cell potential of the overall reaction. The half reactions are written as a reduction (gain of electrons).

	E^0 (volts)
$F_2\ (g)\ +\ 2\ e^-\ \rightarrow\ 2\ F^-\ (aq)$	2.87
$Cu^{2+}\ (aq)\ +\ 2\ e^-\ \rightarrow\ Cu\ (s)$	0.34
$Ag^+\ (aq)\ +\ e^-\ \rightarrow\ Ag\ (s)$	0.80
$2\ H^+\ (aq)\ +\ 2\ e^-\ \rightarrow\ H_2(g)$	0.0
$Zn^{2+}\ (aq)\ +\ 2\ e^-\ \rightarrow\ Zn\ (s)$	-0.76
$Li^+\ (aq)\ +\ e^-\ \rightarrow\ Li\ (s)$	-3.05

In each of the half reactions, the substance on the left is reduced because it gains electrons. When a substance is reduced, it is an oxidizing agent. The substances on the right side of these reactions are reducing agents that can be oxidized. Each half-reaction has a certain tendency to occur. The more positive the cell potential, the greater the tendency for reaction to occur. For example, the reduction of F_2 is very favorable as indicated by the large positive cell potential. This is not surprising considering the fact that fluorine is highly electronegative and strongly attracts electrons. At the other extreme, lithium metal wants to donate electrons. As a result, the reduction of Li^+ is not favorable as indicated by the large negative reduction potential. The reverse reaction is favorable as indicated by the large positive cell potential.

$$Li\ (s)\ \rightarrow\ Li^+\ (aq)\ +\ e^-\qquad\qquad E^0 = 3.05\ V$$

When the reaction is reversed, the sign of the cell potential is reversed.

The potential of a half-reaction can not be measured in isolation because a flow of electrons is required. Thus, two half-reactions are combined and the relative potential is measured. In the table above and the Table of Standard Reduction Potentials in your text, the half-reaction potentials are measured relative to the hydrogen electrode. That is, a series of galvanic cells are constructed and one electrode is always the hydrogen electrode. In the first part of this experiment, reduction potentials of metals relative to each other will be measured.

With a table of reduction potentials available you can predict the spontaneity of oxidation-reduction reactions. For example, what if you wanted to know if a piece of zinc metal dissolves in an aqueous solution of Cu^{2+} ions. In other words, can Zn (s) reduce Cu^{2+} to produce Cu(s)? That is, will copper metal be produced?

The reduction half-reactions are given as follows.

$$Zn^{2+}\ (aq)\ +\ 2\ e^-\ \rightarrow\ Zn\ (s)\qquad\qquad E^0 = -\ 0.76$$

$$Cu^{2+}\ (aq)\ +\ 2\ e^-\ \rightarrow\ Cu\ (s)\qquad\qquad E^0 = 0.34\ V$$

If Cu^{2+} is reduced, Zn (s) must be oxidized. The first reaction is therefore reversed and the cell potential must be reversed accordingly.

$$\begin{array}{ll}
Zn\ (s)\ \rightarrow\ Zn^{2+}\ (aq)\ +\ 2\ e^- & E^0\ =\ 0.76\ V \\
\underline{Cu^{2+}\ (aq)\ +\ 2\ e^-\ \rightarrow\ Cu\ (s)} & \underline{E^0\ =\ 0.34\ V} \\
Zn\ (s)\ +\ Cu^{2+}\ (aq)\ \rightarrow\ Zn^{2+}\ (aq)\ +\ Cu\ (s) & E_{cell}^{\ 0}\ =\ 1.10\ V
\end{array}$$

The overall reaction is obtained by adding the half reactions and the cell potential is obtained by adding the half-cell potentials. $E_{cell}^{\ 0} = 0.76 + 0.34\ V = 1.10\ V$. Because $E_{cell}^{\ 0} > 0$ the overall reaction is spontaneous and Zn (s) does reduce Cu^{2+} (aq). Thus, the zinc metal dissolves and copper metal appears in the solution. Also, as the reaction occurs, the color of the solution changes from blue to clear. The aqueous Cu^{2+} solution is blue and becomes clear as Cu^{2+} ions are reduce to Cu (s) in the reaction. In the second and third parts of this experiment you will be given half-cell reduction potentials so you can predict the direction in which reactions will be spontaneous. You will then observe these reactions.

Electrolytic Cells

In electrolytic cells, the electrical energy provided by an external circuit is used to drive a reaction in the direction opposite the spontaneous direction. The external circuit provides the energy needed to carry out a chemical reaction which would otherwise not occur. Consider an electrolytic cell constructed with two copper electrodes immersed in a dilute H_2SO_4 solution. If copper metal is oxidized to produce Cu^{2+} ions in solution and H^+ ions are removed from solution to produce H_2 (g), the overall reaction has a negative cell potential.

$$
\begin{array}{llll}
Cu\ (s) & \rightarrow & Cu^{2+}\ (aq)\ +\ 2\ e^- & E^0\ =\ -0.34\ V \\
2\ H^+\ (aq)\ +\ 2e^- & \rightarrow & H_2(g) & E^0\ =\ 0.0\ V \\
\hline
Cu\ (s)\ +\ 2\ H^+ & \rightarrow & Cu^{2+}\ +\ H_2(g) & E_{cell}^0\ =\ -0.34\ V
\end{array}
$$

Because $\Delta E^0 < 0$, this reaction will not occur spontaneously. However, if a power supply provides a voltage greater than 0.34 V, the reaction will occur. The amount of H_2 gas produced and the amount of copper metal dissolved in the reaction is directly proportional to the number of electrons transferred. The charge carried by one mole of electrons is a Faraday. In the last part of this experiment you will determine the Faraday constant by measuring the amount of charge required per mole of electrons consumed or produced in the half reactions.

SAFETY
WEAR SAFETY GLASSES

Please keep voltmeters and wires clean, dry and away from all solutions. Avoid contact with $AgNO_3$, it will stain skin brown. In case of contact with $AgNO_3$, rinse thoroughly. The brown color will wear off in a few days. H_2SO_4 is a strong acid. In case of contact, rinse thoroughly with water. Clean up spills immediately.

PROCEDURE
This experiment will be performed in pairs but you must record all the data, do the calculations and write up your lab reports individually. All calculations must be completed and checked by your instructor before you leave the laboratory.

Part 1. The Electrochemical Series of Metals
1. Obtain a piece of filter paper, 9 cm in diameter. Fold it in half twice, sequentially. Cut the folded filter paper along the dashed lines and unfold.

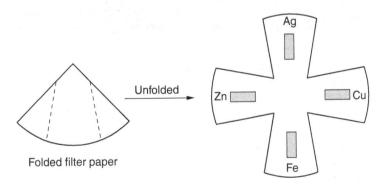

Folded filter paper

2. Using a pen, label the filter paper, Ag, Cu, Fe, and Zn, in the order specified, near the outer edge of the filter paper as shown.

3. Place the filter paper in a clean, dry petri dish or petri dish lid.

4. Place a sample of each of the metals, Ag, Cu, Fe, and Zn just below each of the labels, as shown in the figure. The pieces of metal must be flat to make good contact.

5. Place two drops of the corresponding metal ion solutions onto the paper at the edge of each metal piece so the metal is in contact with the solution. The solution of the given metal ion must remain within the boundaries of the wedge containing the metal.

6. Put a couple drops of 1 M KNO_3 salt bridge solution in the middle of the filter paper, it will absorb outward. Continue to add the solution until it just touches each of the other metal ion solutions. Avoid using too much!

7. Obtain a voltmeter equipped with a black and a red probe. The black probe is the reference to ground. Switch the voltmeter to measure DC voltage.

8. Using the black probe, touch the piece of silver metal, Ag (s), and with the red probe touch the piece of copper metal, Cu (s). Read and record the voltage. Be sure to note the sign of the voltage, negative or positive.

9. Leave the black probe on the Ag (s) and move the red probe to each of the metals clockwise, Fe (s) and Zn (s). Read and record the voltage for each metal in the table below.

10. Repeat the above procedure but with the black probe on the piece of copper metal. Read and record the voltage for each metal.

STANDARD REDUCTION POTENTIALS AT 25° C			
Half-reaction	E^0 **(volts) Referenced to the Hydrogen Electrode**	E^0 **(volts) Referenced to the Silver Electrode**	E^0 **(volts) Referenced to the Copper Electrode**
$Ag^+ + e^- \rightarrow Ag$ (s)	0.80	0.0	
$Cu^{2+} + 2\,e^- \rightarrow Cu$ (s)	0.34		0.0
$2\,H^+ + 2\,e^- \rightarrow H_2$ (s)	0.0	Not measured	Not measured
$Fe^{2+} + 2\,e^- \rightarrow Fe$ (s)	− 0.41		
$Zn^{2+} + 2\,e^- \rightarrow Zn$ (s)	− 0.76		

Part 2. Aluminum-Copper Reduction Potentials

1. Given the following half reactions, predict if aluminum will dissolve in a $CuCl_2$ solution.

$$Al^{3+} + 3e^- \rightarrow Al\ (s) \qquad E^0 = -1.70\ V$$
$$Cu^{2+} + 2e^- \rightarrow Cu\ (s) \qquad E^0 = 0.34\ V$$

2. Put 6 mL of 0.5 M $CuCl_2$, in a medium test tube.

3. Obtain a strip of aluminum foil, approximately 1-2 cm wide and 6-8 cm long. Form it into any shape you like.

4. Put the aluminum into the copper chloride solution.

5. Record your observations as the reaction takes place. Is this reaction exothermic or endothermic?

6. Write the half-reactions that are occurring, the balanced overall reaction and the corresponding E_{cell}^0.

Part 3. Silver-Copper Reduction Potentials

1. Given the following half reactions, predict if copper will dissolve in a $AgNO_3$ solution.

$$Ag^+ + e^- \rightarrow Ag\ (s) \qquad E^0 = 0.80\ V$$
$$Cu^{2+} + 2e^- \rightarrow Cu\ (s) \qquad E^0 = 0.34\ V$$

2. Put 4 mL of 1 M $AgNO_3$ in a small test tube. Avoid contact with $AgNO_3$, it will stain skin brown. In case of contact with $AgNO_3$, rinse thoroughly. The brown color will wear off in a few days.

3. Coil a 6-8 cm piece of copper wire and place it in the $AgNO_3$ solution.

4. Record your observations.

5. Write the half reactions that are occurring, the balanced overall reaction and the corresponding E_{cell}^0.

6. Set the test tube aside until the end of the lab and record your observations.

Part 4. Faraday's Constant and Avogadro's Number

1. Obtain a digital timer. Also obtain a rectangular piece of copper, $8 \times 2 \times 0.15$ cm, and weigh it to the nearest 0.001 g. This will be the anode.

2. Fill a 250-mL beaker with 175 mL of DI water, and 30 mL of 3 M H_2SO_4.

■ **EXPERIMENT 19**

3. Set up a ring-stand with a burette clamp and an inverted burette as shown in Figure 1.

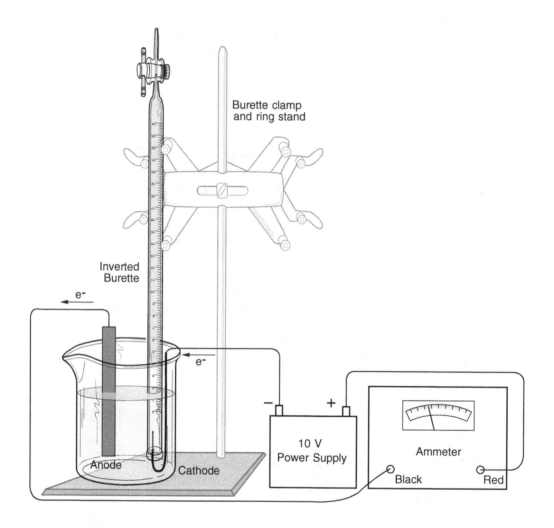

Figure 1. A schematic diagram of an electrolytic cell with two copper electrodes immersed in a dilute H_2SO_4 solution. Electrical energy, provided by a 10 V power supply, is required to oxidize Cu (s) to Cu^{2+} at the anode and reduce H^+ to H_2 gas at the cathode. The ammeter reads the current in amps.

4. Place the inverted burette in the beaker of aqueous H_2SO_4 solution.

5. Using a rubber pipette bulb, the solution is drawn into the burette. To do this, squeeze the pipette bulb and place it on the tip of the burette, open the stopcock and draw the solution into the burette, then close the stopcock. Repeat this procedure until the burette is filled to the stopcock with the solution. There should be no air inside the burette.

6. The cathode is a piece of copper wire, partly covered with plastic. Place the end of the copper wire in the inverted burette so that the bare wire end is completely inside the burette. This ensures that all the hydrogen gas is produced and collected inside the burette. See Figure 1. Connect the other end of the copper cathode to a power supply and ammeter.

7. Hook the copper anode up to the ammeter. Start the digital timer as you immerse the anode into the beaker. The ammeter should read a current between 0.4 and 0.8 amps. If it reads only 0.2 amps, the experiment will take much longer. If the ammeter reads less than zero, immediately remove the copper anode and reverse the leads. Read and record the current on the ammeter after 15 seconds have elapsed and at 30 second intervals thereafter. If everything is hooked up correctly and no H_2 bubbles are produced at the cathode (in the burette) try another power supply and turn over the ammeter to check for loose wires.

8. Stop the electrolysis by removing the anode (the rectangular piece of copper) when the level of the solution in the burette is just **above** the last gradation mark on the burette (at or near the level of solution in the beaker). <u>Record the total electrolysis time</u>. Adjust the height of the burette or beaker until the levels of the solution inside the burette, and inside the beaker are equal (you can add water to the beaker if needed). <u>Record the burette reading</u>.

9. Measure and record the temperature of the solution in the beaker. What color is the solution? What is the color due to?

10. To determine the total volume of gas inside the burette you must determine the volume between the stopcock and the first gradation on the burette and add it to the remaining volume. Remove the burette from the ring-stand, turn it right side up, fill it to the first gradation mark with water. Tare a small beaker on the balance. Transfer the water inside the burette to the beaker and record the weight. Use the density of water, 1 g/mL, to calculate the volume of water. This corresponds to the total volume of H_2 gas produced. Record the volume.

11. Obtain the barometric pressure from the instructor.

12. Gently rinse the anode with DI water and dry it. Weigh and record the mass of the copper anode to the nearest 0.001 g.

■ **EXPERIMENT 19**

Data: Faraday's Constant and Avogrado's number					
Mass of Copper Anode before Electrolysis (g)					
Current after 15 seconds of reaction time (amps)					
Current at 30-second intervals (amps)					
Total Electrolysis Time (s)					
Final Burette Reading (mL)					
Temperature of Solution (°C)					
Mass of Copper Anode after Electrolysis (g)					
Barometric Pressure (atm)					
Vapor Pressure of Water (See Appendix 2) Interpolate the Value					

Calculate Faraday's Constant and Avogadro's Number from the moles of H_2 gas produced at the cathode.

1.   Total volume of hydrogen gas produced.

2.   Calculate the partial pressure of hydrogen gas, P_{H_2}, produced.

$$P_{total} = P_{H_2} + P_{H_2O}$$

or $$P_{H_2} = P_{total} - P_{H_2O}$$

In this equation P_{total} is the barometric pressure and P_{H_2O} is the vapor pressure of water at the temperature of the solution (see Appendix 2).

3.   Calculate the moles of H_2 produced using the ideal gas law, $PV = nRT$. Watch units carefully: $R = 0.08206$ L atm mol^{-1} K^{-1}; P_{H_2} is in units of atmospheres; V_{H_2} in liters, and T is the absolute temperature in units of Kelvin.

4.   The reaction that occurs at the cathode is as follows.

$$2\,H^+ + 2\,e^- \rightarrow H_2\,(g)$$

From the reaction stoichiometry, calculate the moles of electrons consumed from the moles of hydrogen produced.

5. Calculate the total reaction time, t, and the average current, I.

6. Calculate the charge, Q, transferred in units of coulombs.

$$Q = I\,t$$

In this equation, the current, I, passed through the circuit is in units of coulombs/second and the electrolysis time, t, is in seconds. 1 Amp = 1 Coulomb/sec; 1 A = 1 C/sec.

7. Calculate Faraday's constant, F, the charge per mole of electrons (C/mol).

$$F = \frac{Q}{\text{moles of electrons consumed}}$$

8. Calculate Avogadro's number, N_A.

$$N_A = \frac{F}{e} \qquad \text{where } e = 1.602 \times 10^{-19}\ C$$

9. Calculate the percent error in Faraday's constant and in Avogadro's number.

Calculate: Faraday's Constant and Avogrado's number	
Total Volume of Hydrogen Gas Produced (mL)	
Partial Pressure of Hydrogen, P_{H_2} (atm)	
Moles of H_2 Produced	
Moles of Electrons Consumed	
Total Reaction time, t (sec)	
Average Current, I (C/sec)	
Charge Transferred, Q (C)	
Faraday's Constant, F (C/mol of electrons)	
Avogrado's Number, N_A	
Percent error in Faraday's Constant, F	
Percent error in Avogrado's Number, N_A	

Calculate Faraday's Constant and Avogadro's Number from the moles of copper dissolved from the copper anode.

1. Calculate the moles of copper dissolved from the copper anode.

2. The reaction that occurs at the anode is as follows.

$$Cu\ (s)\quad \rightarrow\quad Cu^{2+} + 2\ e^-$$

   From the reaction stoichiometry, calculate the moles of electrons produced from the moles of copper dissolved.

3. You have calculated the total reaction time, t, the average current, I, and the charge, Q, in the previous set of calculations. Include these values in the table here.

4. Calculate Faraday's constant, F, the charge per mole of electrons (C/mol).

$$F = \frac{Q}{\text{moles of electrons consumed}}$$

5. Calculate Avogadro's number, N_A.

$$N_A = \frac{F}{e} \quad \text{where } e = 1.602 \times 10^{-19}\ C$$

6. Calculate the percent error in Faraday's constant and in Avogadro's number.

Calculate: Faraday's Constant and Avogrado's number	
Mass of Copper Reacted	
Moles of Copper Reacted	
Moles of Electrons Produced	
Total Reaction time, t (sec)	
Average Current, I (C/sec)	
Charge Transferred, Q (C)	
Faraday's Constant, F (C/mol of electrons)	
Avogrado's Number, N_A	
Percent error in Faraday's Constant, F	
Percent error in Avogrado's Number, N_A	

WASTE DISPOSAL

All waste is discarded in the appropriately labeled waste containers in the hood.

PRE-LAB QUESTIONS

1. Consider the reaction of copper reacting with silver ions in aqueous $CuSO_4$ and $AgNO_3$ solutions.

$$Cu\ (s)\ +\ 2\ Ag^+\ (aq)\ \rightarrow\ Cu^{2+}\ (aq)\ +\ 2\ Ag\ (s)$$

   a) Indicate which substance loses electrons and which substance gains electrons.
   b) When a substance is oxidized it loses electrons. Write the oxidation half-reaction.
   c) When a substance is reduced it gains electrons. Write the reduction half-reaction.
   d) Add the oxidation and reduction half reactions to give the overall reaction of copper reacting with silver ions. In order to conserve charge, the electrons lost and gained must be balanced.

2. Complete the following electrochemical cell. The anode is where oxidation takes place and the cathode is where reduction takes place.
   a) Label the anode and cathode.
   b) Write the half reactions that occur at the anode and cathode.
   c) Indicate the direction of electron flow.

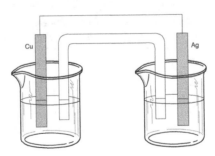

   d) What is the purpose of the salt bridge? What would happen if the half-cell compartments were not connected with a salt bridge?

3. What causes electrons to flow?

4. Write the equation that relates the change in free energy, ΔG, to the change in cell potential, E_{cell}. Define all the variables in the equation.

5. Consider the following reaction.

$$Cu\ (s)\ +\ 2\ Ag^+\ (aq)\ \rightarrow\ Cu^{2+}\ (aq)\ +\ 2\ Ag\ (s)\ \qquad E_{cell}^{\,o}\ =\ 0.46\ V$$

a) Calculate $\Delta G°$ for this reaction.

b) Is this reaction spontaneous? Explain why or why not. What is the sign of $E_{cell}°$ for a spontaneous reaction?

c) Determine $\Delta G°$ and $E_{cell}°$ for the following reaction.

$$2\ Cu\ (s)\ +\ 4\ Ag^+\ (aq)\ \rightarrow\ 2\ Cu^{2+}\ (aq)\ +\ 4\ Ag\ (s)$$

6. Write the overall reaction of zinc metal reacting with copper ions in aqueous solution. Calculate $E_{cell}°$ for the reaction, given the following reduction half-reactions.

$$Zn^{2+}\ (aq)\ +\ 2\ e^-\ \rightarrow\ Zn\ (s) \qquad\qquad E° = -0.76\ V$$

$$Cu^{2+}\ (aq)\ +\ 2\ e^-\ \rightarrow\ Cu\ (s) \qquad\qquad E° = 0.34\ V$$

7. Standard reduction potentials are given for reduction half-reactions relative to the hydrogen half reaction. In Part 1 of this experiment, you will determine reduction potentials relative to the reduction of silver and copper. Predict what the reduction potentials should be relative to the silver and copper electrodes.

	STANDARD REDUCTION POTENTIALS AT 25˚ C		
Half-reaction	$E°$ **(volts) Referenced to the Hydrogen Electrode**	$E°$ **(volts) Referenced to the Silver Electrode**	$E°$ **(volts) Referenced to the Copper Electrode**
$Ag^+ + e^- \rightarrow Ag\ (s)$	0.80	0.0	
$Cu^{2+} + 2\ e^- \rightarrow Cu\ (s)$	0.34		0.0
$2\ H^+ + 2\ e^- \rightarrow H_2\ (s)$	0.0	Not measured	Not measured
$Fe^{2+} + 2\ e^- \rightarrow Fe\ (s)$	– 0.41		
$Zn^{2+} + 2\ e^- \rightarrow Zn\ (s)$	– 0.76		

8. In Part 2 of this experiment you will observe the reaction of aluminum in an aqueous $CuCl_2$ solution.

a) Given the following half reactions, predict if aluminum will dissolve in a $CuCl^2$ solution.

$$Al^{3+}\ +\ 3e^-\ \rightarrow\ Al\ (s) \qquad\qquad E° = -1.70\ V$$
$$Cu^{2+}\ +\ 2e^-\ \rightarrow\ Cu\ (s) \qquad\qquad E° = 0.34\ V$$

b) The more positive the cell potential the more spontaneous the reaction will be. What precautions should you take in performing this experiment if E_{cell}^0 is positive and large?

9. In Part 3 of the experiment you will observe the reaction of copper metal in an aqueous $AgNO_3$ solution. Given the following half reactions, predict if copper will dissolve in $AgNO_3$ (aq).

$$Ag^+ + e^- \rightarrow Ag\ (s) \qquad\qquad E^0 = 0.80\ V$$
$$Cu^{2+} + 2e^- \rightarrow Cu\ (s) \qquad\qquad E^0 = 0.34\ V$$

10. In Part 4 of this experiment, you will construct an electrolytic cell in which copper metal is oxidized to produce Cu^{2+} ions in solution and H^+ ions are removed from solution to produce hydrogen gas.

$$Cu\ (s) \rightarrow Cu^{2+}\ (aq) + 2\ e^- \qquad\qquad E^0 = {}^-0.34\ V$$
$$2\ H^+\ (aq) + 2e^- \rightarrow H_2(g) \qquad\qquad E^0 = 0.0\ V$$

a) Write the overall reaction and determine the corresponding cell potential.
b) Is this reaction spontaneous? Explain why or why not.
c) How can we get this reaction to occur?

11. The amount of H_2 gas produced and the amount of copper metal dissolved in the reaction is directly proportional to the number of electrons transferred. A faraday represents the charge carried by one mole of electrons. In Part 4 of this experiment you will determine Faraday's constant by measuring the amount of charge required per mole of electrons consumed or produced in each of the half-reactions.

a) Write the half-reaction that occurs at the anode and that occurs at the cathode.

b) The cathode is a copper wire, partly covered with plastic. Why is it important to make sure all the bare copper wire is inside the burette.

DISCUSSION QUESTIONS

How did the relative half-cell potentials measured for Ag, Cu, Fe and Zn compare to the actual values? What are the possible errors in these measurements? Was there a difference between using the two reference electrodes? Was one more accurate then the other?

What did you observe when aluminum foil was immersed in an aqueous $CuCl_2$ solution and when copper wire was immersed in an aqueous $AgNO_3$ solution. Write the half reactions and overall reactions which occurred. For each reaction, indicate which substance was reduced and which substance was oxidized.

In the electrolysis of copper, Faraday's constant and Avogadro's number were determined in two ways: 1) by measuring the volume of hydrogen gas produced and 2) by measuring the

■ EXPERIMENT 19

amount of copper metal dissolved. What were the values determined for the Faraday constant and Avogadro's number? How did the values compare? Is one method more accurate than the other? What are the possible sources of error in each case. What were the percent errors calculated for Faraday's constant and Avogadro's number?

QUESTIONS

1. In part 4 of the experiment, hydrogen gas was produced in the electrolysis of copper.
   a) If the current (amps) supplied was increased by a factor of two, how would this affect the time required to produce the same number of moles of hydrogen gas?
   b) The copper anode is weighed before and after the electrolysis reaction. If the copper anode is not completely dry when it is weighed after the electrolysis, how would this affect the value of the Faraday constant calculated?

2. In the electrolysis of an aqueous NaCl solution, Cl_2 gas is produced.

   $$2\ Cl^- (aq)\ \rightarrow\ Cl_2\ (g)\ +\ 2\ e^-$$

   a) How many moles of electrons need to be transferred at the anode to release 0.02 moles of Cl_2 gas?
   b) How many coulombs of charge is required to release 0.02 mol of Cl_2 gas?

3. Calculate the mass of aluminum produced in 1.00 hr by the electrolysis of molten $AlCl_3$ if the electrical current is 8.0 A.

4. Answer the questions using the following half reactions:

	E^o (V)
$Cl_2\ +\ 2e^-\ \rightarrow\ 2\ Cl^-$	1.36
$O_2\ +\ 4\ H^+\ +4\ e^-\ \rightarrow\ 2\ H_2O$	1.23
$ClO_2\ +\ e^-\ \rightarrow\ ClO_2^-$	0.95
$Ag^+\ +\ e^-\ \rightarrow\ Ag\ (s)$	0.80
$Cu^{2+}\ +\ 2e^-\ \rightarrow\ Cu\ (s)$	0.34
$2\ H^+\ +\ 2\ e^-\ \rightarrow\ H_2$	0.00
$Co^{2+}\ +\ 2\ e^-\ \rightarrow\ Co\ (s)$	-0.28
$Cd^{2+}\ +\ 2\ e^-\ \rightarrow\ Cd\ (s)$	-0.40
$Cr^{3+}\ +\ 3\ e^-\ \rightarrow\ Cr\ (s)$	-0.76

   a) Which is the strongest reducing agent?
   b) Is Cr^{3+} capable of oxidizing Ag (s)?
   c) Is the following reaction spontaneous? $Cd\ (s)\ +\ 2\ H^+\ \rightarrow\ H_2\ +\ Cd^{2+}$
   e) Does Cu (s) dissolve in hydrochloric acid?
   f) Calculate ΔG° for the following reaction at 25°C.

   $$2\ NaClO_2(aq)\ +\ Cl_2(g)\ \rightarrow\ 2\ ClO_2\ (g)\ +\ 2\ NaCl(aq)$$

Experiment **20**

20

Thermodynamics of Electrochemical Cells

PURPOSE AND LEARNING OBJECTIVES

To study the effects of temperature and concentration on cell potentials. From the temperature dependence of cell potentials ΔG, ΔH and ΔS are calculated. The Nernst equation is used to calculate cell potentials as a function of concentration.

PRINCIPLES

Dependence of Cell Potential on Temperature

In this experiment electrochemical cells will be constructed to measure the cell potential as a function of temperature and concentration. These are galvanic (or voltaic) cells in which the oxidation-reduction reaction occurs spontaneously to produce a current. The half-reactions take place in separate compartments connected by a salt bridge.

By measuring the cell potential, E_{cell}, the change in free energy, ΔG, can be determined.

$$\Delta G = -n F E_{cell}$$

When 1 M solutions are used, the standard cell potential, E_{cell}^{0}, is measured and the standard free energy change, $\Delta G°$, is calculated.

$$\Delta G° = - \text{n} \, F \, E_{cell}{}^{o}$$

In these equations, n is the number of moles of electrons transferred in the reaction and F is Faraday's constant, the charge on one mole of electrons.

$$F = 96{,}485 \ C/mol$$

The equilibrium constant is calculated from the standard free energy change.

$$\Delta G° = -RT \ln K$$

$$K = e^{-\Delta G°/RT}$$

In this equation, R is the universal gas constant ($8.314 \ J \ mol^{-1} \ K^{-1}$) and T is the absolute temperature in Kelvin.

The change in free energy is also related to the change in enthalpy, ΔH, and the change in entropy, ΔS, of the reaction.

$$\Delta G = \Delta H - T\Delta S$$

In the first part of this experiment, the cell potential is measured as a function of temperature. The change in free energy is calculated from the cell potentials. Plotting ΔG versus temperature gives a straight line with the slope equal to $-\Delta S$ and the intercept is ΔH.

Dependence of Cell Potential on Concentration
Recall from thermodynamics, the relationship between the change in free energy and the reaction quotient, Q, from the thermodynamic description of the equilibrium state.

$$\Delta G = \Delta G° + RT \ln Q$$

Substituting $\Delta G = -\text{n} \, F \, E_{cell}$ and $\Delta G° = -\text{n} \, F \, E_{cell}{}^{o}$ into this equation results in the Nernst equation.

$$-\text{n} \, F \, E_{cell} = -\text{n} \, F \, E_{cell}{}^{o} + RT \ln Q$$

$$E_{cell} = E_{cell}^{o} - \frac{RT}{nF} \ln Q$$

Using the Nernst equation the cell potential can be calculated for oxidation-reduction reactions as a function of concentration. The cell potential calculated is the maximum potential before any current flows. As the cell discharges, current flows from the anode to the cathode, concentrations change and the cell potential decreases until equilibrium is attained. At equilibrium Q = K, E_{cell} = 0 and ΔG = 0.

$$E_{cell}^{o} = \frac{RT}{nF} \ln K$$

SAFETY

WEAR SAFETY GLASSES

Please keep voltmeters and wires clean, dry and away from all solutions.

EQUIPMENT

For this experiment large test-tubes (25 mm by 150 mm) are needed along with 12-inch long tubing (3/16 I.D.) to construct the salt bridge. The $Pb(NO_3)_2$ solutions must be freshly made.

PROCEDURE

Part 1. Effect of Temperature on the Cell Potential

1. Obtain two 6-inch test tubes, supplied especially for this experiment. Label the test tubes, copper and lead. Add 15-20 mL of the corresponding 1.0 M metal nitrate solution to the test tubes. Use a beaker to hold the test tubes.

2. Obtain a 7-inch strip of copper and lead.

3. Obtain a 12-inch piece of tubing supplied in the lab. Place the tube in an empty 150-mL beaker so the ends are pointing up and out of the beaker, in the shape of a U. Using a dropping pipette fill the tube with 1 M KNO_3.

4. Pull two small pieces of cotton from a cotton ball. Wet each piece and put them in the ends of the tubing. After the first piece of cotton is placed in one end, some KNO_3 may have spilled out the other end. If so, add more 1 M KNO_3 to completely fill the tube. Plug the other end with the second piece of cotton. The cotton plugs should protrude from the ends of the U-tube. Make sure there are no air bubbles in the tube. This salt bridge can be used throughout the experiment.

5. Set up a ring stand with a ring and wire gauze, over a Bunsen burner. Put a 400-mL beaker filled with 200 mL of tap water on the wire gauze as shown in Figure 1.

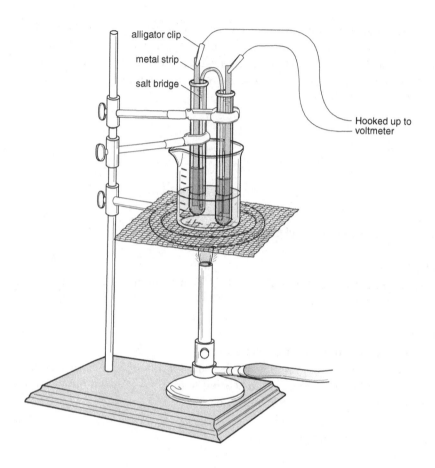

Figure 1. The test tubes are firmly secured to the ring stand using clamps. Allow for some space between the bottom of the test tubes and the bottom of the beaker.

6. Put the test tube containing the lead solution and the test tube containing the copper solution in the 400-mL beaker. Secure the test tubes with clamps to the ring stand. The bottom of the test tubes should be 1 to 2 inches above the bottom of the beaker.

7. Put the U-tube ends into the test tubes as a salt bridge, making sure the ends are submerged in the solutions and that no air bubbles are trapped in the salt bridge. The same salt bridge can be used throughout the experiment.

8. Clean the surface of the lead and copper metal strips in 1 M HNO_3 provided in the hood. Scrub the metal surfaces SHINY CLEAN, rinse with DI water and immediately place the lead strip into the lead nitrate solution and the copper strip into the copper nitrate solution. The surface oxidizes very quickly in air. If the surface is oxidized, the experiment will not work.

9. Obtain a voltmeter and attach the leads to the metal strips so the voltmeter reads positive values. If a negative potential is measured, reverse the leads. Make sure the leads are in good contact with the metal.

10. Put a thermometer in the beaker of water. Measure and record the voltage and temperature of the cell in your notebook.

11. Start heating the water in the beaker using the Bunsen Burner. Heat the water to 75°C. Remove the heat from the system by turning off the gas. When the temperature of the water reaches 70.0°C, record the temperature and the voltage. When measuring the temperature, the thermometer should be in the solution, away from the sides or bottom of the beaker.

12. Let the solution cool to approximately 55.0°C. Measure and record the voltage and temperature.

13. Carefully replace the warm water bath with an ice water bath. Allow the ice bath to come to equilibrium for 15 minutes. Measure and record the voltage and temperature.

14. Calculate $\Delta G°$, using the measured cell potential, E_{cell}^{0}, at each temperature. Also calculate the corresponding values of the equilibrium constant, K.

$$\Delta G° = -n\, F\, E_{cell}^{0}$$

$$K = e^{-\Delta G^{0}/RT}$$

15. Plot $\Delta G°$ versus temperature. From the equation, $\Delta G° = \Delta H° - T\Delta S°$, the slope of the line equals $-\Delta S°$ and the intercept equals $\Delta H°$.

Pb (s) + Cu²⁺ (aq) → Cu (s) + Pb²⁺ (aq)			
Temperature	**Cell Voltage, E_{cell}°**	**$\Delta G°$**	**K**

■ EXPERIMENT 20

16. Calculate the values of ΔG°, ΔS°, and ΔH° and the equilibrium constant, K, at 298 K from the following thermodynamic data, at 25°C.

	ΔH_f° (kJ/mol)	S° (J K^{-1} mol^{-1})	ΔG_f° (kJ/mol)
Cu^{2+} (aq)	64.77	−99.6	65.49
Pb^{2+} (aq)	−1.7	10.5	−24.25
Cu (s)	0	33.15	0
Pb (s)	0	64.81	0

Experimental Values (Room Temperature)		Calculated Values (298 K)	
ΔG°		ΔG°	
ΔH°		ΔH°	
ΔS°		ΔS°	
K		K	

Part 2. Concentration Effects and the Nernst Equation

1. Construct an electrochemical cell using a lead metal strip in a 0.1 M $Pb(NO_3)_2$ solution and a copper metal strip in 1.0 M $Cu(NO_3)_2$ solution. Use a 1.0 M KNO_3 salt bridge.

2. Measure and record the voltage and temperature.

3. Measure and record the temperature and voltage of a cell using a 1.0 M $Pb(NO_3)_2$ solution and a lead metal strip in 0.1 M $Pb(NO_3)_2$ solution.

4. Calculate the cell potential, E_{cell}, as a function of concentration using the Nernst equation.

$$E_{cell} = E_{cell}^o - \frac{RT}{nF} \ln Q$$

In this equation, Q is the reaction quotient.

$Pb (s) + Cu^{2+} (aq) \rightarrow Cu (s) + Pb^{2+} (aq)$			
Concentration	**Cell Voltage, E_{cell}**		**Temperature**
	Measured	**Calculated**	
1.0 M $Pb(NO_3)_2$ 1.0 M $Cu(NO_3)_2$			
0.1 M $Pb(NO_3)_2$ 1.0 M $Cu(NO_3)_2$			
1.0 M $Pb(NO_3)_2$ 0.1 M $Cu(NO_3)_2$			

WASTE DISPOSAL

Dispose of all waste in the appropriate labeled waste containers in the hood.

PRE-LAB QUESTIONS

1. In Part 1 of the experiment you will study the effect of temperature on the cell potential. A $Pb^{2+} \mid Pb$ half cell is connected to a $Cu^{2+} \mid Cu$ half cell to make a galvanic cell. The concentrations of Pb^{2+} and Cu^{2+} are both 1.00 M. The reaction is carried out at 25°C.

   a) Define Galvanic cell. In a Galvanic cell, is the cell potential, E_{cell}^{0}, positive or negative?
   b) Write the reaction for the $Pb|Pb^{2+}||Cu^{2+}|Cu$ galvanic cell.
   c) What is a salt bridge? Would a galvanic cell function without the salt bridge? Explain why or why not.
   d) Small air bubbles in the salt bridge may not be a problem. How can the presence of air bubbles in the salt bridge alter the effectiveness of this salt bridge?
   e) Why is it important to clean the surface of the lead and zinc electrodes with 1 M HNO_3 immediately before using them in this experiment?

2. Calculate, E_{cell}^{0}, $\Delta G°$ and the equilibrium constant K, for the following reaction at 25°C, for 1 M solutions.

   $$Pb (s) + Cu^{2+} (aq) \rightarrow Cu(s) + Pb^{2+} (aq)$$

3. Calculate E_{cell} for the following reaction at 25,C, if $[Cu^{2+}] = 0.1$ M and $[Pb^{2+}] = 0.2$ M.

   $$Pb (s) + Cu^{2+} (aq) \rightarrow Cu(s) + Pb^{2+} (aq)$$

4. Consider the electrolytic cell constructed with two silver electrodes in 0.1 M and 1.0 M silver nitrate solutions. Will electrons flow in this cell? If so, in what direction? Label the anode and the cathode. Write the half reactions occurring at the anode and the cathode. If current flows will it ever stop? When?

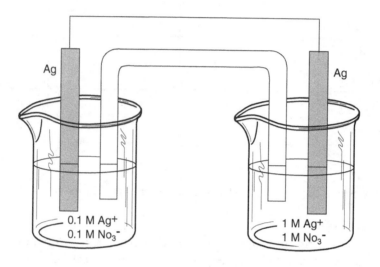

DISCUSSION QUESTIONS

Is the cell potential, $E_{cell}^{\,0}$, and the change in free energy, $\Delta G°$, strongly dependent on the temperature? In your plot of $\Delta G°$ versus T, were the points on a straight line? Compare your experimental values of $\Delta S°$, $\Delta H°$, $\Delta G°$ and K to the values of $\Delta S°$, $\Delta H°$, $\Delta G°$ and K calculated using accepted thermochemical values at 25°C. Is the reaction endothermic or exothermic?

Is the cell voltage strongly dependent on concentration? Were the differences in cell potential large enough to be accurately measured? How close were the measured and calculated cell potentials as a function of concentration? Discuss the possible and actual sources of error in this experiment. Are the errors systematic or random?

QUESTIONS

1. Consider the following cell reaction.

$$Cu\ (s)\ +\ 2\ Ag^+\ (aq)\ \rightarrow\ 2\ Ag\ (s)\ +\ Cu^{2+}\ (aq)\qquad E_{cell}^{\,0}\ =\ 0.46\ V$$

Predict if the cell potential, $E_{cell} > E_{cell}^{\,0}$ or $E_{cell} < E_{cell}^{\,0}$, for each of the following cases.
a) $[Cu^{2+}]\ =\ 2.0\ M,\ [Ag^+]\ =\ 1.0\ M$
b) $[Cu^{2+}]\ =\ 1.0\ M,\ [Ag^+]\ =\ 2.0\ M$

2. Consider the following reaction at 25°C, $[Al^{3+}] = 2.0$ M and $[Zn^{2+}] = 1.0$ M.

$$2\ Al\ (s)\ +\ 3\ Zn^{2+}\ (aq)\ \rightarrow\ 3\ Zn(s)\ +\ 2\ Al^{3+}\ (aq)$$

a) Predict if the cell potential, $E_{cell} > E_{cell}^{0}$ or $E_{cell} < E_{cell}^{0}$? Explain why.
b) Calculate E_{cell}^{0} given the half-cell reduction potentials.

$$Zn^{2+}\ (aq)\ +\ 2\ e^{-}\ \rightarrow\ Zn(s) \qquad\qquad E^{0}\ =\ -0.76\ V$$
$$Al^{3+}\ (aq)\ +\ 3\ e^{-}\ \rightarrow\ Al(s) \qquad\qquad E^{0}\ =\ -1.66\ V$$

c) How many electrons are transferred in the reaction?
d) Calculate E_{cell} for the reaction using the Nernst equation.

■ EXPERIMENT 20

22

Synthesis of Aspirin and Oil of Wintergreen

PURPOSE AND LEARNING OBJECTIVES

To synthesize and purify organic molecules and determine the purity through analytical techniques.

PRINCIPLES

Organic chemistry is the study of molecules containing the element carbon. Carbon is unique in its ability to bond to other carbon atoms in long chains and rings to make large molecules, many of which are found in biological systems. Fuels, pharmaceuticals, shampoos, perfumes, cotton, silk, are all made of organic compounds that occur naturally or are extracted from living systems. For example, ethyl alcohol is obtained from grain; soap from fats; organic dyes and drugs from plants; and urea from animal waste. Prior to the 1800s chemists believed organic compounds could only be produced in the cells of living systems. Organic compounds were thought to have some "vital force" possessed by all living things. However, in 1828, a German chemist, Freidrich Wöhler, synthesized the organic compound, urea, in the lab by heating ammonium cyanate, an inorganic compound.

$$NH_4NCO \xrightarrow{\text{heat}} H_2N{-}\overset{\displaystyle \overset{O}{\|}}{C}{-}NH_2$$

ammonium cyanate   urea

Scientists found that there is no fundamental difference between the chemistry of molecules from living sources and molecules from non-living sources.

Organic chemistry encompasses a large number of molecules with many different properties, characteristics, and reactivities. Even simple hydrocarbons (compounds that contain only the two elements carbon and hydrogen) consist of a diverse group of compounds. In spite of the incredible variety of organic compounds, organic chemistry can be understood in terms of characteristic behavior of functional groups. Functional groups are comprised of atoms that contain non-carbon atoms such as oxygen, nitrogen, sulfur, phosphorous or halogens, which are attached to a chain of carbons (the carbon backbone) or are imbedded within the carbon chain itself. They are also double or triple carbon-carbon bonds in hydrocarbons. Functional groups give a family of compounds its name and dominate the properties and reactions of these compounds. Look up examples of functional groups in a table in your text. Each type of functional group reacts in a predictable way. They are the reactive sites of organic molecules. Simple hydrocarbons with only single C–C and C–H bonds are relatively unreactive.

In this experiment, you will synthesize two organic molecules, aspirin and oil of wintergreen, via an esterification reaction. As the name suggests, esterification is the production of an ester, an organic compound with the general formula:

$$R - \overset{\displaystyle O}{\overset{\displaystyle \|}{C}} O - R' \quad \text{or simply} \quad R - COO - R'$$

where R represents either a hydrocarbon or hydrogen atom and R' represents hydrocarbons only. Esters tend to be responsible for the pleasant odor of fruits and flowers. For example, bananas contain 3-methylbutyl acetate, $CH_3COOCH_2CH(CH_3)_2$ and oranges contain octyl acetate, $CH_3COOCHCH_3C_6H_{13}$. The cosmetic industry exploits the fragrant properties of esters in the manufacture of cosmetics and perfumes. Esters are also used as flavoring agents in soft drinks.

Prior to the 1800s willow bark was chewed to relieve pain. Salicylic acid in this bark was effective in reducing pain but was found to irritate the stomach lining. Near the end of the nineteenth century (1899), the German chemical company Bayer, converted salicylic acid to the ester, acetylsalicylic acid, commonly called aspirin, an effective pain killer which is much less irritating to the stomach lining.

The functional group in an ester is the –COOR group. In esterification reactions, a compound containing a hydroxyl group (–OH) reacts with a compound containing a carboxylic acid group (–COOH). This reaction is catalyzed with a strong acid, H_2SO_4.

salicylic acid   +   acetic acid   ⇌   acetylsalicylic acid (aspirin)   Water

The reaction of salicylic acid and acetic acid to produce aspirin is slow and does not go to completion. Instead, an equilibrium mixture of the reactants and products is produced. In the reverse reaction, aspirin reacts with water to produce salicylic acid and acetic acid. You can detect the odor of the acetic acid (like that of vinegar) when aspirin is exposed to moisture.

In this experiment, acetic anhydride is used instead of acetic acid to drive the reaction to completion. Combining two acetic acid molecules and eliminating water produces acetic anhydride. Because no water is produced in the reaction of salicylic acid and acetic anhydride, the reverse reaction will not occur and significantly more aspirin will be produced.

salicylic acid   +   acetic anhydride   →   acetylsalicylic acid (aspirin)   +   acetic acid

In this experiment, you will also synthesize oil of wintergreen, methyl salicylate. Oil of wintergreen has the odor and flavor of spearmint. It can be used as an ointment because it penetrates the skin and produces heat to relieve aching muscles.

salicylic acid   + CH_3OH methanol   ⇌   methyl salicylate   + H_2O water

Equilibrium will be established and because there is no simple alternative to methanol to force the reaction to go to completion, the product yield of oil of wintergreen is maximized by adding an excess of methanol. Excess methanol drives the equilibrium to the right as predicted by Le Chatelier's Principle.

An important characteristic of salicylic acid is its bifunctionality, meaning it has two different functional groups. In the reaction to synthesize aspirin, the alcohol group on the salicylic acid reacts with a carboxylic acid to form the ester, whereas in the production of wintergreen oil, the carboxylic acid on the salicylic acid reacts with an alcohol to form an ester. This is a good example of the reactivities and properties of different functional groups.

The Purity Test and Recrystallization

In the synthesis of aspirin and oil of wintergreen, the products are relatively impure. The main impurities are unreacted salicylic acid and acetic acid. The acetic acid is soluble in water and rinsing the aspirin removes the acetic acid. Dealing with the unreacted salicylic acid is more complicated. Like aspirin, salicylic acid is a solid that is insoluble in water. In order to determine if salicylic acid is present in your aspirin, a 1% $FeCl_3$ solution is added as a purity test. Three salicylic acid molecules coordinate to the iron (III) ion to produce a brightly colored magenta complex.

salicylic acid

Phenols are a family of compounds with a hydroxyl group (–OH) attached to an aromatic ring (benzene, C_6H_6). These compounds are known to react with metal ions to form colored complexes. The hydroxyl group in the salicylic acid is the reactive site necessary to produce the magenta colored complex with the iron. Aspirin does not have a hydroxyl group and therefore will not complex with the iron.

Once salicylic acid is detected in the product, what can we do to remove it? In organic chemistry a number of methods have been developed to isolate the desired product. One of the most common methods utilizes differences in solubility of the components of the crude mixture to isolate the desired product. The crude mixture is dissolved in a warm solvent in which one of the components is more soluble. The solution is cooled and the less soluble component crystallizes out of the solution and the more soluble component remains in solution. The compounds can then be separated by filtration. This technique is known as **recrystallization**. In this experiment you will recrystallize the aspirin by dissolving the crude product in warm ethanol. As the solution is cooled, the salicylic acid will remain in solution while aspirin recrystallizes.

Melting Point and Back-Titration of Aspirin

A common method for identifying an organic molecule is by measuring its melting point, T_m. Every molecule has a unique temperature range, $T_m \pm 1°C$, in which it changes from a solid to a liquid at a given pressure. This is called the melting point. If the melting point of a compound has been determined experimentally, scientists use the known value as a means to characterize a synthesized substance. If a new molecule is synthesized the melting point is determined and recorded for future reference. The melting point of the aspirin synthesized in this laboratory will be compared to the known melting point of acetylsalicylic acid, 135°C, to ensure the correct molecule was synthesized.

The melting point can also be used to check for the presence of impurities. If a sample is not entirely pure, the melting point will be lower and the temperature range at which it melts will be larger. The melting point of the sample will be lower, if an impurity is present, due to freezing point depression.

In the last part of this experiment, you will test the purity of your aspirin in the recrystallized and crude products. Impurities such as salicylic acid and acetic acid are likely to be present. At low temperature the acetylsalicylic acid (the aspirin) can be neutralized according to the above reaction.

The quantity of aspirin in the sample could be determined by titrating the sample with a base. However, the base will also neutralize any acid impurities. From this titration, the total moles of acid in the sample would be determined.

In order to determine the amount of acetylsalicylic acid in the sample we take advantage of a hydrolysis reaction, which is observed only for the neutralized acetylsalicylic acid at elevated temperatures.

According to this reaction, once all the acid in the sample is neutralized, additional base will hydrolyze the acetylsalicylic acid. This process is reasonably fast at elevated temperatures. This reaction is the reverse of esterification and is referred to as saponification of esters or base-promoted hydrolysis.

You will add excess base to ensure the hydrolysis process is complete. This is necessary because there is no physical change that takes place to indicate hydrolysis is complete. Because you know the amount of base added, back-titration with hydrochloric acid will allow you to determine the amount of excess base in the solution. Once this back titration is performed you can calculate the amount of base required for the hydrolysis and from the reaction stoichiometry, the amount of aspirin in the sample is determined.

In the back-titration with HCl, it is assumed that the products formed in the hydrolysis reaction, the acetate and salicylate, do not compete effectively with the OH^- for protons. For a strong acid, strong base titration, the equivalence point is at pH = 7. At pH = 7, $[H^+] = 1 \times 10^{-7}$. Consider the acid ionization constant, K_a, of acetic acid.

$$CH_3COOH \ (aq) \ \rightleftharpoons \ H^+ \ (aq) + CH_3COO^- \ (aq) \qquad\qquad K_a = 1.76 \times 10^{-5}$$

$$K_a = \frac{[H^+][CH_3COO^-]}{[CH_3COOH]}$$

$$\frac{[CH_3COO^-]}{[CH_3COOH]} = \frac{K_a}{[H^+]} = \frac{1.76 \times 10^{-5}}{1 \times 10^{-7}} = 176$$

The ratio of the acetate ion to acetic acid is 176 to 1 at pH = 7. Thus, only 1 of 176 acetate ions in solution will have accepted a proton when all of the OH^- is neutralized. For salicylic acid, $K_a = 1.06 \times 10^{-3}$, and this ratio is 10,600. It is therefore reasonable to assume that the acetate and salicylate do not compete effectively with the OH^- for protons.

Example Calculation

A 0.425g sample of recrystallized aspirin is titrated with 38.6 mL of a 0.106 M NaOH solution.

$$(38.6 \text{ mL NaOH})(0.106 \text{ M NaOH}) = 4.09 \text{ mmol NaOH}$$

An additional 25.0 mL of 0.106 M NaOH solution was added to the sample to hydrolyze the neutralized acid. The excess base was back-titrated with 11.1 mL of 0.0998 M HCl solution.

$$(25.0 \text{ mL NaOH})(0.106 \text{ M NaOH}) = 2.65 \text{ mmol NaOH}$$

$$(11.1 \text{ mL HCl})(0.0998 \text{ M HCl}) = 1.11 \text{ mmol HCl}$$

The mmoles of HCl used in the back-titration is equal to the mmole of excess base that was added to ensure hydrolysis was complete.

$$\text{mmol HCl} = \text{mmol excess NaOH} = 1.1 \text{ mmol NaOH}$$

To determine how much base was needed for the hydrolysis process itself, the mmoles of excess base determined by the back-titration is subtracted from the total mmoles of base used for the hydrolysis process.

$$2.65 \text{ mmole NaOH} - 1.11 \text{ mmole NaOH} = 1.54 \text{ mmole NaOH}$$

Thus, 1.54 mmoles of NaOH was needed to complete the hydrolysis process and this corresponds to the mmoles of acetylsalicylic acid (aspirin) in the sample.

$$1.54 \text{ mmol aspirin}$$

The mass of the aspirin can be calculated using its molecular weight, 180.2 g/mol.

$$\text{Mass of aspirin in sample} = (1.54 \text{ mmol})(180.2 \text{ mg/mmol}) = 278 \text{ mg}$$

The percent aspirin in the sample is calculated relative to the total mass of the sample.

$$\frac{278 \text{ mg}}{425 \text{ mg}} \times 100\% = 65.4\%$$

The product obtained from the reaction only contains 65.4% aspirin. Recrystallization would be necessary to increase the purity of this sample. You definitely do not want to ingest this sample.

CHEMICALS:

WEEK 1

5 g salicylic acid
6 mL acetic anhydride
5 mL methyl alcohol
1% $FeCl_3$ solution
50 mL 95% ethanol
Ice

WEEK 2

Generic Aspirin
2.4 g potassium hydrogen phthalate
6 M NaOH
0.1 M HCl, standardized
95 % ethanol
Phenolphthalein indicator
Boiling Chips

SAFETY
WEAR SAFETY GLASSES

Concentrated sulfuric acid and acetic anhydride can cause **severe chemical burns**. In case
of contact with skin, rinse immediately with copious amounts of water. Many of the chemicals
used in this laboratory are flammable. **Extreme caution should be used when using any
open flame.**

PROCEDURE

This is a two-week experiment. You will work with a partner. Parts 1-4 are completed the first
week of lab. The analysis of aspirin will be performed the second week.

Part 1. Synthesis of Aspirin (Week 1)

1. Weigh 2-3 grams of salicylic acid and record the weight to the nearest 0.001 g in your
    notebook. Place the salicylic acid in a 125-mL Erlenmeyer flask.

2. Carefully add 5 mL of acetic anhydride to the flask. Add 5 drops of concentrated sulfuric
    acid. Cautiously swirl the flask to mix the reagents.

3. Using a Bunsen burner, heat approximately 250 mL of water in a 400-mL beaker to ap-
    proximately 85°C. Place the flask in the beaker and secure the flask to the ring stand using
    a clamp. Heat the solution for 25 minutes. Be very careful with an open flame because
    many of the chemicals used in this lab are flammable.

4. Turn off the Bunsen burner and carefully add 2 mL of DI water to the flask. This will react
    with any excess acetic anhydride to produce acetic acid. Avoid breathing in the hot acetic
    acid vapor.

5. Allow the reaction to cool to approximately 45°C. Add 30 mL of DI water to the flask and
    swirl. Crystals should form.

6. Place the flask in an ice bath for 30 minutes to ensure complete crystallization. While you are waiting, do Part 5.

7. Set up a vacuum filter flask with a rubber adapter, Buchner funnel, filter paper, and a piece of tubing. Remove the flask from the ice bath and filter the crystals using the vacuum filter. Rinse the crystals with three 5 mL portions of cold DI water. Allow suction to continue for a few minutes to help dry the aspirin crystals.

8. Weigh and record the product in the tables above. The density of acetic anhydride is 1.082 g/mL.

Chemical	Salicylic acid	Acetic anhydride	Aceylsalicylic acid	Acetic acid
Molecular Formula				
Molar Mass (g/mol)				
Mass (g)				
Moles				

9. Calculate the percent yield of the crude product.

Part 2. Purity Test (Week 1)

1. Clean and dry two medium test tubes.

2. To one test tube, add a few crystals of your product and label the tube. To the other test tube, add a few crystals of salicylic acid and label it.

3. Add 5 mL of DI water and a drop of 1% $FeCl_3$ solution to each test tube. Record you observations.

Part 3. Recrystallization of Aspirin (Week 1)

1. Obtain two vials and caps. Put half of the product in one of the vials and label it CRUDE. Put this in your lab drawer for analysis next week.

2. Weigh the other half of your product. Place it in a small Erlenmeyer flask.

3. Heat 5-10 mL of 95% ethanol in a hot water bath. CAUTION: Ethanol is flammable. The boiling point of ethanol is 78°C, so make sure the water bath does not boil. The ethanol should be around 60°C. Add the warm ethanol drop wise to the crude product in the Erlenmeyer flask. Add just enough ethanol to dissolve the solid.

4. Heat the flask in a warm water bath for a few minutes.

5. When all of the aspirin has dissolved, add approximately 20 mL of 50°C water. Swirl the flask. If crystals form at this point, warm the solution in the hot water bath until the crystals dissolve.

6. Put a watch glass over the flask and let the solution cool slowly to room temperature. If crystals do not form after the flask has reached room temperature, scratch the inside wall of the flask to initiate crystal formation.

7. After crystals begin to form allow the flask to sit undisturbed for an extra 20 minutes to ensure complete crystallization.

8. Filter the crystals using a vacuum filter and Buchner funnel.

9. Weigh and record the mass of the product. Calculate the percent yield of the recrystallization.

10. Put this product in the other vial and label it PURIFIED. Put it in your lab drawer for analysis next week.

Part 4. Melting Point Determination (Week 1 or Week 2)
1. Obtain two capillary tubes, a watch glass and a spatula.

2. Put approximately 25 mg of the **dry** crude product in a small pile on a watch glass.

3. Push the open end of the capillary tube through the sample. Press some of the solid into the top of the capillary tube with the help of the spatula. The tube should only be filled with 2-3 mm of sample.

4. The tube is very narrow so the solid will probably need to be forced to the bottom. This can be done by shaking the tube, gently tapping the tube on the benchtop, or dropping the tube through a hollow piece of tubing onto the bench top.

5. Check the temperature of the melting point apparatus. **Be careful it may be hot.** Do not put your sample in the apparatus unless the temperature is less than 85°C. The sample needs sufficient time to come to equilibrium with the temperature of the melting point apparatus.

6. Place the packed capillary tube in the melting point apparatus. This apparatus can hold 3 capillary tubes and should be used as efficiently as possible.

7. The volt dial should be turned on low to ensure the temperature increases approximately 1-2°C/min. If the temperature is increased at a faster rate the melting point range will be too wide because the crystals will not be able to reach thermal equilibrium.

8. Record the temperature as soon as the crystals begin to liquefy. Then record the temperature when all of the crystals have melted. This is the melting point of the product.

9. Repeat this for the purified product.

Part 5. Synthesis of Methyl Salicylate (Week 1)

1. In a large test tube, place 1 gram of salicylic acid and 5 mL of methanol. Add 3 drops of concentrated sulfuric acid.

2. Place the test tube in a 70°C water bath for 15 minutes. The boiling point of methanol is 65°C. Some of the methanol may boil off; add more methanol to the test tube, keeping the solution level constant while heating. Take caution when adding the methanol because it is flammable.

3. Remove the solution from the water bath and let it cool to room temperature.

4. Add a drop of 1% $FeCl_3$ solution to the test tube and record your observations.

Part 6. Standardization of NaOH Solution (Week 2)

1. Weigh and record three samples of potassium hydrogen phthalate (KHP) between 0.4 and 0.6 g to the nearest 0.001 g. Put the samples in three separate, labeled Erlenmeyer flasks, indicate the mass of KHP on each flask. Add 50.0 mL of DI water to each flask.

2. Warm the KHP solutions with a low flame Bunsen burner until the KHP is completely dissolved. **Do not boil the KHP solutions.** Let solutions cool to room temperature.

3. In a 500-mL Erlenmeyer flask, prepare 400.0 mL of 0.1 M NaOH solution starting from 6 M NaOH. Calculate the amount of 6 M NaOH needed to prepare this solution. The volume of the NaOH solution does not have to be known too accurately because this solution will be titrated to determine the exact concentration. Stopper the flask.

    NOTE: The NaOH solution must be stopstoppered when not in use because the NaOH slowly reacts with CO_2 (g) in the air to produce carbonic acid, H_2CO_3.

    $$CO_2 \text{ (g)} + H_2O \text{ (l)} \quad \rightarrow \quad H_2CO_3 \text{ (aq)}$$

The carbonic acid dissociates to increase the hydrogen ion, H^+, concentration in solution.

$$H_2CO_3 \text{ (aq)} \rightleftharpoons HCO_3^- \text{ (aq)} + H^+ \text{ (aq)}$$

$$HCO_3^- \text{ (aq)} \rightleftharpoons CO_3^{2-} \text{ (aq)} + H^+ \text{ (aq)}$$

H^+ (aq) reacts with OH^- (aq) in solution, decreasing the concentration of OH^-, which would affect the end point in the titration.

$$H^+ \text{ (aq)} + OH^- \text{ (aq)} \rightarrow H_2O \text{ (l)}$$

4. Clean a 50.0 mL burette with soap and water. Do a final rinse of the burette with DI water. Make sure to run water through the tip of the burette. If the burette is clean, water runs uniformly down the burette without adhering to the glass.

5. Rinse the burette with two 5 mL portions of the 0.1 M NaOH solution. Drain some of the NaOH through the tip.

6. Fill the burette with the NaOH solution to the zero mark or below the zero mark. If the burette is filled beyond the zero mark drain some of the solution into an empty 600-mL beaker (this beaker will be your waste beaker for the remainder of this experiment). To make sure there are no air bubbles in the tip, briefly open the stopcock to drain some of the solution through the tip and into your waste beaker.

7. Allow the solution to sit for a minute to let the liquid settle in the burette. Read and record the initial volume of the NaOH in the burette.

8. Select one of the flasks containing KHP. Record the mass of KHP in your notebook.

9. Add two drops of phenolphthalein to the KHP solution and swirl it.

10. Slowly titrate the KHP solution with sodium hydroxide solution while gently swirling the flask. As the NaOH solution is added, a pink color will appear in the KHP solution. When the KHP solution is swirled the color disappears. As the end point is approached, the pink disappears more slowly, at which point the base should be added drop wise until the solution remains pink when swirled. A single drop can be sufficient to reach the end point. Remove any hanging drops from the burette tip by rinsing the tip with DI water into the flask, using a squirt bottle.

11. Once the end point is reached, record the final volume of the NaOH solution in the burette.

12. Repeat steps 6-11 for the other two KHP samples. At least two of the NaOH concentrations determined have to be the same within 1.0 % (in the table above).

13. Calculate the molarity of NaOH for each of the trials.

Data	Trial 1	Trial 2	Trial 3
Mass of KHP			
Moles of KHP			
Initial Burette Volume NaOH (mL)			
Final Burette Volume NaOH (mL)			
Total Volume of NaOH used in titration (mL)			
Moles of NaOH			
Molarity of NaOH (mol/L)			

14. Calculate the average molarity and the average deviation.

Part 7. Aspirin Analysis (Week 2)

1. Weigh to the nearest milligram 0.5 g of your crude aspirin product. Put it in a 250-mL Erlenmeyer flask.

2. Clean, dry, and set up two burettes. One burette is for hydrochloric acid and the other for sodium hydroxide. Label the burettes and rinse one with standardized 0.1 M HCl and the other with standardized 0.1 M NaOH.

3. Chill approximately 25 mL of 95% ethanol to about 15°C. Add the chilled ethanol to the aspirin in the Erlenmeyer flask. Swirl the flask to dissolve the aspirin. If some aspirin does not dissolve, the remainder will dissolve as you titrate the solution with NaOH.

4. Add 2 drops of phenolphthalein to the solution and titrate immediately with standardized 0.1 M NaOH solution until a faint pink end point is reached (be sure to record the initial and final volume of NaOH). Calculate the volume of NaOH used.

5. To hydrolyze the acetylsalicylic acid, add an additional 15 mL of the standardized 0.1 M NaOH solution from the burette. If you refill the burette be sure to record the initial volume.

6. Heat the flask in a boiling water bath for 15 minutes. Swirl the flask periodically.

7. Remove the flask from the water bath and cool it to room temperature in cold tap water or an ice bath. Do not let any water get in the flask. If the solution is not pink add an additional 10 mL of 0.1 M NaOH. Be sure to include this additional NaOH when you record the total volume of NaOH used.

8. Back titrate the excess NaOH with standardized 0.1 M HCl solution until the pink has disappeared. Record the volume of HCl used.

Data	Crude Aspirin Sample 1	Crude Aspirin Sample 2	Pure Aspirin Sample 1	Pure Aspirin Sample 2
Mass of aspirin sample				
Initial Burette Volume NaOH (mL)				
Final Burette Volume NaOH (mL)				
Total Volume of NaOH titrated (mL)				
Molarity of standardized NaOH (mol/L)				
Moles of NaOH titrated (mmoles)				
Volume of NaOH for hydrolysis (mL)				
Moles of NaOH hydrolysis (mmoles)				
Initial Burette Volume HCl (mL)				
Final Burette Volume HCl (mL)				
Total Volume of HCl titrated (mL)				
Moles of HCl (mmoles)				
Moles of Aspirin (mmoles)				
Mass of Aspirin in Sample (g)				
Percent Aspirin in Sample				

9. Repeat this procedure with another sample of crude product and two samples of purified product.

WASTE DISPOSAL

Dispose of all waste in the appropriately labeled waste bottle in the hood.

PRE-LAB QUESTIONS

1. In Part 1 of this experiment, you will synthesize aspirin.

   a) Salicylic acid reacts with acetic acid to produce aspirin and water. Write the balanced equation for this reaction showing the structures of the reactants and products.
   b) Identify and name each of the functional groups in salicylic acid, acetic acid and aspirin.
   c) Why is acetic anhydride used instead of acetic acid in the synthesis of aspirin?
   d) Calculate the molecular weight of salicylic acid, acetic anhydride, acetic acid, and acetylsalicylic acid. Enter these values in the table in Part 1.

2. Draw the structure for each of the following functional groups:

   a) carboxylic acid
   b) alcohol
   c) aldehyde
   d) ketone
   e) ester

3. Draw the structure of two esters with the molecular formula $C_3H_6O_2$.

4. In Part 2 of this experiment you will test for the purity of the aspirin.

   a) What are the main impurities expected in the crude aspirin synthesized?
   b) Which of the expected impurities can be removed? How?
   c) What test is done to determine if unreacted salicylic acid is present in the crude aspirin product?
   d) Why is it difficult to remove the unreacted salicylic acid from the aspirin?
   e) How will we test for the presence of phenols? What will be observed?

5. In Part 3, aspirin is recrystallized.

   a) What is the purpose of recrystallizing the aspirin? How does it work?
   b) Ethanol is used as a solvent in the recrystallization process. What temperature will the ethanol be warmed to and why should the temperature be below the boiling point of ethanol?

■ EXPERIMENT 22

6. You will determine the melting point of the crude and purified aspirin.

    a) What is the purpose of determining the melting point for the crude and recrystallized aspirin? What is the known melting point for pure aspirin?

    b) Why must you wait until the melting apparatus is below 85°C?

    c) Why is it important to have the voltage dial set to low?

    d) You will record the temperature at which the aspirin crystals just start to melt and the temperature when all the crystals have melted. Do you expect a larger range in temperature for the crude or recrystallized aspirin? Explain your answer.

NOTE: The melting apparatus holds three capillary tubes at once. The most efficient way to use the apparatus is to have two or three samples of aspirin tested at once. Waiting for the apparatus to cool down takes time.

7. Salicylic acid reacts with methanol to produce methyl salicylate and water.

    a) Write the balanced equation for this reaction showing the structures for the reactants and products.

    b) Identify and name the functional groups in methyl salicylate.

    c) Does this reaction go to completion? How can we maximize the product yield?

    d) In the presence of an acid catalyst, salicylic acid reacts with methanol to produce oil of wintergreen and water. If water is added to the solution, a precipitate is formed. Identify the precipitate and explain why it is formed.

8. a) Write the balanced equation for the neutralization reaction of acetylsalicylic acid.

    b) If this reaction were carried out at elevated temperatures, what other reaction may occur? Write the balanced equation for this reaction.

9. What volume of 0.1 M NaOH would be required to neutralize 0.5 g of aspirin?

DISCUSSION QUESTIONS

Write the balanced equation for the synthesis of aspirin. Which reactant was the limiting reagent? What was the percent yield of acetylsalicylic acid? Discuss the possible sources of error in the synthesis of aspirin.

How pure was the crude product? How pure was the recrystallized product? Was the recrystallization process effective? Discuss the possible sources of error associated with the recrystallization process and the analysis of the products?

QUESTIONS

1. The synthesized aspirin was washed with cold water. Why is it better to use cold rather than hot water?

2. If $FeCl_3$ is added to oil of wintergreen would a color change be observed? Explain why or why not.

3. Explain how a percent yield of aspirin, greater than 100%, can be obtained.

4. Complete each of the following reactions by drawing the structures of the products.

a) 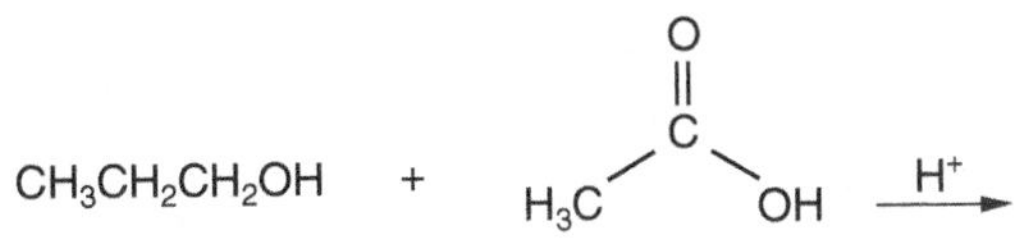 $CH_3CH_2CH_2OH$ + $\xrightarrow{H^+}$

b) 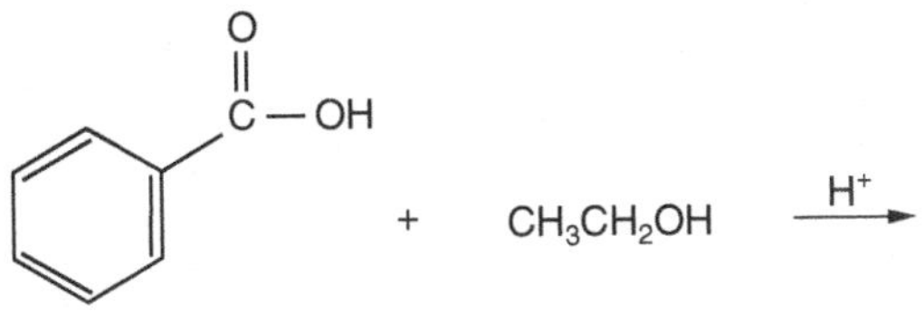   + CH_3CH_2OH $\xrightarrow{H^+}$

c) $CH_3CH_2CH_2OH$ + CH_3CH_2COOH $\xrightarrow{H^+}$

5. Novocain is a local anesthetic that is made by an esterification reaction. Given the structure of Novocain, draw the structures of the alcohol and carboxylic acid that would react to produce Novocain.

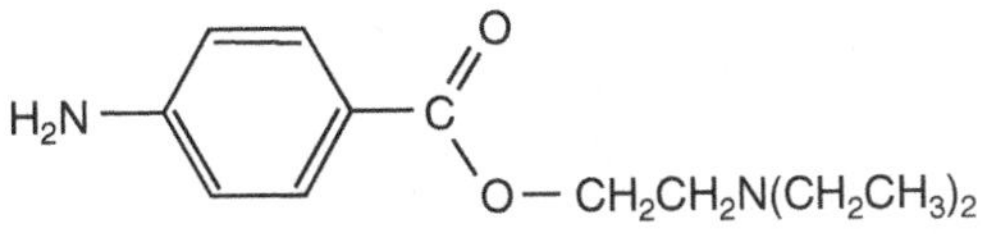

Novocain

6. The legal blood alcohol content (BAC) in California is 0.08% by mass. Blood samples are titrated with $K_2Cr_2O_7$ to determine the alcohol content according to the following reaction.

$$6\,CH_3CH_2OH + 4\,K_2Cr_2O_7 + 16\,H_2SO_4 \rightarrow 6\,CH_3COOH + 4\,Cr_2(SO_4)_3 + 4\,K_2SO_4 + 22\,H_2O$$

In this reaction, the chromium is reduced, from Cr^{6+} to Cr^{3+}, causing a color change in the solution, signaling the end-point. Determine the mass percent ethanol in a 50.0 g blood sample, if the sample required 25.6 mL of 0.05 M $K_2Cr_2O_7$ to react completely with all the ethanol. Was this person intoxicated above the legal limit?

■ **EXPERIMENT 22**

APPENDIX 1 - SOLUBILITIES OF IONIC COMPOUNDS IN WATER

Anions	Soluble*	Slightly Soluble*	Insoluble*
NO_3^- nitrate	All	—	—
CH_3COO^- acetate	Most	—	$Be(CH_3COO)_2$
ClO_3^- chlorate	All	—	—
ClO_4^- perchlorate	Most	$KClO_4$	—
SO_4^{2-} sulfate	Most	$CaSO_4$, Ag_2SO_4	$BaSO_4$, $SrSO_4$, $PbSO_4$, Hg_2SO_4
Cl^- chloride	Most	$PbCl_2$	$AgCl$, Hg_2Cl_2
Br^- bromide	Most	$PbBr_2$, $HgBr_2$	$AgBr$, Hg_2Br_2
I^- iodide	Most	—	AgI, Hg_2I_2, PbI_2, HgI_2
F^- fluoride	Group I, AgF, BeF_2	SrF_2, BaF_2, PbF_2	MgF_2, CaF_2
OH^- hydroxide	Group I, $Ba(OH)_2$, NH_4OH	$Sr(OH)_2$, $Ca(OH)_2$	Most
PO_4^{3-} phosphate	Group I, $(NH_4)_3PO_4$	—	Most
SO_3^{2-} sulfite	Group I, $(NH_4)_2SO_3$	—	Most
CO_3^{2-} carbonate	Group I, $(NH_4)_2CO_3$	—	Most
S^{2-} sulfide	Group I and II, $(NH_4)_2S$	—	Most

Soluble: dissolves to the extent of > 10 g/L **Slightly Soluble:** 0.1 to 10 g/L **Insoluble:** < 0.1 g/L

■ APPENDIX 1

APPENDIX 2 - VAPOR PRESSURE OF WATER AT SELECTED TEMPERATURES

Degrees Centigrade	Vapor Pressure (torr)	Degrees Centigrade	Vapor Pressure (torr)
-10	2.149	30	31.824
-5	3.163	35	42.175
0	4.570	40	55.320
5	6.543	45	71.881
10	9.209	50	92.510
15	12.788	55	118.04
16	13.634	60	149.38
17	14.530	65	187.54
18	15.477	70	233.7
19	16.477	75	289.1
20	17.535	80	355.1
21	18.650	85	433.6
22	19.827	90	525.8
23	21.068	95	633.9
24	22.377	100	760.00
25	23.756	125	1740
26	25.209	150	3570
27	26.739	175	6694
28	28.349	200	11659
29	30.043	300	64432

■ APPENDIX 2

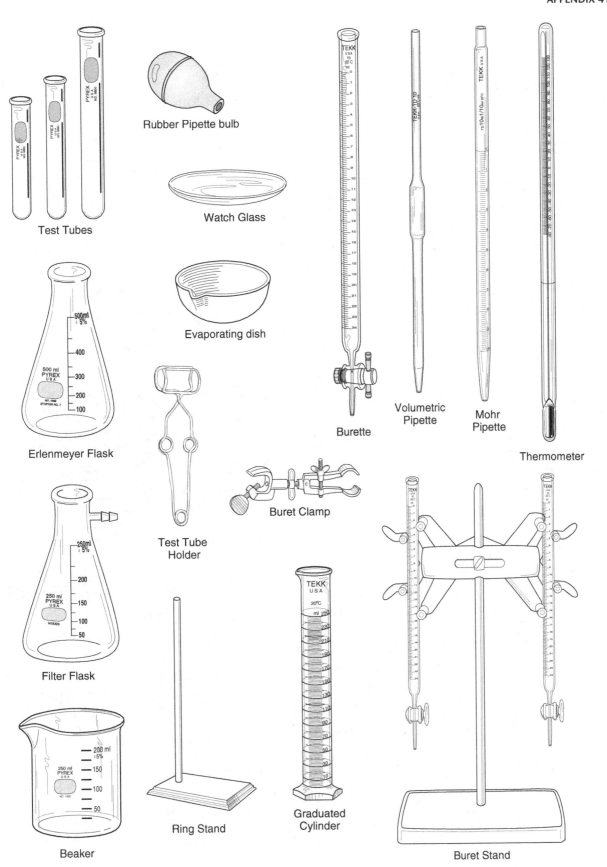

Test Tubes

Rubber Pipette bulb

Watch Glass

Evaporating dish

Burette

Volumetric Pipette

Mohr Pipette

Thermometer

Erlenmeyer Flask

Test Tube Holder

Buret Clamp

Filter Flask

Ring Stand

Graduated Cylinder

Buret Stand

Beaker

■ APPENDIX 4

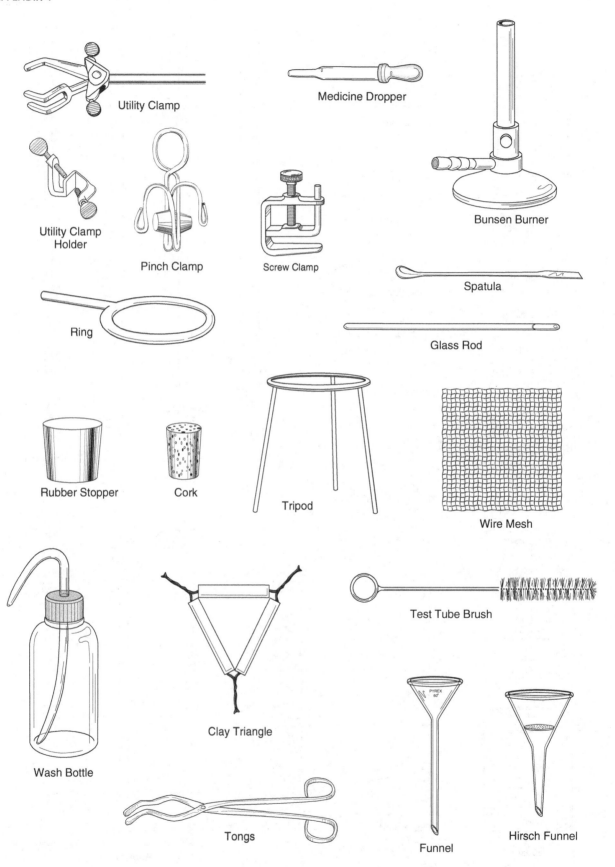

Utility Clamp

Medicine Dropper

Bunsen Burner

Utility Clamp
Holder

Pinch Clamp

Screw Clamp

Spatula

Ring

Glass Rod

Rubber Stopper

Cork

Tripod

Wire Mesh

Wash Bottle

Clay Triangle

Test Tube Brush

Tongs

Funnel

Hirsch Funnel

APPENDIX 5 - IONIZATION CONSTANTS OF ACIDS IN AQUEOUS SOLUTION AT 25°C

Acid	HA	A⁻	K_a	pK_a	Acid	Conjugate Base
Hydriodic	HI	I⁻				
Hydrobromic	HBr	Br⁻				
Perchloric	$HClO_4$	ClO_4^-				
Hydrochloric	HCl	Cl⁻				
Chloric	$HClO_3$	ClO_3^-				
Sulfuric (1)	H_2SO_4	HSO_4^-				
Nitric	HNO_3	NO_3^-				
Hydronium ion	**H_3O^+**	**H_2O**	**1**	**0.0**		
Iodic	HIO_3	IO_3^-	1.6×10^{-1}	0.80	Increase in	Increase in
Oxalic (1)	$H_2C_2O_4$	$HC_2O_4^-$	5.9×10^{-2}	1.23	Acid Strength	Base Strength
Sulfurous (1)	H_2SO_3	HSO_3^-	1.54×10^{-2}	1.81		
Sulfuric (2)	HSO_4^-	SO_4^{2-}	1.2×10^{-2}	1.92		
Chlorous	$HClO_2$	ClO_2^-	1.1×10^{-2}	1.96		
Phosphoric (1)	H_3PO_4	$H_2PO_4^-$	7.52×10^{-3}	2.12		
Arsenic (1)	H_3AsO_4	$H_2AsO_4^-$	5.0×10^{-3}	2.30		
Chloroacetic	$CH_2ClCOOH$	CH_2ClCOO^-	1.4×10^{-3}	2.85		
Hydrofluoric	HF	F⁻	6.6×10^{-4}	3.18	HF	F⁻
Nitrous	HNO_2	NO_2^-	4.6×10^{-4}	3.34	Moderately	Very Weak
Formic	HCOOH	HCOO⁻	1.77×10^{-4}	3.75	Weak Acid	Base
Benzoic	C_6H_5COOH	$C_6H_5COO^-$	6.46×10^{-5}	4.19		
Oxalic (2)	$HC_2O_4^-$	$C_2O_4^{2-}$	6.4×10^{-5}	4.19		
Hydrazoic	HN_3	N_3^-	1.9×10^{-5}	4.72		
Acetic	CH_3COOH	CH_3COO^-	1.76×10^{-5}	4.75		
Propionic Acid	CH_3CH_2COOH	$CH_3CH_2COO^-$	1.34×10^{-5}	4.87		
Pyridinium ion	$HC_5H_5N^+$	C_5H_5N	5.6×10^{-6}	5.25		
Carbonic (1)	H_2CO_3	HCO_3^-	4.3×10^{-7}	6.37		
Sulfurous (1)	HSO_3^-	SO_3^{2-}	1.02×10^{-7}	6.91		
Arsenic (2)	$H_2AsO_4^-$	$HAsO_4^{2-}$	9.3×10^{-8}	7.03		
Hydrosulfuric	H_2S	HS⁻	9.1×10^{-8}	7.04		
Phosphoric (2)	$H_2PO_4^-$	HPO_4^{2-}	6.23×10^{-8}	7.21		
Hypochlorous	HClO	ClO⁻	3.0×10^{-8}	7.53		
Hydrocyanic	HCN	CN⁻	6.17×10^{-10}	9.21		
Ammonium ion	NH_4^+	NH_3	5.6×10^{-10}	9.25		
Phenol	HOC_6H_5	$OC_6H_5^-$	1.6×10^{-10}	9.80	Very Weak	Moderately
Carbonic (2)	HCO_3^-	CO_3^{2-}	4.8×10^{-11}	10.32	Acid	Weak Base
Arsenic (3)	$HAsO_4^{2-}$	AsO_4^{3-}	3.0×10^{-12}	11.53		
Hydrogen Peroxide	H_2O_2	HO_2^-	2.4×10^{-12}	11.62		
Phosphoric (3)	HPO_4^{2-}	PO_4^{3-}	2.2×10^{-13}	12.67		
Water	**H_2O**	**OH⁻**	**1.0×10^{-14}**	**14.00**	H_2O	OH⁻
					Ineffective Acid	Strong Base

Note: *Strong Acids Dissociate Completely to form Ions in Aqueous Solution. Conjugate Bases of Strong Acids are Ineffective as a Base* (applies to the first seven acids).

$pK_a = -\log K_a$

$pH = -\log [H^+]$

$K_w = 1 \times 10^{-14}$ at 25°C

$pH = pK_a + \log ([A^-]/[HA])$

$[H^+] = 10^{-pH}$

$K_w = [OH^-][H^+]$

$K_w = K_a K_b$

■ APPENDIX 5

MHEonline.com

Send all inquiries to:
McGraw-Hill Education
8787 Orion Place
Columbus, OH 43240

ISBN: 978-0-02-684749-0
MHID: 0-02-684749-3

Printed in the United States of America.

22 23 24 25 26 27 QVS 22 21 20 19 18

SRA
Reasoning and Writing

Workbook 1

Level A

Siegfried Engelmann

Ann Brown Arbogast

Karen Lou Seitz Davis

McGraw Hill Education

A.

5☐ 9☐ 4☐ 1☐ 6☐ 2☐

B.

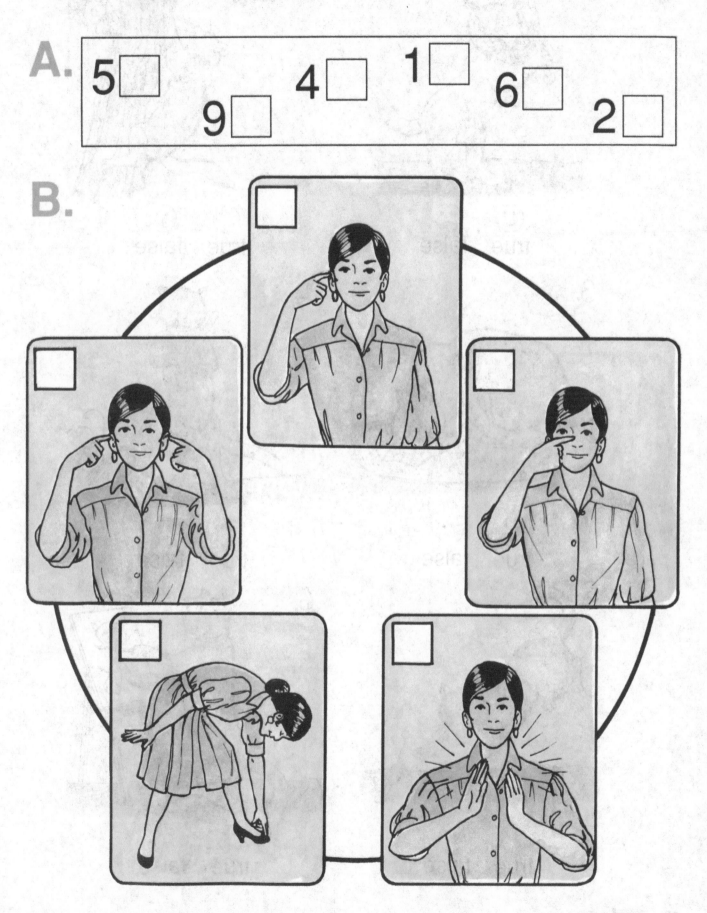

C.

1. true false

2. true false

3. true false

4. true false

5. true false

6. true false

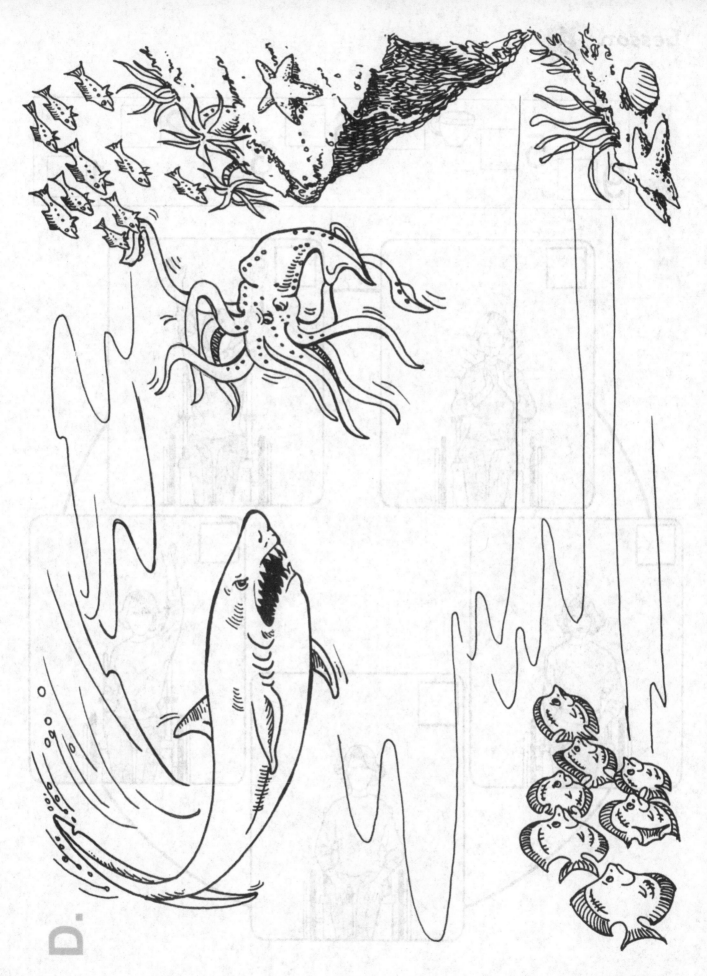

D.

A.

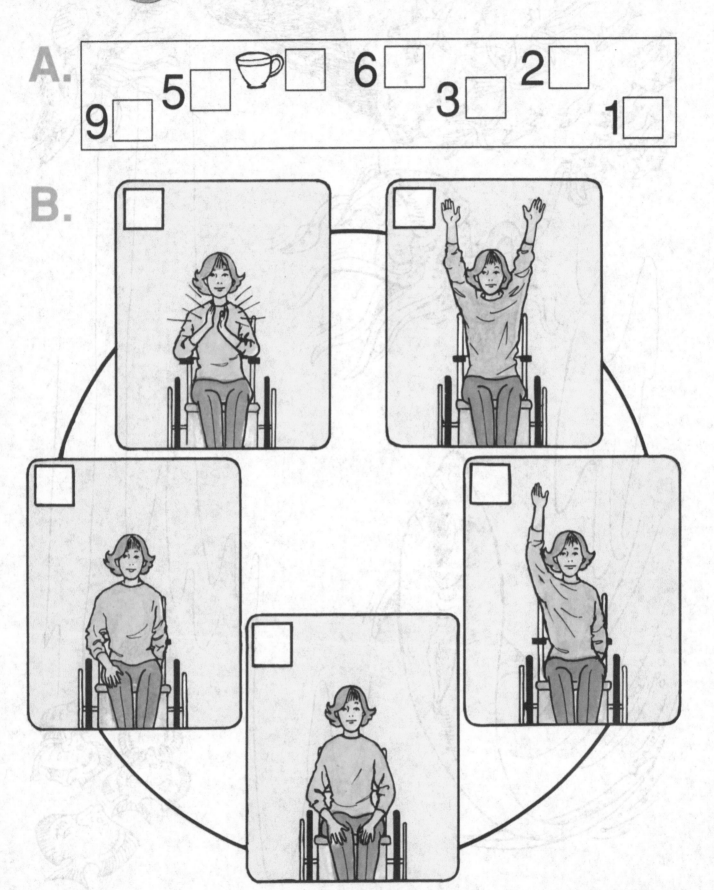

B.

C.

1. true false

2. true false

3. true false

4. true false

5. true false

6. true false

D.

E.

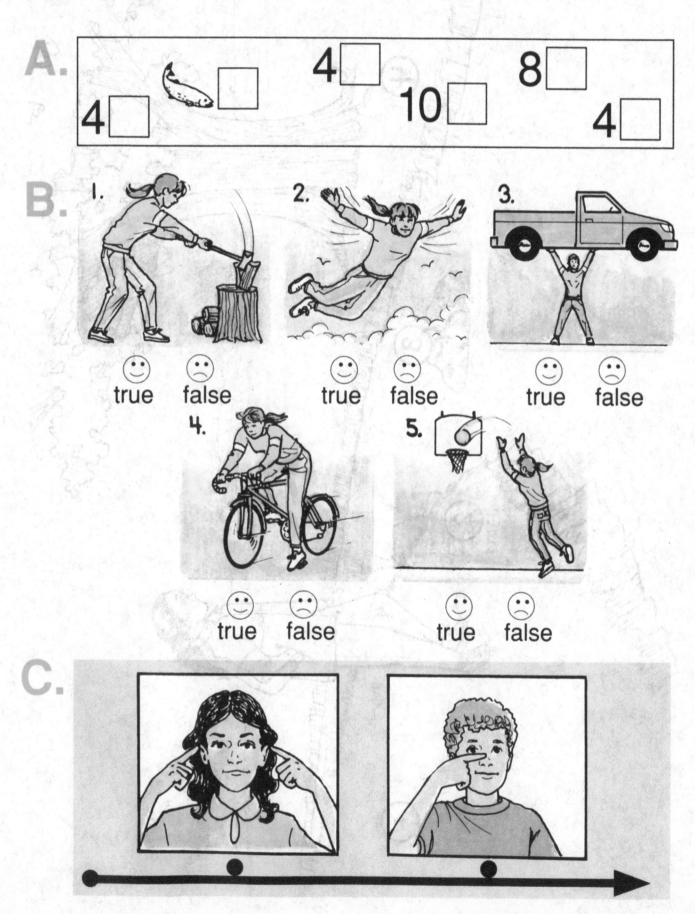

A.

4 ☐   🐟 ☐   4 ☐   8 ☐
                 10 ☐   4 ☐

B.

1.   2.   3.

☺ true   ☹ false   ☺ true   ☹ false   ☺ true   ☹ false

4.   5.

☺ true   ☹ false   ☺ true   ☹ false

C.

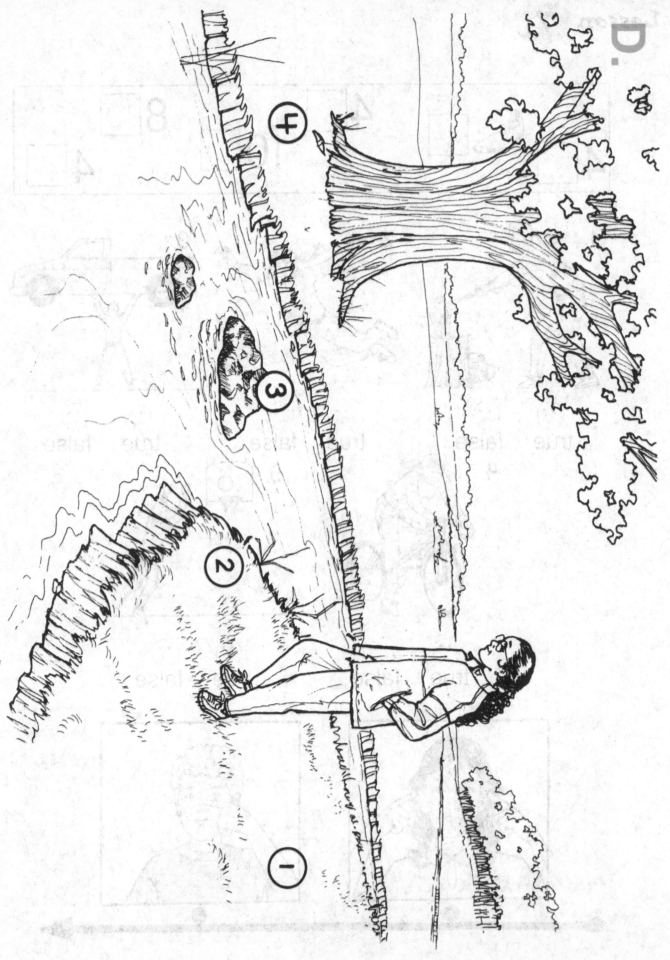

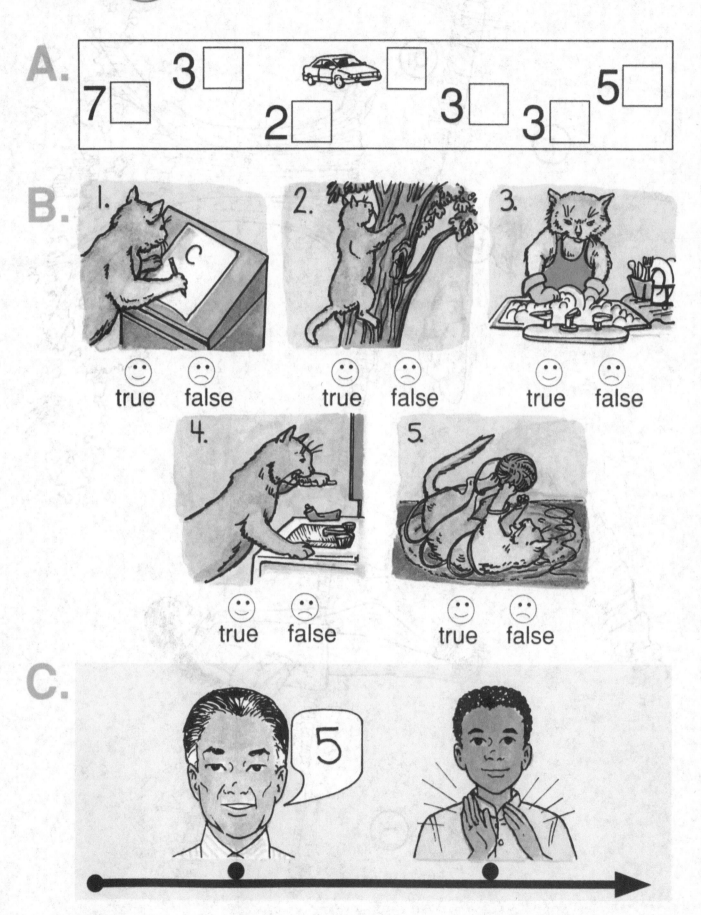

A.

7☐ 3☐ ☐ 2☐ 3☐ 3☐ 5☐

B.

1. true false
2. true false
3. true false
4. true false
5. true false

C.

5

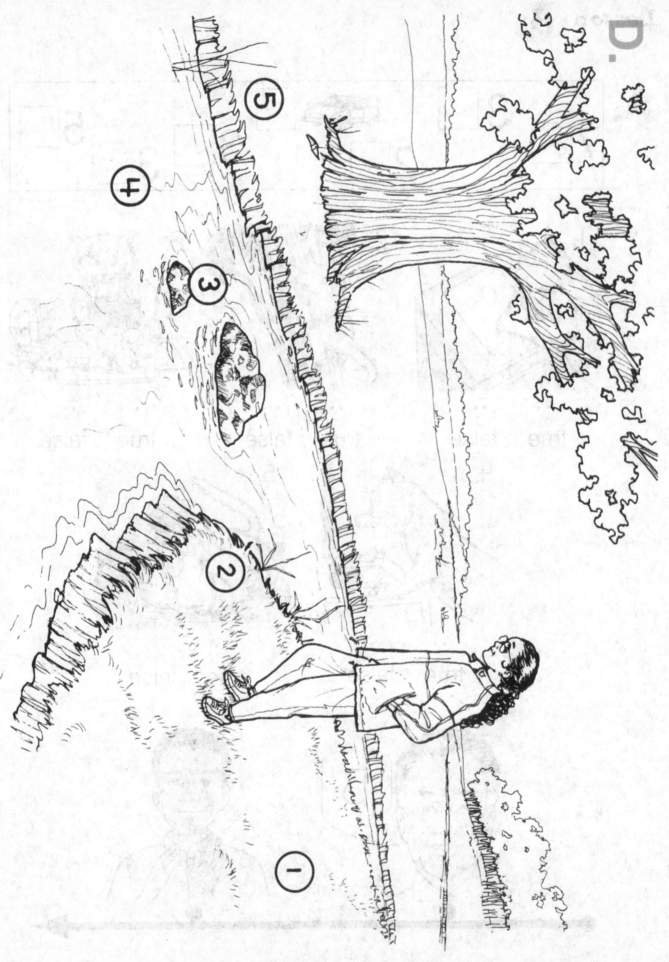

Lesson 9

A.

3☐ 5☐ 7☐ 9☐ 7☐ 2☐ 3☐ 7☐

B.

1. true false

2. true false

3. true false

4. 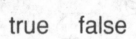 true false

5. true false

C.

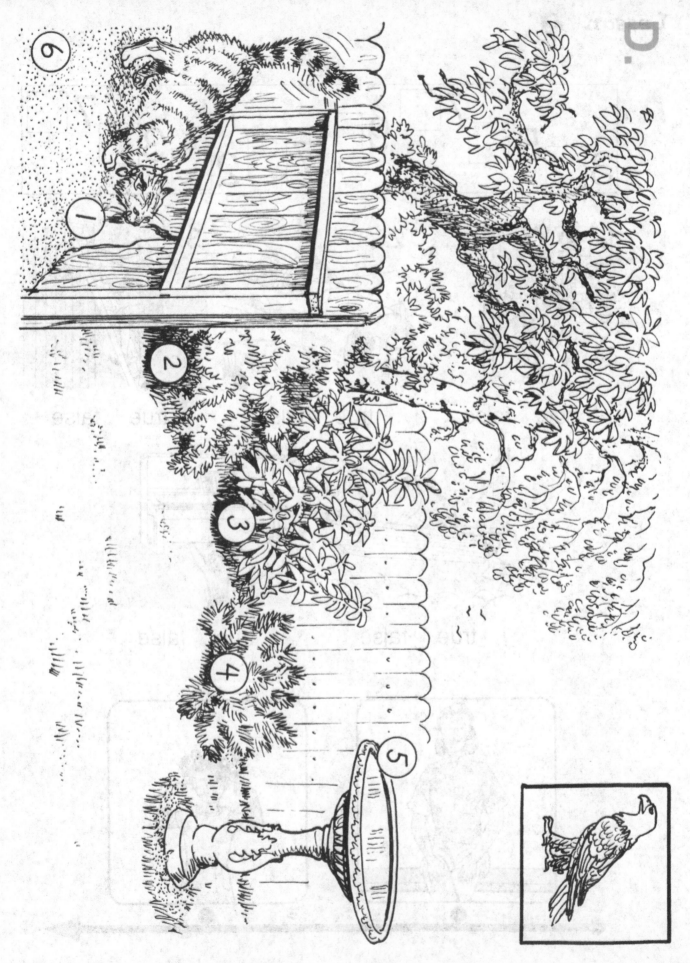

A.

5☐   7☐   5☐   8☐
2☐   5☐   5☐

B.

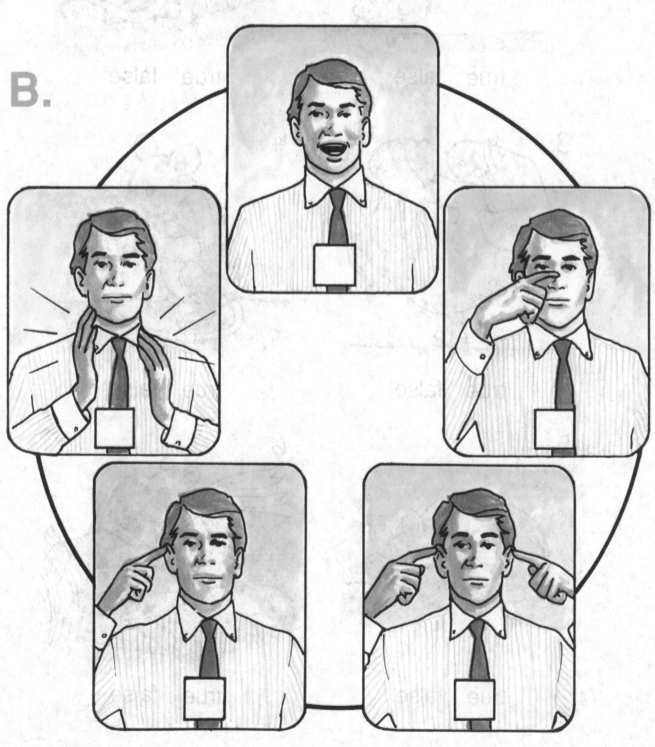

C.

1.

true   false

2.

true   false

3.

true   false

4.

true   false

5.

true   false

6.

true   false

Lesson 11

A.

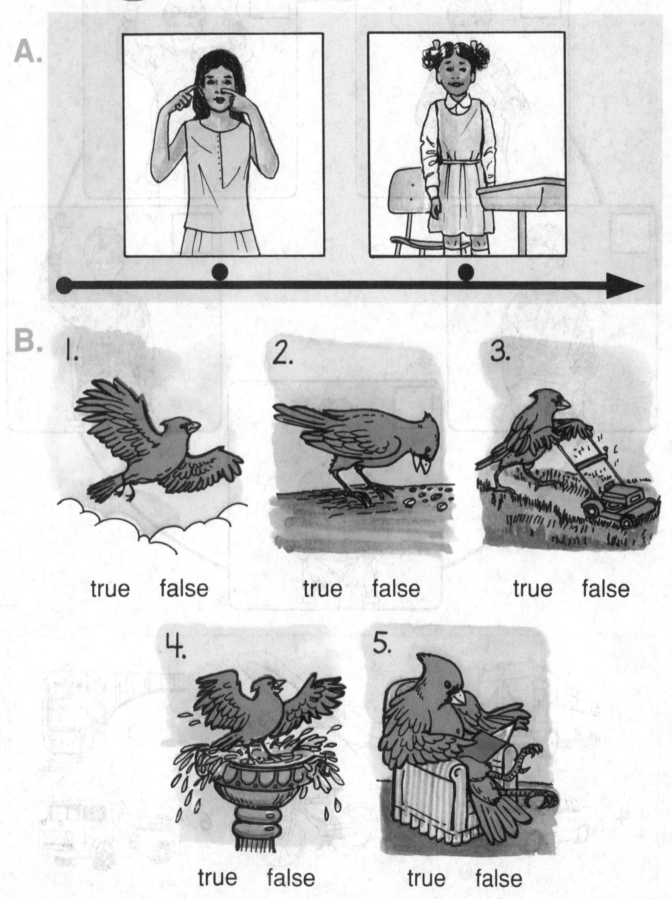

B.

1. true   false

2. true   false

3. true   false

4. true   false

5. true   false

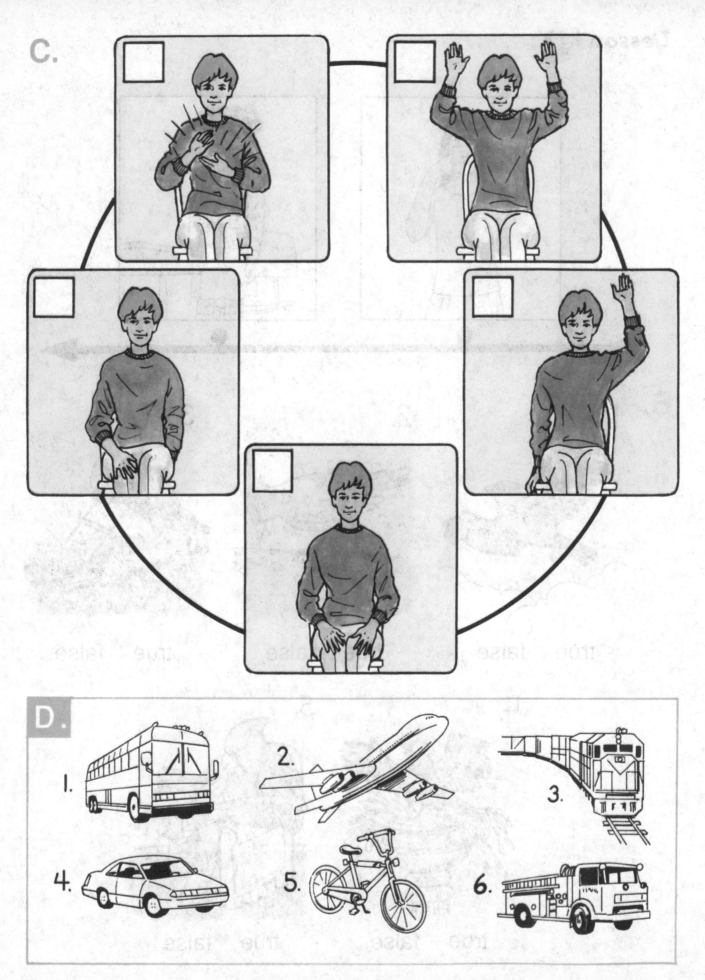

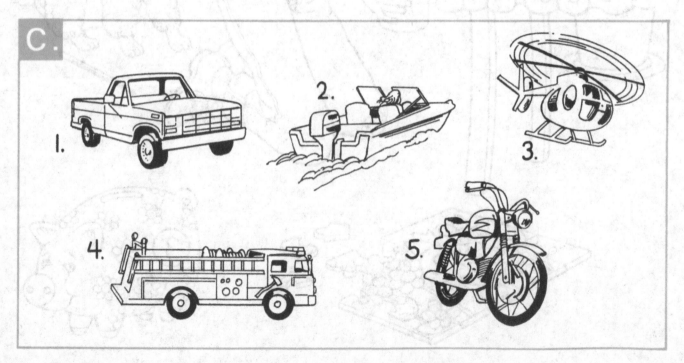

A.

B.

1. true   false
2. true   false
3. true   false
4. true   false
5. true   false
6. true   false

C.

1.

2.

3.

4.

5.

D.

A.

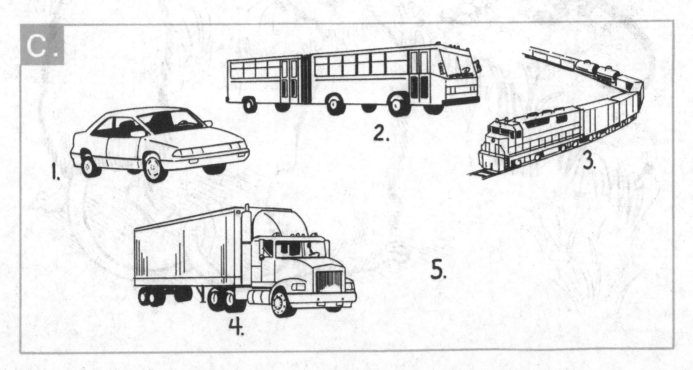

B.

1. true   false

2. true   false

3. true   false

4. true   false

5. true   false

6. true   false

C.

1.

2.

3.

4.

5.

D.

Lesson 14

A.

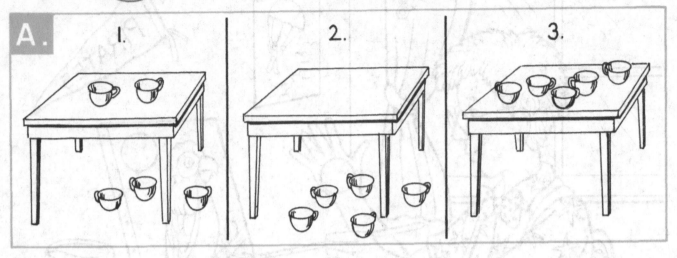

1.   2.   3.

B.

C.

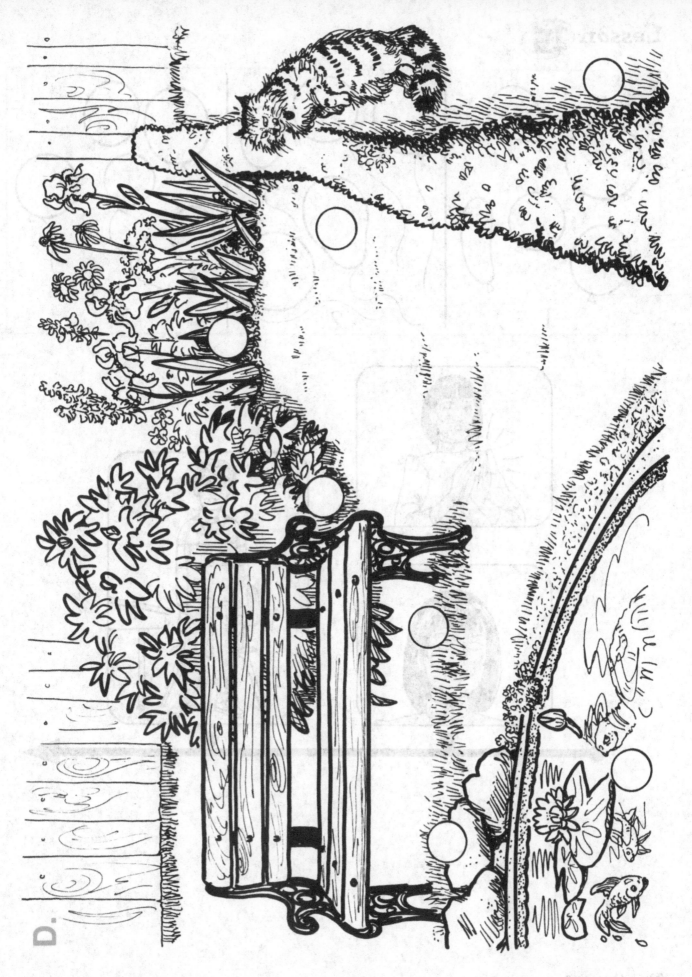

Lesson 15

A.

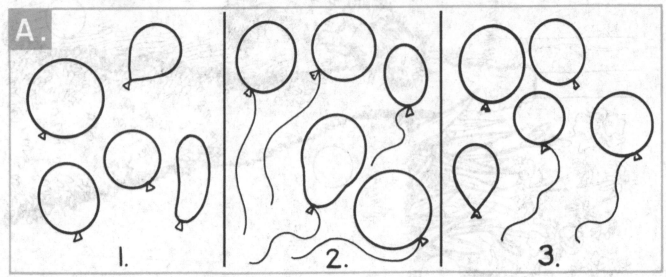

1.   2.   3.

B.

C.

D.

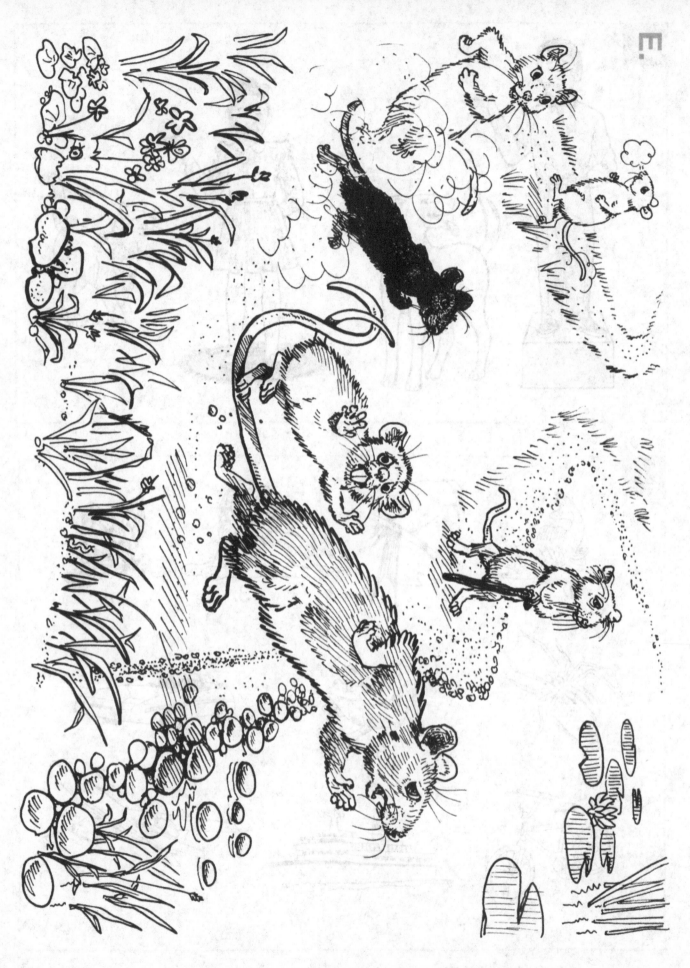

Lesson 16

A.

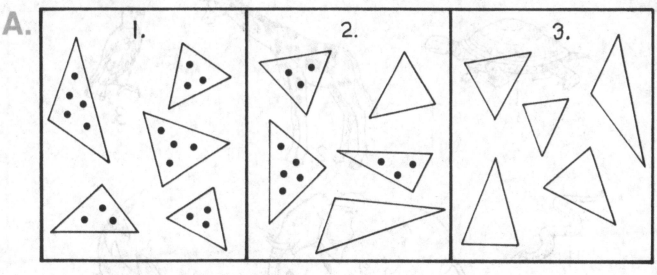

B.

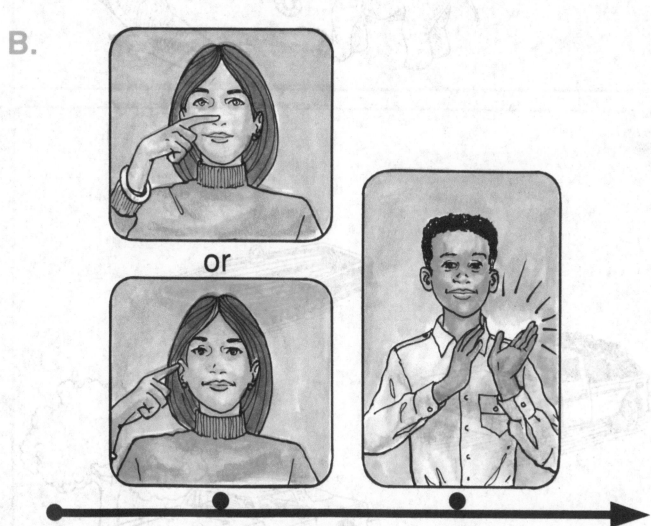

or

C.

1.

2.

3.

4.

D.

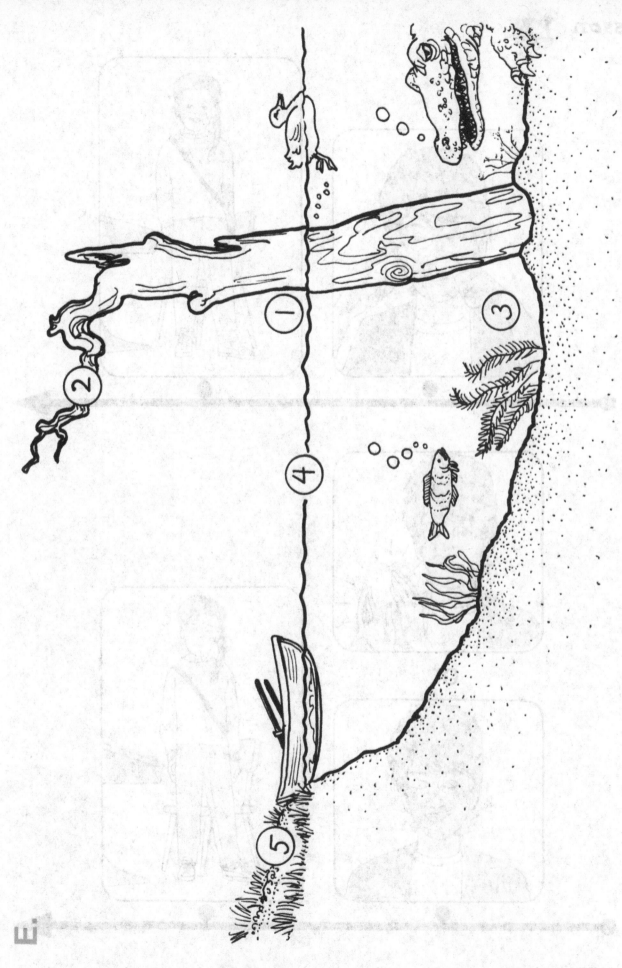

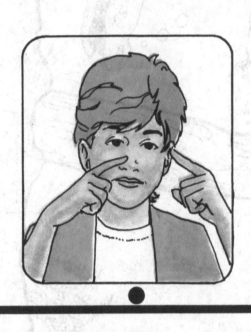

or

B.

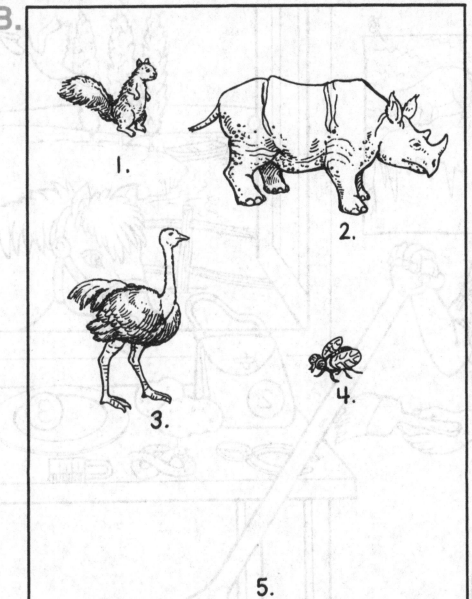

1.

2.

3.

4.

5.

C.

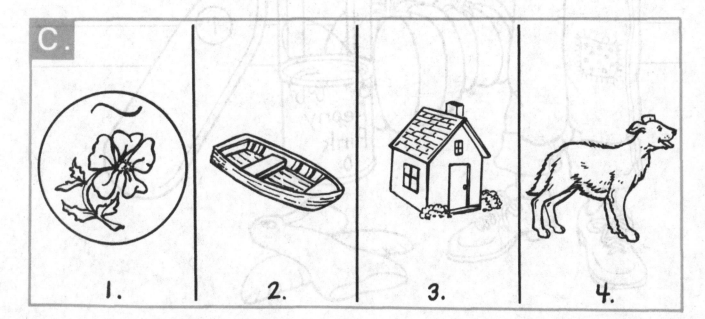

1.

2.

3.

4.

D.

Peony
Pink

Lesson 18

A.

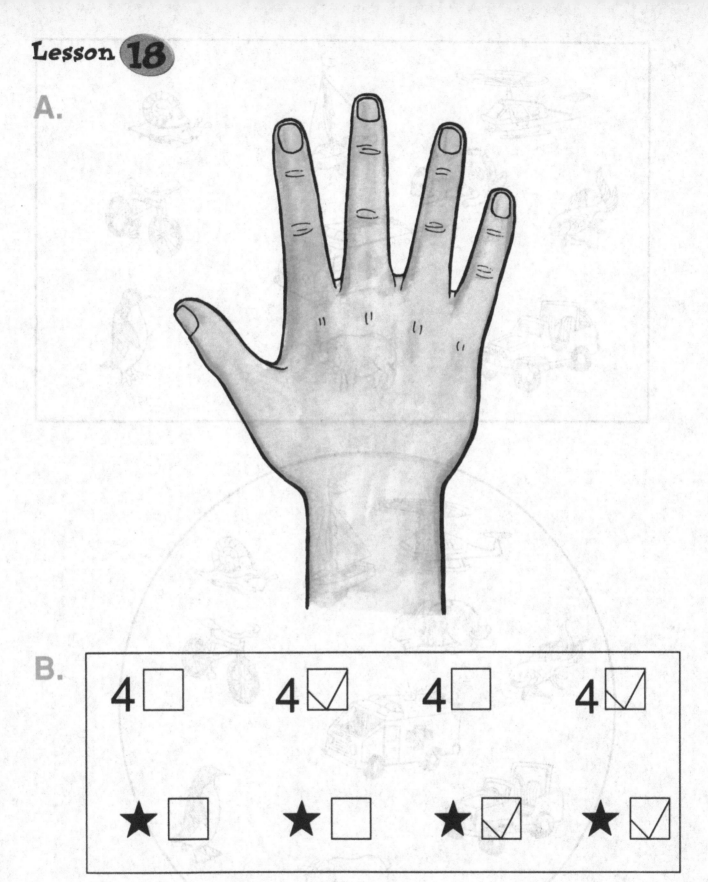

B.

4 ☐   4 ☑   4 ☐   4 ☑

★ ☐   ★ ☐   ★ ☑   ★ ☑

C.

D.

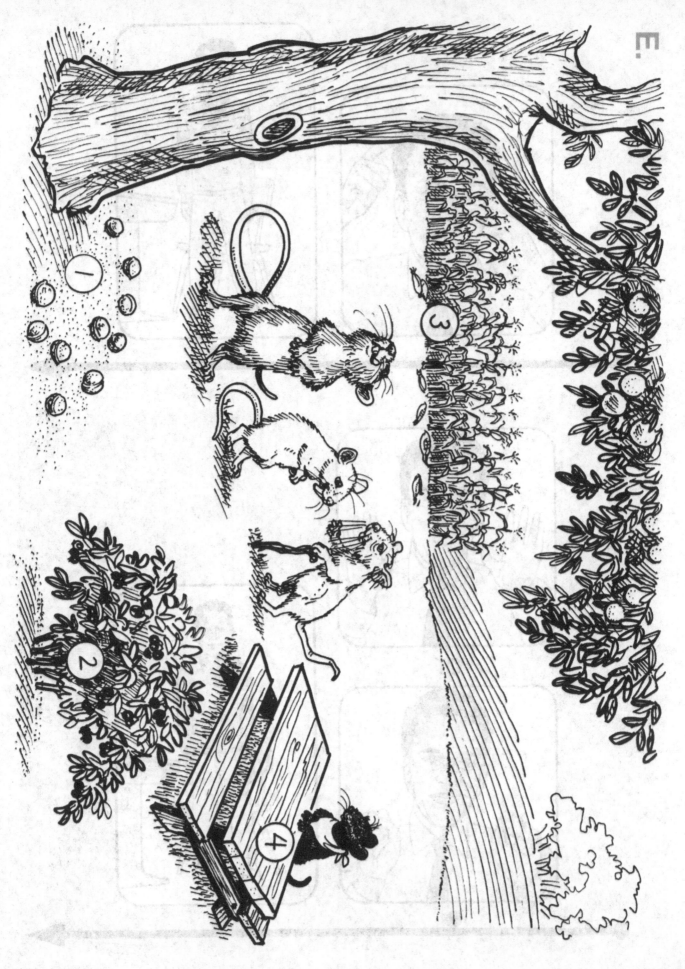

Lesson 19

A.

1.   2.   3.   4.

B.

C.

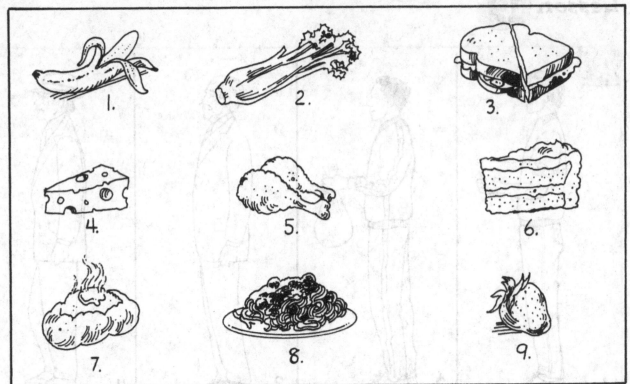

A.

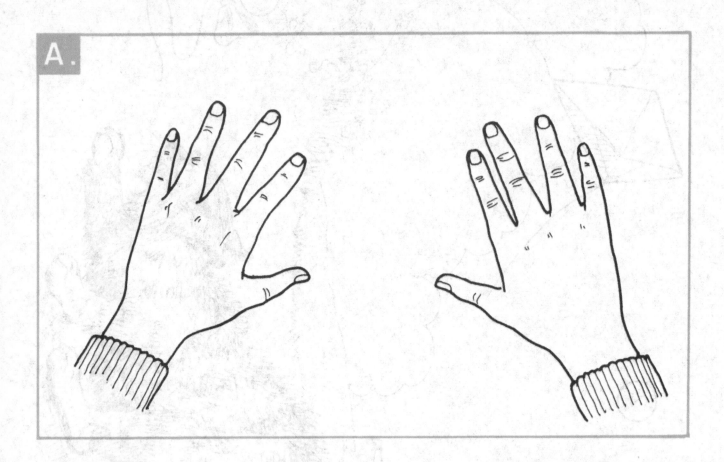

B.

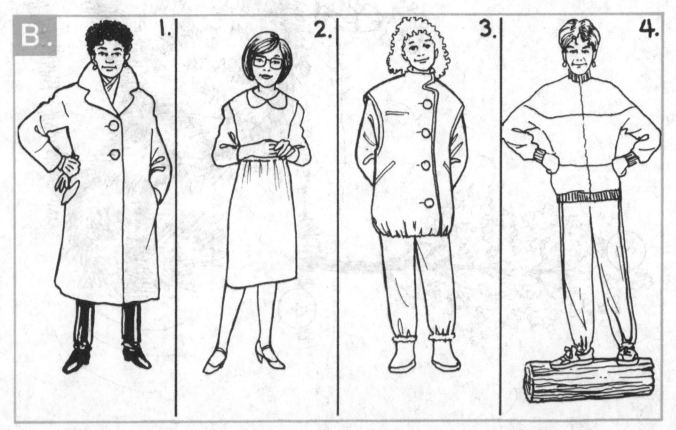

1. 2. 3. 4.

C.

D.

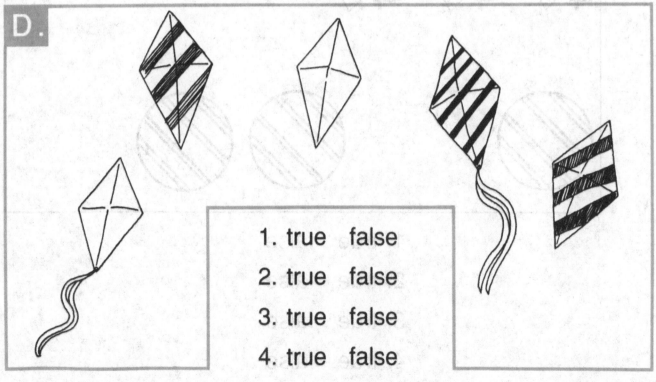

1. true   false
2. true   false
3. true   false
4. true   false

A.

B.

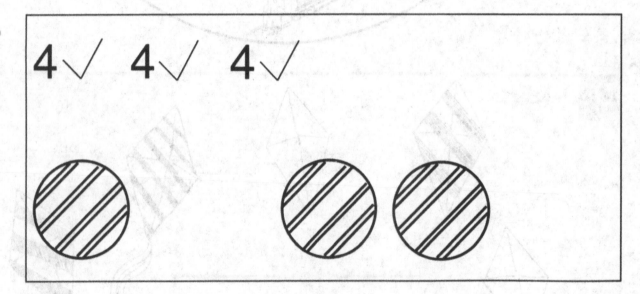

4 ✓   4 ✓   4 ✓

1. true   false

2. true   false

3. true   false

4. true   false

C.

or

A.

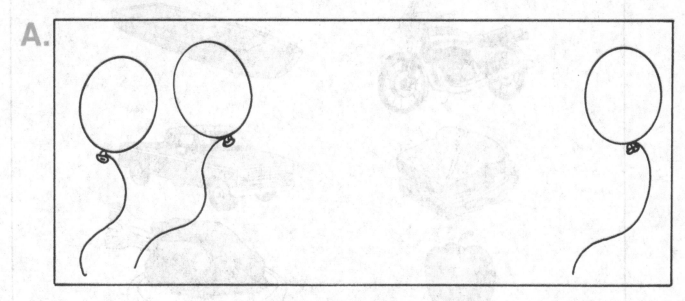

1. true   false

2. true   false

3. true   false

4. true   false

B.

C.

D.

A.

3

3

3

1. true   false

2. true   false

3. true   false

4. true   false

B.

or

C.

D.

A.

1. true   false
2. true   false
3. true   false
4. true   false

B.

1.

2.

3.

C.

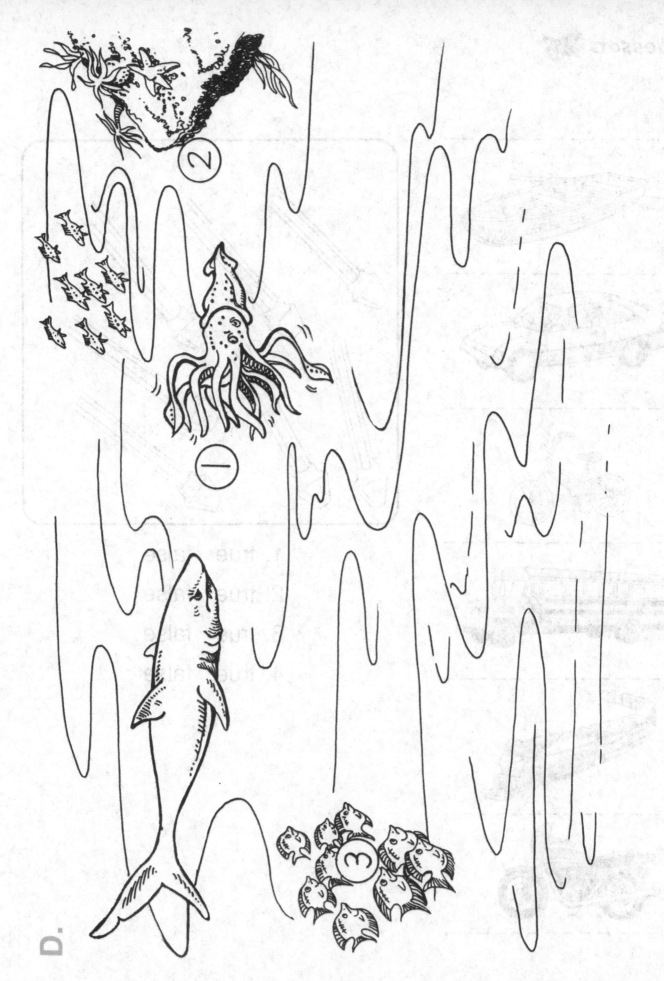

D.

Lesson 25

A.

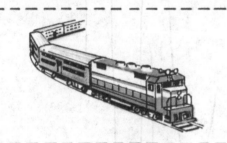

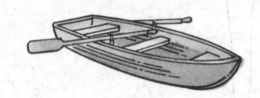

B.

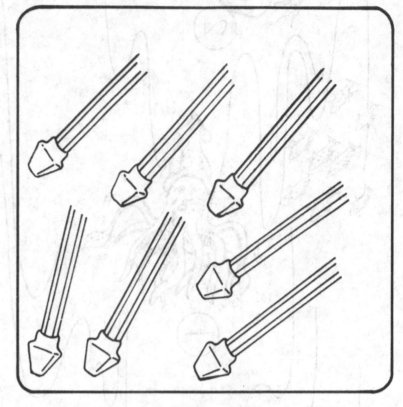

1. true   false

2. true   false

3. true   false

4. true   false

C.

A.

1. true   false

2. true   false

3. true   false

4. true   false

5. true   false

B.

or

A.

B.

C.

1. true   false
2. true   false
3. true   false
4. true   false

D.

A.

B.

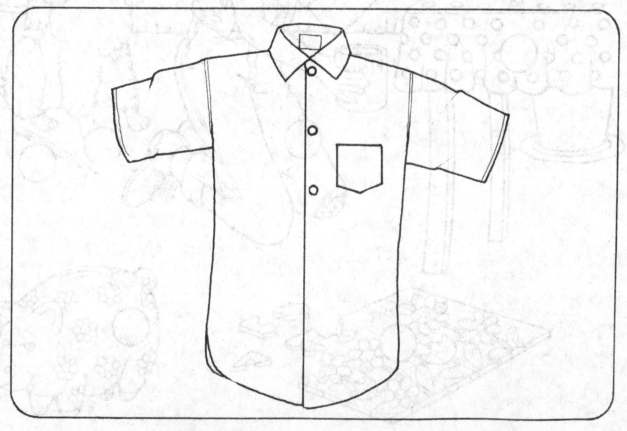

C.

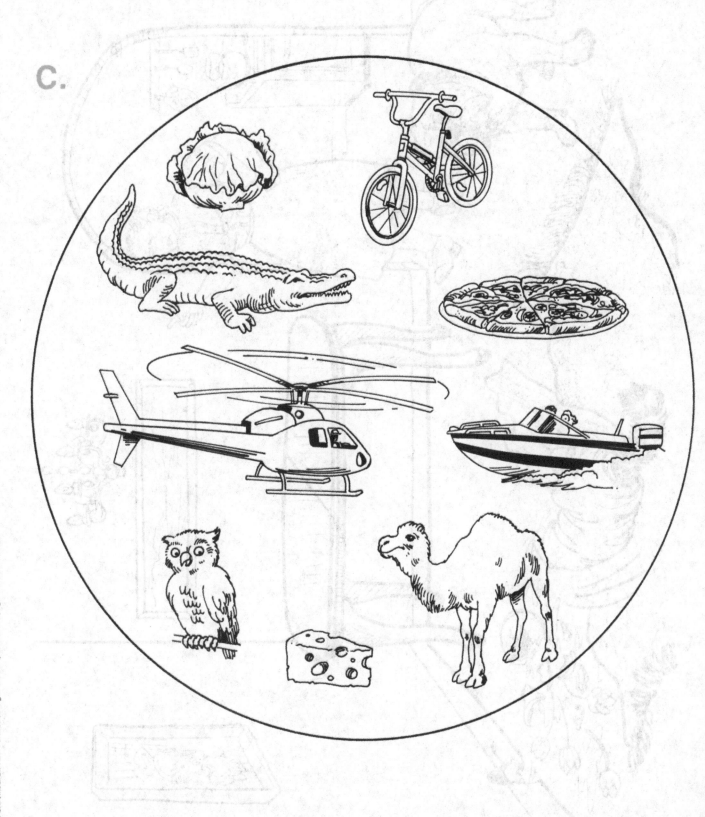

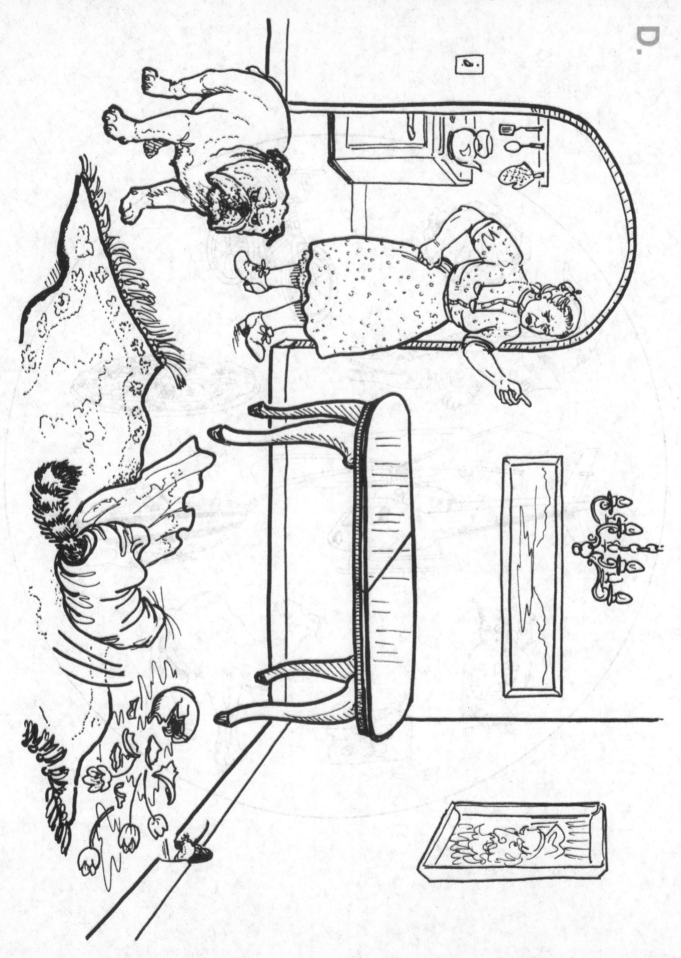

A.

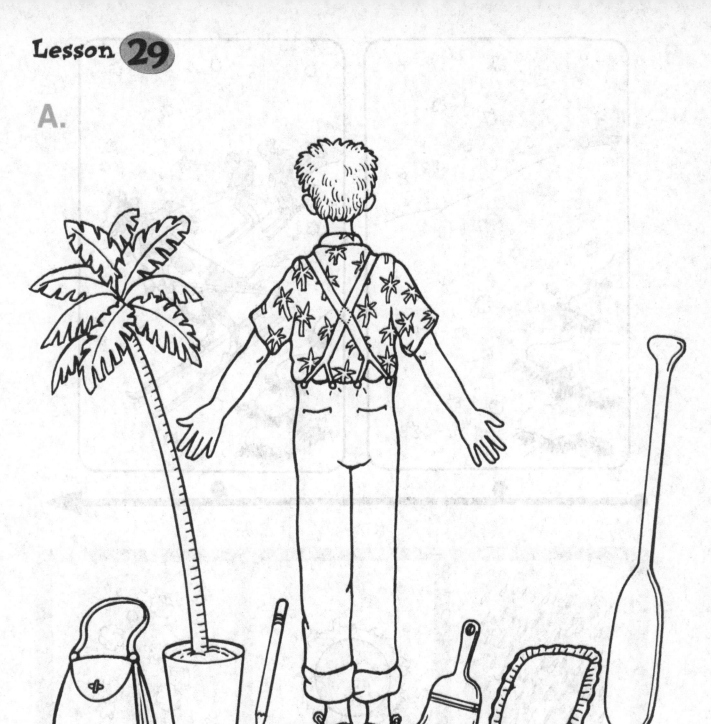

B.

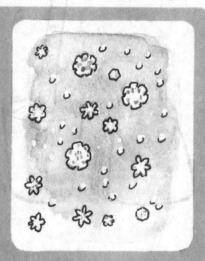

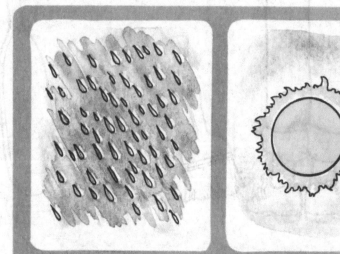

C.

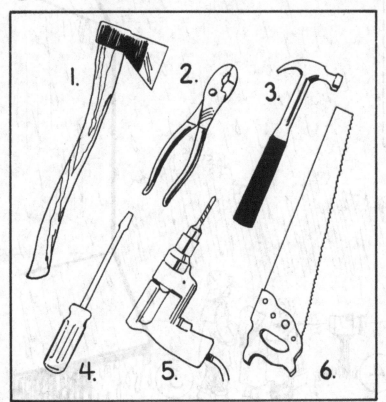

1. 2. 3.

4. 5. 6.

D.

A.

1. true   false
2. true   false
3. true   false

4. true   false
5. true   false

B.

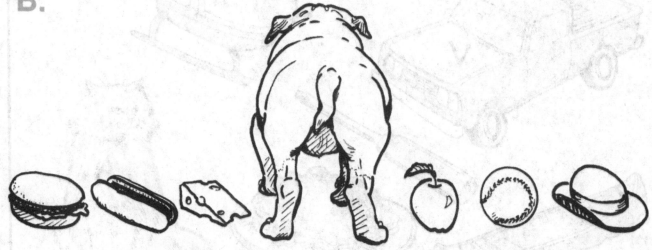

1. true   false
2. true   false
3. true   false

4. true   false
5. true   false

E.

Lesson 32

A.

B.

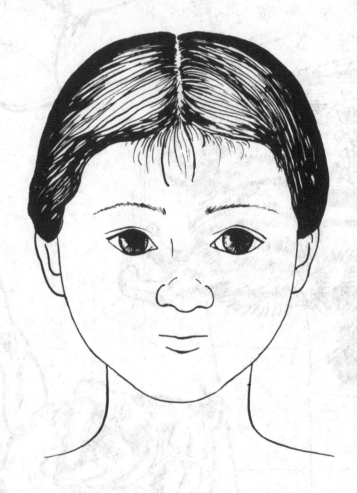

1. true   false

2. true   false

3. true   false

4. true   false

C.

A.

1. true   false
2. true   false
3. true   false

B.

C.

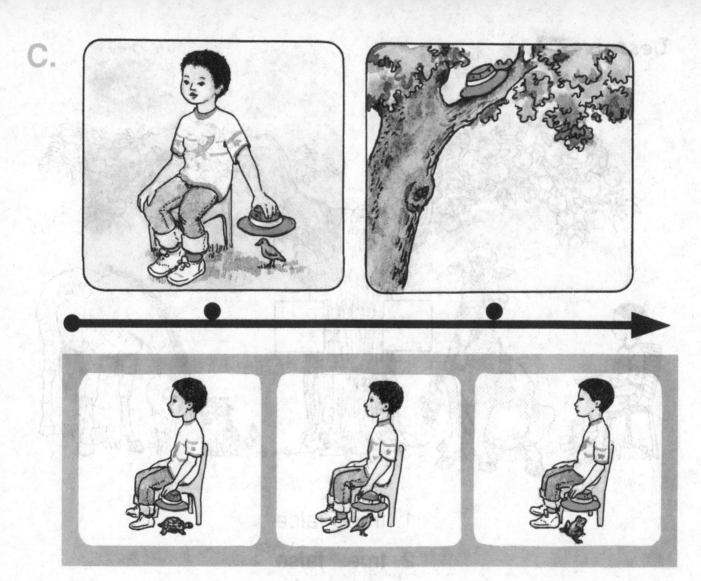

D.

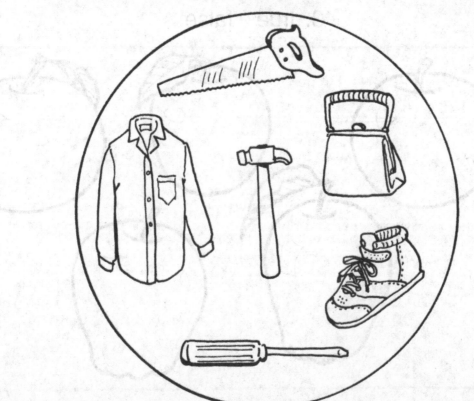

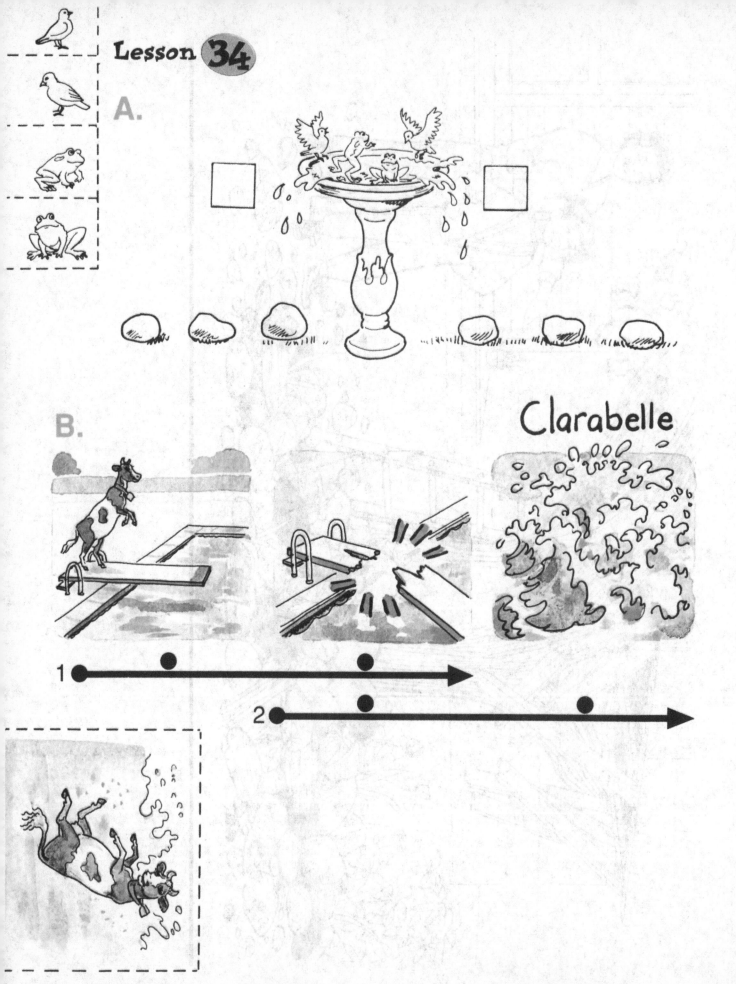

Lesson 34

A.

B.

Clarabelle

1

2

C.

Lesson 35

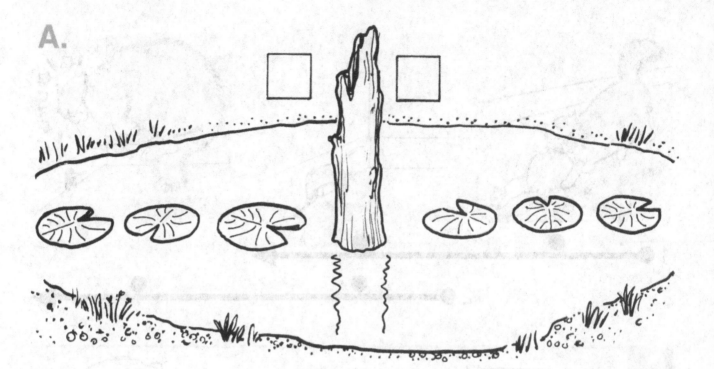

A.

B.

1. true   false

2. true   false

3. true   false

4. true   false

C.

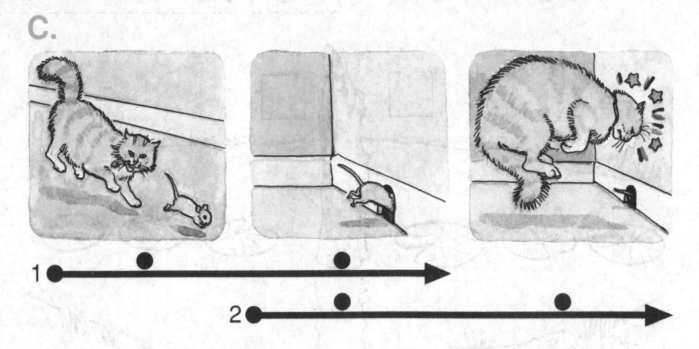

1

2

D.